Man's Poor Relations

Photograph James Brewster Courtesy Harvard Film Serv.

THE POTTO, A SLOW LEMUR

MAN'S POOR RELATIONS

23

EARNEST HOOTON

WITH MANY LINECUT AND
HALFTONE ILLUSTRATIONS

DOUBLEDAY, DORAN & COMPANY, INC.

GARDEN CITY 1942 NEW YORK

PRINTED AT THE *Country Life Press*, GARDEN CITY, N. Y., U. S. A.

60419
7-44

To
ROBERT MEARNS YERKES
STUDENT OF PRIMATES
TEACHER OF PRIMATOLOGISTS

*"For he taught them as one having
authority, and not as the scribes."*

Preface

Paradoxically enough, I am abashed at my own effrontery in writing a book about the infrahuman primates, because I have never made the slightest scientific contribution to knowledge of the subject. A general book on apes, monkeys, and lemurs might appropriately flow from the pen, or click from the typewriter, of such an eminent authority as Robert M. Yerkes, or C. R. Carpenter, or Adolph H. Schultz, or S. Zuckerman, or many another primatologist whose researches are summarized in the following pages. Probably the reading public does not realize that it is much harder to write a general book on a subject in which you are vastly erudite than upon some field of knowledge of which you have a mere smattering. The specialist has an embarrassment of choice of innumerable facts and theories and is all too aware of the pitfalls and gaps in his knowledge. Consequently, he is reluctant to generalize and unwilling to spread himself thinly and precariously over an entire field when he can be profound and secure in some restricted area of it. The enthusiastic amateur has no such inhibitions. He can go right ahead and tell all he knows (and often more) without burying his readers under the weight of factual mass or suffocating them with qualifying statements and ambivalent interpretations. Moreover, he blithely places the responsibility for his material upon the firsthand experimenters and observers whose work he quotes and summarizes (and perhaps distorts and misinterprets).

I have not assumed this vicarious task in response to any concerted demand from real primatologists that I synthesize their original works. I have simply "butted in." Brigadier General Theodore Roosevelt, in a publishing rather than a military capacity, asked me last summer to do a book about primates, probably because he thought that anyone who writes about them as much as I do ought to know something about them. This request happened to catch me in a period of exaltation (as regards infrahuman primates only), because I had just returned from a most stimulating sojourn at the Yale Laboratories of Primate Biology, near Jacksonville, Florida. I had made this visit in acceptance of a long-standing invitation from Professor Yerkes, who had suggested, altogether properly and with the most delicate tact, that anyone who persistently talks about apes ought to fortify his verbiage with at least a glimpse of them and their investigators.

As a matter of fact, the longer I study man, the more interested I become in apes and monkeys, because human physique, temperament, and behavior are rooted in the lower primates. Consequently, I think that the splendid research work of primatologists ought to be made available in a simplified form to educated persons. I have attempted to do this service for man with a full consciousness of my own limitations.

The principal acknowledgments of the author are naturally due to those scientists upon whose studies this book has been based. The names appear in the text and in the footnote references. My indebtedness is in some cases so heavy that it would be oppressive, were it not for the generous and gracious spirit in which these students have contributed the fruits of their labor to my harvest. I have already mentioned the names of Yerkes, Carpenter, Schultz, and Zuckerman. All persons interested in the nature of man ought to rise up and call them blessed, together with the names of W. K. Gregory, Wolfgang Köhler, Henry Nissen, Heinrich Klüver, A. H. Maslow, Le Gros Clark, P. B. Candela, Walter F. Grether, and many others which may be run down in the Bibliography. As a self-selected, eponymous ghost writer for these scientists, I thank them.

For the photographs of primates used to illustrate this book I am grateful to the Zoological Society of Philadelphia and to Roger Conant, curator of the Philadelphia Zoological Garden; to Dr. C. R. Carpenter of Pennsylvania State College; to Miss Hansel Mieth and *Life* magazine; to John Haeseler; to Dr. Florence Lowther of Barnard College; to Frederick P. Orchard of the Peabody Museum, Harvard University. To Dr. W. K. Gregory and Dr. Milo Hellman of the American Museum of Natural History I am grateful for permission to adapt sundry drawings of primate teeth. Professor Adolph H. Schultz of Johns Hopkins has kindly permitted me to reproduce his admirable drawings showing the proportions of man and the great apes. Paul B. Hoeber, publisher of Frederick Tilney's *The Brain from Ape to Man,* has graciously allowed me to redraw and use illustrations from that work.

In addition to the tremendous contribution to this work which Dr. C. R. Carpenter has made by permitting me to summarize his original investigations and to utilize many of his photographs, this generous collaborator has piled Ossa upon Pelion by reading the galley proof and making invaluable suggestions and corrections.

In the onerous task of preparing the manuscript for publication, reading proof, compiling indices, checking footnotes, etc., I have had the splendid services of Dorothea Kelly and Charity Kidd. No one except the author can possibly realize the extent to which their skillful and intelligent editorial work has improved this book.

I hope that anyone who reads this volume will not skip the Preface, because the acknowledgments are far more meaningful than the polite and perfunctory thanks which one distributes hither and yon for mechanical or other services performed in the production of a really original work. The stark reality of the situation is that the person whose name appears on the title page has contributed to the book little more than its organization (which may be defective), its literary style (which many may think deplorable), an occasional gratuitous personal opinion, and an enthusiastic interest in apes, monkeys, and lemurs. However, he feels pretty virtuous about the objectivity of the book and the extent to which it caters to readers who associate soundness in science with dullness. He trusts that they will overlook sundry rare lapses from sobriety.

EARNEST HOOTON

Peabody Museum,
Cambridge, Massachusetts,
June 28, 1942

Contents

PART III. NEW WORLD DEMOCRATS AND PROLETARIANS

Halftone Illustrations

LIST OF PLATES

Text Illustrations

INTRODUCTION

*An Anthropologist Looks at the Primates
—— And Then Looks Back at Himself*

Introduction

AN ANTHROPOLOGIST LOOKS AT THE PRIMATES—

THE COMPLEAT ANTHROPOLOGIST professes to study man in his entirety, with all his doings and thinking, his machinations, and his machines. That he does not always fulfill these grandiose specifications is neither here nor there. He, at any rate, puts in an impressive bid. Assuming some sort of Olympian detachment, the anthropologist is wont to say that he studies man just as he would study any other animal, meaning, of course, that he will show no human bias in appraising his own fellows. However, the anthropologist rarely, if ever, studies any other animal than man. He leaves the rest of the fauna to zoologists, comparative anatomists, physiologists, and other specialists. In this book an anthropologist will attempt to study some other animals as he would study man. The animals thus to be victimized are a group which the zoological classifiers call primates—lemurs, tarsiers, monkeys, and apes. These are supposed to be man's poor relations—some of them very distant, others uncomfortably near.

The systematic zoologist starts out by explaining that such and such animals are characterized by a certain community of characters in structure and development and therefore constitute a generally related group. He classifies this group in one of the broader or narrower zoological categories, according to the number of different kinds of animals it contains and the extent to which they differ from each other. He assumes that they have sprung originally from the same primitive, "generalized" ancestors, and, in the course of evolution, have differentiated into smaller and more intimately related groups, each with its own peculiarities of physique and habit. This method is comparatively valid, or at least as good as any other. It stresses structure—bones, viscera, integument, and so on—and the implications of relationship which are based upon similarities in these features.

The anthropologist goes at the study of men the other way round. He takes a group of human beings as he finds them, living together, and proceeds to describe their physical appearance, their habitations, arts, industries, and general behavior. He tries to find out "what they are like" and why. Questions of ultimate relationship are postponed for treatment until the people and their culture have been observed and the significance of their idiosyncrasies as a group has been worried out. Anthropologists assume that human groups which they approach, however primitive, are fundamentally like themselves in anatomy, physiology, and psychology, and that their peculiarities of material and social culture are developed by the same processes of human reasoning or irrationality as are used by civilized man. The students of animal behavior, who sometimes regrettably call themselves psychobiologists, are very fearful of departing from the inhumanly objective attitude of the zoologists and of explaining the habits and characteristics of subhuman animals in human terms. They are afraid of anthropomorphizing the apes. This attitude is perfectly proper and altogether scientific, but it results in a strained dehumanization of data gathered on the animals, which, combined with a terminology devised to be non-committal in regard to human parallels, renders a fascinating subject unspeakably dreary and barely comprehensible. I suppose you have to write that way in order to safeguard your scientific reputation, if you value it, because dullness and soundness are apparently judged to be synonymous in scientific literature. A scientist who writes a "popular" book is like a girl who has an illegitimate child; the stigma remains, no matter how large and respectable a brood she may have produced in dull and virtuous wedlock. Since nothing can "make her an honest woman," she might as well have a good time.

So, deliberately, I am going to deal with lemurs, monkeys, and apes as if they were "people." I have no intention of perverting the truth, but I shall not refrain from speculating in an anthropocentric fashion upon the human implications of primate morphology and behavior. After all, I am interested in these animals only because they are, as Yerkes says, "almost human," and I see no reason why I should try to be almost inhuman in my description and interpretation of them and their doings.

So we shall approach these various primate populations and in each case tell where they live and the nature of the country they inhabit, describe their personal and collective physical appearances, their dwelling places, their diet, their familial and larger social groupings, and their individual life histories—from birth to death. Then we shall outline their culture, if any, descant upon their psychology, and pronounce upon their evolutionary status, not without some human comparisons, odious though these may be. After we have worked through this primate ethnography, we shall be in a position to discuss the relationships of the various groups one to another and to our own kind, as well as the questions of origins and destiny.

Of course, we cannot go and live with the many different kinds of primates in their own natural surroundings, as anthropologists live among the savages they study. It is obviously impossible to chase each monkey up his particular tree, although one or two field primatologists have virtually attempted that method in the case of a few. Naturally, the best information that we possess has come from such studies. Nowadays, the anthropologist who wants to study North American Indians usually has to observe them on reservations into which they have been herded and where they live lives considerably different from those which they enjoyed in a state of nature. They are, so to speak, captive animals. Yet a good deal of information upon the former life and behavior of Indians in the wild can be gathered from these tame, domesticated specimens. Of course, you cannot interview an aged baboon in the zoo and ask him to describe for you life in the old days on the veldt. The interviewing method and the use of an informant, so favored among social anthropologists, break down here. We have to depend entirely upon observations of the behavior of the brute. But Professor Arnold Gesell of Yale secures his unique information upon human infants in just this way. He isolates them in a sort of cage with various experimental objects and then peeks at them through a one-way screen, photographing and recording their reactions to various stimuli.

The present book is not intended to be a compendium of all known facts about the primates; its style, form, and content are not encyclopedic. It is not a "handbook" of the primates, because a handbook is a volume to be handled briefly and then laid down—thumbed over hastily in search of some specific fact. It even includes a certain amount of primate fiction, plainly designated as such, because folklore is a part of anthropology and even of what used to be called "natural history." Some of these romantic tales about monkeys and apes at least serve to season an otherwise tasteless mess of facts. In any event, it is almost impossible to prove that they are not true.

It is hoped that the reader who entertains a temperate curiosity about the primates and their habits and even the moderately serious student will find in this volume the desired information not too grimly presented. For the benefit of the more avidly scientific some pages of smaller print have been added to the end of each chapter. To these pages have been relegated sundry technical minutiae of the anatomy and physiology of the various animals which would slow down a running account of the primates to a virtual standstill if included in the body of the text. In this unobtrusive small type are also printed brief accounts of little-known or less-interesting primates with which the casual reader need not bother. Their existence has to be recognized lest some ferocious seeker of primate knowledge be balked of his prey and turn upon the author to rend him.

Instead of beginning with the lowliest, humblest, and least-known of the primates and working slowly and painfully up to the great anthropoid apes, I have started at the top with the chimpanzee, which is perhaps closest to man and about which we know the most. It is not a good idea to keep the best wine until the last, because some guests are likely to be under the table before the end of the banquet, having "passed out" without ever tasting anything worth while. On the other hand, if they become initially exhilarated with the fine vintages of the apes, the effect may carry them through subsequent potations of the *vin ordinaire* of the monkeys and the small beer of the lemurs. Then, if they are still on their feet and thus have proved themselves able to carry their primatology like scientists, we shall present them with a final and potent draught of synthetic spirit—a few swallows of strongly fortified but mellow conclusions.

—AND THEN LOOKS BACK AT HIMSELF

Man usually takes himself for granted, without really knowing what he is. When he directs his "insatiable curiosity" toward other animals, he ought to have some precise gauge of his own peculiarities, so that he will not mistake subhuman symmetry of organism and behavior for lopsidedness by comparing it with his own exclusive malformations and dysfunctions. If we have a brief, preliminary look at ourselves, we shall be able the better to appreciate the other primates whom we patronizingly call "poor relations." Nearly all the human characteristics which we regard with complacent pride are really freaks of nature, or, better, the excesses of organic evolution gone haywire. If we should see ourselves as the apes see us, the view would be appalling. I once tried to get an ape's-eye view of man, and the prospect was so unflattering to our own species that it put me on the defensive and I had to call the thing "Apology for Man."[1] It was miserably insufficient.

I have no intention in this book of flogging man over the shoulders or rumps of apes, unduly glorifying the latter at the expense of the former. All this section purports to be is a description of human deviations from the general norms of the Order of Primates, to which man belongs, together with the apes, monkeys, and lemurs. We are not so much interested in evaluating man's divergences as in emphasizing the fact that related animals are not to be depreciated because they do not follow human eccentricity.

We ordinarily think of man as departing from the standard primate pattern by reason of his enormous brain, shrunken jaws, elongated legs, abbreviated arms, erect posture, and biped gait, and, for good measure, his comparatively hairless and absolutely tailless condition. By no means all these supposedly human characteristics are peculiar to man, even among the primates. The brain of the humble marmoset, most primitive of all monkeys, is probably much larger than that of man relative to body size, although the surface is almost smooth and unconvoluted. It is true that man has absolutely the largest brain of the primates, exceeding the brain of the giant gorilla, who is more than 3 times his body weight, by 2 to 2½ times. Probably human jaws and teeth are more reduced than those of any other primate, but the short-faced tarsiers, lemurs, and, again, the marmoset, press man closely in shrinkage of the snout, while the grub-eating aye-aye, a curious Madagascar lemur, has considerably fewer teeth than man.

Again, short arms and long legs are common enough in the small primates below the monkey level, although I am not sure that any of them equal man in relative elongation of the lower extremity. Certainly, man has absolutely the longest primate legs and the only non-prehensile, supporting feet to be found in the order. He is also the only primate which walks completely erect on fully extended legs and thighs, and he alone possesses the full development of a forward kink in his spine just above the pelvis which permits him to keep his trunk vertical and his center of gravity directly in the axis of his sustaining hind limbs. There can be no argument also about man's relative sparsity of body hair, in which he surpasses all monkeys, apes, and lemurs. However, the human head hair is longer than that of other primates, with few exceptions. Of course, there are non-primate mammals which have even less body hair than man—the whale and other sea-dwelling mammals, for instance. As for the lack

[1]Hooton 1937, pp. 19–42. Footnotes in the present volume are keyed to the Bibliography, pp. 395–403, where full reference forms are given.

of a tail in our species—we are still better endowed caudally than any of the anthropoid apes, in all of whom the external tail is equally absent and the vestigial vertebrae of this terminal part of the spine are fewer and more degenerate than in man. For that matter, some monkeys and lemurs are also far advanced in caudal decay.

There are many skeletal features in which man differs widely, in degree rather than in kind, from all apes, monkeys, and the low-grade lemurs. Most of them are bony structural correlates of the differences in body proportions, stance, and gait which we have just discussed, or of the contrast in relative size of the brain case (which has to cover the swollen brain somehow) and the conversely shrunken teeth and jaws. Almost the only uniquely human feature of the skull is, however, the jutting chin eminence. Nothing of the sort occurs in any other primate. Again, the skeleton of the nose is much more developed in height and breadth in man than in any ape, monkey, or lemur. Perhaps the same could be said of the external human nose, were it not for the proboscis monkey of Borneo, which has a nasal appendage that would put Cyrano de Bergerac to the blush. Yet this peculiar and elongated soft tip of the nose in the Borneo monkey is an excrescence structurally diverse from the nasal tip in man, and, to go with it, the proboscis monkey has no high and arched bony bridge of the nose.

Highest marks must also be awarded to man for his thumbs, which are relatively and absolutely the longest, and capable of being rotated so as to oppose the finger tips in fine grasping movements to an extent unequaled in other members of the order.

I am not aware of any important physiological feature in which man stands apart from all other primates. Of course, there are many minor variations in physiological functioning between man and his nearest relatives, and it may be discovered, when more is known of primate physiology, that man has a few unique properties. The processes of prenatal and postnatal growth are slightly to markedly different in man from those in any of the apes or monkeys, but subhuman primates probably differ among themselves in these respects as much as, if not more than, some of them diverge from man. When you have considered this very general and non-technical summary of man's physical uniqueness, you are likely to conclude that he is just another primate after all and not so godlike in his aberrances as we commonly fancy him to be.

On the mental or psychological side, we may perhaps anticipate a greater gap between man and the rest of the animal kingdom. Serious and competent scientific attempts to measure animal intelligence do not antedate the present century. Even now the chimpanzee is probably the only subhuman primate whose psychology and intelligence have been explored with moderate thoroughness. We have always assumed that the superiority of our brain mass over that of any anthropoid ape or monkey is more or less a measure of our greater intelligence, and that may indeed be the case. It seems clear, however, that man habitually overestimates his own intelligence and is prone to depreciate that of other animals without investigating them. Individual variation in human intelligence certainly ranges over a vast scale, even if idiots and imbeciles are excluded. The average is much lower than we ordinarily rate it to be. Yet, even if we take the most ungifted groups of savages, with material cultures which seem almost non-existent and social organization meagerly developed, we find them to be using articulate language and, apparently, employing roughly the same reasoning processes which civilized man is supposed to exercise.

It is this faculty of language which seems to be the overt expression of a mental ability which is uniquely human. We shall have occasion to note that apes and other lower primates have a large variety of vocal sounds which they use to express emotion and for signaling purposes. But they cannot, of course, communicate thoughts and ideas, assuming that they have any. How closely the various subhuman primates approximate man in intelligence is a problem which has commanded the attention of some of our most skilled investigators during the past quarter-century and more without resulting in any very precise gradation of primate variation. One of the conclusions of which we are almost certain is that the great apes, which resemble man most closely in physical characteristics, are also closest to man psychologically. The insurmountable obstacle which blocks the way to cultural and mental progress in the anthropoids is dumbness. In vulgar speech we call a person dumb who is stupid, although the word really means inarticulate. However, the colloquial use is justified by the fact that animals which have not the power of speech are enormously limited thereby in intelligence, or in capitalizing upon such intelligence as they may possess by communicating ideas and building culture. As far as I am aware, there is no serious anatomical impediment to speech in great apes. The speech areas in the brain are there, although not highly developed. It is difficult to decide whether apes do not speak because they are of inferior intelligence, or their intelligence is retarded by their inability to speak. These are not mutually exclusive alternatives; it may work both ways. On the whole, we may have to leave the matter, for the present, with the feeble conclusion that the most important correlated differences between man and the rest of the primates are in absolute size of brain and articulate speech with its mental involvements.

A fair comparison of human sociology with that of the subhuman primates demands that we select as the exemplars of our own species relatively simple and uncultured groups of savages whose social behavior is not complicated by all the gadgetry of civilization, including book learning. In spite of the huge advantage of oral tuition and tradition which even the rudest savages have over apes and monkeys, the sociological gap between them is by no means a yawning and unbridgeable abyss. The family is the unit of primate society all the way down. Maternal care and solicitude is constant, but manifested with an apparent intelligence which is highly variable. The participation of the father in family life, and particularly in looking after the young, is certainly greater in the human species than in any kind of ape or monkey, but some display of paternal concern for offspring in trouble is not at all uncommon in subhuman primates.

The permanence of subhuman primate matings probably differs greatly in the species and genera, just as it does in human races, nations, and individual cases. The monogamous pattern certainly occurs in some of the lower primates and there is undoubtedly polygyny, as in man. A sort of limited promiscuity, or group marriage, in which all the adult females of a small clan are accessible to all the males, is attested for the American howling monkeys. It is certainly not a standard form of sex relationship throughout the subhuman primates. Years ago social anthropologists argued bitterly about the probable existence of a state of promiscuity in primitive human society. Many evolutionists, such as Lewis Morgan, postulated that our early ancestors, like the inhabitants of heaven, were "neither married nor given in marriage." Others, such as Westermarck, attempted a refutation by describing the alleged virtuously monogamous habits of the anthropoid apes, although practically nothing was known of their familial organization. Today it is certain that we cannot prove that our ancestors in prehuman stages were either promiscuous or monogamous by citing the forms of the family in our poor relations, even when, as now, certain of them have been observed accurately in the wild. An even greater debate arose about the existence of promiscuity and group marriage among the native Australians. Virtue triumphed, and the evidences of such a practice among, for example, the Dieri tribe were generally declared insufficient and illusory by good Victorian anthropologists. Yet today I doubt that any social anthropologist would attempt to make monogamy or sexual fidelity an important criterion of distinction between human and subhuman primate behavior.

Social groups larger than the biological family or the somewhat loose clan group have not yet been observed in anthropoid apes, but are fairly common among the monkeys. In spite of the tall tales told about some species, particularly baboons, it seems highly improbable that anything of an elaborate social organization has been achieved by primates below the human stage. Although dominance and subordination are often notable as phenomena pertaining to the relationships between sexes or between individual animals of different sexes, the apes and monkeys appear not to have attained much in the way of formalized leadership, rank, social classes, etc. But some human groups, such as Congo pygmies, are little better off in this respect. On the whole, however, the subhuman primates make a very poor showing in social organization, when compared with any but the most backward and poverty-stricken human groups.

The rudest savages in the world today far exceed the chimpanzee, mechanically the most gifted ape, in manual skill and dexterity in the manipulation of objects. It is strange that the subhuman primates so closely approximate man in the anatomical equipment of the fore-limbs, but lag so far back in the utilization of their five prehensile digits. The fact that all primates except man tend to use their hands for locomotion or for support in the trees may partially explain their mechanical ineptitude. Yet the true answer probably lies in the difference between human and subhuman brains. It is fair to say that no primate except man is habitually a tool-using animal, in spite of feeble efforts in that direction which are sometimes observed in apes and monkeys. The whole intricate mass of material culture which man has developed stems from his ability to devise and to use tools. It is a pity that human achievement in this field of activity should have distorted so completely all of man's valuations of other and even more important biological functions, so that the comparative bulk of machines and gadgetry is taken as a measure of human intellectual ability, moral worth, and evolutionary progress. The possession of efficient and powerful tools does give man a superior control over his physical environment, but such power does not imply biological superiority over the apes and monkeys beyond that already possessed by the simplest savages who purposefully fabricate and use crude stone axes. Most of the subsequent growth of material culture is the result of continuous linguistic tradition which enables each succeeding generation to build cumulatively upon the mechanical achievements of the past. There comes a time when the perfection and power of tools contrived by a few ingenious brains put within the hands of the most moronic human animals almost unlimited constructive and destructive potentialities. Many of us are almost as incapable of inventing and understanding the scientific contrivances which we use as are chimpanzees. It is probably easier to operate an airplane than to make a stone arrowhead. At any rate, Harvard students make a better fist at the former than the latter. I have no doubt that the natural tool-making ability with which the human species has been endowed has been atrophied in a great many or even the majority of individuals by dependence upon machines which really do the work with little demand for skill or intelligence on the part of their human operators.

To summarize the entire matter of human separateness from the rest of the primate order, it may be said that bigger brains on the anatomical side, articulate speech, and the use of the hands in creating and employing tools on the functional side seem to be the only important items which we can enumerate. It is difficult to escape the conclusion that all these differences depend upon the larger brain and better functional organization which man has inherited through long lines of human ancestors and even longer lines of apelike and lower-primate precursors. Some primate strain, in one way or another, got off to an evolutionary start with a much more generous endowment of brains and intelligence than any of the numerous allied lines which ultimately gave rise to the present apes and monkeys. There can be no doubt that the original prehuman endowment of brains and intelligence was enhanced in the course of evolution up to the emergence of the fully developed "erect and featherless biped." I am acquainted with no anatomical, physiological, psychological, or cultural evidences that indicate that progressive evolution of the human brain and of the human intelligence has continued since the fifth millennium before Christ, when man succeeded in domesticating animals and cultivating plants. Anyone who believes that his ability to turn the dial of a radio and immediately hear nonsense from the uttermost parts of the earth is a gauge of the mental superiority of modern man would better close this book at once and dismiss the subhuman primates as too remote and too stupid to be worth his attention.

PART I

Ape Aristocrats

INTRODUCTION

AFTER A GREAT DEAL of study of the anatomy of various animals and a moderate amount of investigation of their physiology, zoologists have agreed that the Order of Primates includes not only man and the anthropoid apes but all the monkeys, the lemurs, and the curious little beast called the tarsier. The resemblance between man and these last two types of animals could easily be overlooked by a superficial observer. But anyone who sees a monkey is sure to be impressed, favorably or unfavorably, by its "human" appearance and behavior. The doglike baboons and mandrills seem to depart farther from our pattern of form, but their anatomical divergence is not paralleled in their behavior. The small anthropoid ape, the gibbon, has to be observed closely before the layman realizes that it is closer to man than is the average monkey. However, no one, however ignorant of zoology, can miss the anthropoid, or humanlike, appearance and behavior of the great apes. Two of them, the chimpanzee and the orang-utan, are roughly the same size as man, while the third, the gorilla, is far larger. We tend to admire the gorilla because he is like ourselves, but bigger and stronger, whereas the equality with us in size enjoyed by the chimpanzee and the orang-utan assure them our attention and respect, since nearly all other primates are much smaller than man.

However, in addition to parity or superiority of size, the three great apes have much more important human resemblances, which are also found in the little gibbon. In the first place, the anthropoid apes, like man, lack external tails, whereas all lower primates have them, although they are sometimes very short, and, in the single case of the monkey which is called the Barbary ape, virtually absent. A much more important characteristic which all the anthropoid apes and man have in common is an adaptation for vertical carriage of the trunk. All sit erect and have chests more or less flattened from front to back. The erect sitting or standing posture is made feasible by the suspension of the viscera in the body cavities from sheets of membrane or mesenteries. Thus the "innards" are hitched up so that they do not slump downward when the trunk is held upright. Lower primates and other quadrupeds are likely to have their cargoes and engines shift toward the stern if they are required to sit bolt upright or stand for protracted periods on their hind legs. There are no other obvious physical similarities of the anthropoid apes to man which other lower primates do not share here and there among the various groups.

All the anthropoid apes have another character in common, which is found in only one lower primate. Their arms are longer than their legs, and they use the former for locomotion in the trees in preference to the latter. The habit of hanging by the arms and progressing by arm swings is closely connected both with the elongation and increased strength of these limbs and with the upright or vertical position of the trunk, the fixation of the viscera for that posture, and the flattening of the chest from front to back. No doubt, man's arms have decreased in length since he took to the ground and began to stand and walk erectly. He certainly derived his flat chest and visceral fixation from ape ancestors.

CHAPTER I

Chimpanzee—The Extravert Ape

HABITAT

THE CHIMPANZEE is the "fair-haired boy" of the subhuman primates, partly because he manages to get along with man and to adapt himself to human habits better than any of his fellow apes. More is known about the chimpanzee than about any other ape, monkey, or lemur. It would be easy enough to fill a bulky volume with the interesting and reliable data concerning this animal, most of which have been accumulated within the past quarter of a century. In spite of this embarrassment of riches, psychobiologists feel that they are only beginning to get acquainted with the chimpanzee. Evidently this ape "takes a lot of knowing."

The chimpanzee is a native of western and central equatorial Africa and has a wider distribution than any other anthropoid ape. Roughly, the habitat of the chimpanzee is included in the areas drained by the Congo and the Niger rivers; yet the animal occurs along the banks of other rivers on the West Coast as far north as Gambia and perhaps south of the Congo in Loanda. Most of the chimpanzees, however, dwell north of the Congo River, except in East Africa where they occur from the southern part of the Anglo-Egyptian Sudan southward to the region of Lake Mweru in latitude 8° S. Probably the easternmost limit of the chimpanzee is somewhat to the west of Lake Victoria. South of the big bend of the Congo the chimpanzee was supposed to be absent until the existence of a pygmy race was established in this area in 1929. Interestingly enough, it is in this region that the pygmy form of the African Negro is principally at home.

SPECIES AND VARIETIES

The scientific nomenclature of the chimpanzee is in a hopeless mess, and the number of recognizable species and varieties ranges from 2 to 14, according to the authority consulted. We shall not venture into this morass. Let us be content with recognizing a common, more or less white-faced chimpanzee, a black-faced, bald-headed chimpanzee, and the pygmy chimpanzee, as yet little known. The following is a general description of the ordinary chimpanzee, culled mostly from the works of Yerkes and Schultz.

DESCRIPTION

SIZE AND WEIGHT

The average weight of adult male chimpanzees is about 50 kilos (110.25 pounds) and of females about 40 kilos (88.2 pounds).[1] Actually 19 captive adult females weighed, on the average, 39.9 kilos, and 9 adult males 45.4 kilos, or 100.1 pounds. Of this group the largest female weighed 55 kilos (121.3 pounds) and the largest male 60 kilos (132.3 pounds).[2] However, there is one female at Orange Park, not included in the above tabulations, who weighs 80 kilos, or 176.4 pounds. This animal, Mona, is a sort of circus fat lady. She happens to be the oldest as well as the fattest of all the chimpanzees. I should think it quite possible that unusually large males might sometimes exceed the relatively prodigious weight of this female, who has the further distinction of having given birth to twins.

Yerkes says that the maximum height of the male chimpanzee is approximately 5 feet, and of the adult female 4 feet. Another authority gives 1.7 meters for males and 1.3 meters for females (66.9 inches and 51.2 inches).

STRENGTH

Bauman tested the strength of several chimpanzees by getting them to pull on a rope attached to a dynamometer fixed outside of the cage.[3] One of his males, having an estimated weight of 165 pounds, made right-hand pulls of 847 and 640 pounds. Two-hand pulls of 1,260 pounds and 905 pounds were recorded for a female thought to weigh 135 pounds. Another female, of approximately the same size as the male, pulled 378 pounds. Seven college football players, weighing from 127 to 210 pounds, averaged 175.4 pounds with right-hand pulls, 368.37 and 377.4 pounds for fast and slow two-hand pulls. The almost in-

---

[1]Grether and Yerkes 1940. For complete references see Bibliography.
[2]Schultz 1940a.
[3]Bauman 1923, pp. 432–39; 1926, pp. 1–9.

credible 1,260-pound pull of the 135-pound female was made in a vicious attempt to wreck the apparatus. It would be fairer to compare the arm strength of the ape with the leg strength of a man, since these are the respective limbs specialized for locomotion in the two species.

At the Orange Park laboratory, in April of last year, Dr. Glen Finch showed me an apparatus devised for weight-pulling tests and induced two of the animals to demonstrate. The device consisted of weights suspended by a rope running through a pulley fixed to a crossbar between two uprights. From the pulley the rope led downward to a block attached horizontally to a bench which extended from the uprights. This apparatus was pushed up to the bars of the cage and the chimpanzees, standing erect, pulled on the horizontal rope. The threading of the rope through the pulley and the block greatly increased the amount of work necessary to lift the weights. Bula, an adult female with an approximate weight of 47 kilos (103.6 pounds), was able to lift 7 weights (140 ± 10 pounds). Frank, the adult male in the same cage, who weighs 51.6 kilos (113.8 pounds), was less efficient and could do no better than Bula. Finch remarked that neither could pull nearly as much as Dolph, a 220-pound human attendant, nor as much as Dr. Vincent Nowlis, one of the research psychologists—a brawny young man of the approximate weight of 190 pounds. It should be noted that this strength test required the animals to use their backs and legs from a bipedal stance. It is quite possible that chimpanzees are not so strong as they are commonly supposed to be, although they are undoubtedly mighty in their hands, arms, and shoulders.

COAT

The coat of the chimpanzee ordinarily consists of coarse, straight, black hairs, but brown, reddish brown, grayish, and white hairs appear on various parts of the body. Schultz records that the hair of a female chimpanzee changed color from deep black to gray-brown and, in parts, white, beginning in her seventh year and starting in the sacral region and the outside of the thighs. When this animal died at the age of 14 years, she had more light hairs than dark on her back and lower limbs. Schultz observed similar graying in 3 other chimpanzees of the Johns Hopkins colony, but the changes began later and were not so pronounced. Yerkes thinks that the thickness, color, and distribution of hair in the chimpanzee vary so markedly with health and environmental factors that it is ridiculous for taxonomists to attempt to establish species on the basis of pelage. Some chimpanzees are nearly bald; others have thick head hair. In some the hair is very long on the back and limbs, in others very sparse.

Schultz reports that a fetal chimpanzee (126 days old) had fine black hair several millimeters long on the scalp, gray eyelashes, and a few hairs on the face. At first the rest of the body of the fetal chimp is hairless. The head hair is longest throughout fetal life. Soon after the hair appears on the scalp, short hair develops on the upper back and shoulders, then on the outside of the limbs, then the lower back. On the other parts of the body the hair is very scanty, even at birth.

Skin Color

Schultz has also studied the development of pigmentation in the chimpanzee. In the youngest fetus known (about 104 days old) the only pigment found was on the ears. In Schultz's 126-day chimpanzee fetus, light pigmentation was present everywhere except on the palms, soles, perineal region, nipples, and lips. The head and face were darkest, and the back more heavily pigmented than the chest and abdomen. The general pigmentation of the younger fetuses is light gray and of the older ones medium gray-brown. There are apparently "white-skinned" and dark-skinned chimpanzees. In both kinds the skin pigment becomes intensified in postnatal life. Yerkes says that the skin around the eyes is darker in the white-skinned type than on other parts of the face, whereas in the dark types the pigmentation of the skin on the head and face is uniform. In a white-skinned chimp, noted by Schultz, brown freckles began to appear in the fifth year and became numerous and larger until they eventually covered nearly one third of his otherwise white skin. The hands and feet are often covered with great pigmented blotches, like giant freckles. In the animals (nearly 40 in number) at the Yale Laboratory in Orange Park, there is much variation in skin color. Some have almost black skin; others are coffee-colored. Age darkening and tanning due to exposure are clearly evident. The ears are often heavily freckled. Contrary to what is observed in Negroes, the chimpanzees seem to have heavier pigment on the palms and soles than on the sides and backs of the hands and feet. Dr. Nissen pointed out to me a very dark-skinned animal, which he said had been brought up indoors, and when transferred to the laboratory was nearly albino. I looked into many open chimpanzee mouths, but observed no pigment patches inside of them. The lining of the oral cavity was invariably bright red.

The iris, according to my observations, varies from a clear *café-au-lait* to a light tea color. The sclerotic or "white" of the eye is dark brown, much darker than the iris. The latter has a black outer rim. No patterning of the iris is visible. Pupils are usually contracted and small.

HEAD AND FACE

The adult chimpanzee has a round, low-vaulted brain case with little or no backward projection above the nape of the neck. The forehead is low and receding and culminates in front in a great transverse bar of bone which overhangs the sockets of the eyes. This brow ridge is small and inconspicuous in the young, but grows larger as the face develops with the eruption of the permanent teeth. Most chimpanzees have very large and outstanding ears, almost naked, and mottled, in many cases, with dark patches of pigment. In many the ear seems very soft and floppy—by no means as stiff and rigid as the human ear. The cartilage of which the ear is composed is not thick. Usually the upper and hinder part of the rim of the ear (the helix) is unrolled. Nevertheless, Yerkes has studied at least one chimpanzee which had small ears, set close to the head, as in the gorilla. The pygmy chimpanzee described by Coolidge also has very small ears. On the whole, however, bigger, less degenerate ears distinguish the chimpanzee from the rest of the anthropoid apes and from man. One might guess that the retention of the well-developed external ear would go with more acute hearing, but I know of no evidence which supports such a speculation.

The eyes of the chimp are recessed under the overhang of the brow ridges. The eye opening seems high and relatively narrow. The upper lids are strongly arched, but the lower lids are almost horizontal in the specimens which I have observed. I could not see any eyelashes. When the eyes are open, a wrinkle of the upper lid extends clear across the eyelid and continues inside of the inner corner of the eye, along the root of the nose. This wrinkle is not a true eyefold, since it does not overhang the free edge of the lid. The little fleshy excrescence in the inner corner of the human eye (the caruncula lacrymalis) is present in the chimp, but inconspicuous. The upper eyefold does not cut across the caruncula as in the so-called Mongoloid fold in man and in the orang. The skin below the eyes is heavily wrinkled, as also on the region of the brows. Adults apparently lack eyebrows.

The root and bridge of the nose in the chimpanzee are depressed rather than elevated. There is actually a trough along the place where the arch of the bridge should be. The root, which is virtually without elevation, has a good many heavy transverse wrinkles, and a vertical wrinkle marks the bottom of the V-shaped trough which extends down the middle of the bridge to the tip. An actual fleshy tip of the nose is practically non-existent; the bulbous swelling of the human nose is quite absent. Instead, there is a flat V-shaped area, with the apex directed forward and continuous with the thin septum which divides the nostrils. The latter are directed diagonally backwards and are not surrounded by wings of flesh and cartilage as in man. Altogether, the chimpanzee nose is most inhuman in appearance. Below it the jaws bulge forward into a prominent, wide, and deep convexity overlaid by the sparsely haired upper lip, which is molded to the curve of the jaws, but, nevertheless, is extremely mobile. There is no furrow or philtrum running down the middle of the fleshy integumental upper lip, as in man. The membranous lips (the true lips which are too often painted by the female of our species) are very thin and inconspicuous, although the mouth slit is prodigiously wide. The lips are capable of great protrusion, especially the lower lip, which can be thrust out like a trough, so that the animal can see what is being held between the lips and the lower front teeth. Chimpanzees frequently funnel their lips, especially when making a curious hoo-hoo sound often emitted by nearly all of them. Below the mouth the deep jaw drops away in a receding curve without any chin eminence. Most adult chimps have very projecting, snouty jaws. There seems to be a considerable individual variation in this muzzle development, which is, presumably, greater in males than in females.

When the animal opens its mouth, the incisors and canines look very large and strong, but the back teeth are not much bigger than those of man, and the canines are massive only by human standards of comparison. The palate is U-shaped. Hair on the face is very sparse except along the sides of the cheeks, the hinder angles of the jaws, and below and behind the place where the chin ought to be.

The head of the chimp seems to be planted directly on its shoulders with little or no neck. However, this illusion is due to the heavy and bulging musculature which necessarily supports the overbalanced jaws. Very young chimps have short but slender necks.

TRUNK AND LIMBS

The shoulders of the chimpanzee are sloping and rounded. They appear to be massive, more because of the depth of the shoulder region than its width. The chest is very deep and proportionately narrow. The breasts in the female are disklike and relatively inconspicuous. On the whole, the trunk of the chimpanzee gives the

YOUNG CHIMPANZEE

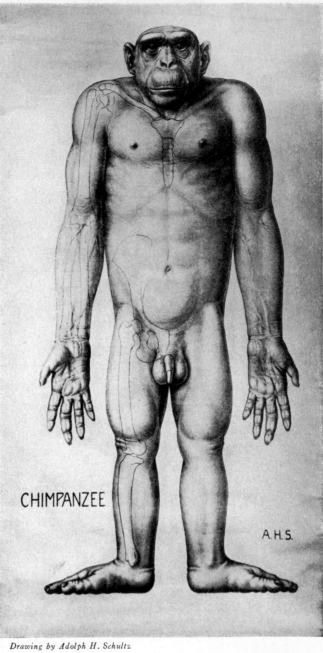

CHIMPANZEE

A.H.S.

Drawing by Adolph H. Schultz

PROPORTIONS OF ADULT CHIMPANZEE

impression of length and narrowness, rather than of great breadth. The pelvis is narrow and the buttocks almost undeveloped. The bulk of this animal is not so great as often described; nor is the abdominal region necessarily protrusive except in obese individuals.

The upper limbs of the chimpanzee are long and massive, so that in the erect position the finger tips of the hanging arms reach to the knees or even farther. However, there is undoubtedly a good deal of variation in arm length. The greater part of this upper-limb elongation is in the forearm and the hand, rather than in the upper arm. The excessive development of the upper extremity is correlated with locomotion through the trees by arm-swinging and also with suspension from the arms. The arms are so strong that a chimp can easily hang for a long time by one arm, employing the other for a variety of purposes. The thumb is usually diminutive and short, the fingers very long and coarse in comparison with the breadth of the palm. Yet in some chimpanzees the fingers are said to be stubby. Usually the middle knuckles of the fingers are covered with thick, calloused skin, as a result of the habit of resting upon these knuckles in four-footed progression. Commonly the four outer fingers are webbed part way up the first joint. The backs of the hands and fingers are more or less hairy, the palms naked and showing flexure lines and papillary ridges similar to those of the human hand. The nails are narrow and curved. The index finger is definitely shorter than the fourth and the thumb hardly reaches to the base of the former.

The legs of the chimpanzee are short and clumsy, and the foreleg is not elongated with reference to the thigh as is the forearm in comparison with the upper arm. The foot of the chimpanzee is generally described as long and narrow, but the great toe is massive, set back, and projecting inward like a thumb. It can be opposed to the other digits in grasping, so that the foot grip is undoubtedly very strong. The four outer toes are relatively and absolutely long and partially webbed. The third toe is invariably the longest and the fourth usually is second in length. The nails are oval and usually dark brown to black in color. The heel is rather small and narrow.

Genitals

The external genital organs of chimpanzees are profoundly different in appearance from those of man. In the female the genital area is a great mound which projects posteriorly like a bustle. The anus and the vulva present a very large expanse of bright red, naked, and smooth skin which looks like mucous membrane. The size of the genital mound and of the vulva and anus depends to a great extent upon the phase of the sexual cycle, but they are always very large, even when not swollen. There seems to be no specialized pubic hair. Lateral to the vulva on the genital mound are areas of thick, horny skin which correspond to the ischial callosities found in many Old World monkeys. In Frank, a vigorous adult male at Orange Park, there are large, saucerlike, gray-blue patches of thickened skin on each side of the anus. The anus is not recessed in a fold between the buttocks in these animals, since the buttocks are very poorly developed. Schultz found that 42 of 116 chimpanzees examined had ischial callosities (36 per cent). A few of his fetal specimens had incipient callosities.

The penis is very thin, elongated, and pencil-like. Usually in adults it is difficult to discern the scrotum, since the inguinal region is covered with long hair. In a newborn baby a few hours old the scrotum was visible and well developed.

The genital mound in the female has so much bright red skin exposed that it looks tender and sore. However, the region is apparently not sensitive, since the animals sit upon it without apparent discomfort and rub it casually against the bars and netting of their cages.

THE CHIMP AT HOME

Dr. Henry Nissen of Yale University has made the pioneer study of the chimpanzee in his native haunts.[4] Such a task necessitates a great amount of skill, endurance, patience, and disregard of hardship. The results are not always exciting, but they are worth much more than travelers' tales, which are likely to be more picturesque than accurate. Nissen stalked the chimpanzee in the forests of French Guinea for 64 days, on 49 of which he managed to observe one or more groups. He observed in all between 56 and 63 groups, but probably not more than 20 to 25 different groups. The number of chimpanzees in a group ranged from 4 to 14, with an average of 8.5. In two instances a couple of groups were combined, apparently temporarily, so that the number was increased to 16 and 18. Several times he saw groups mingle, but he could not ascertain whether this mixing up resulted in reorganization.

The composition of the chimpanzee group is hard to determine accurately, because it is difficult to sex the animals from a distance. In 6 cases Nissen saw at least 2 mature males in the same group, and in

[4] Nissen 1931.

9 cases more than one mature female. He could sex only about one quarter of the animals observed, but of these 65 per cent were female. This result checks with the fact that the chimpanzees collected at the Pastoria Laboratory in French Guinea are three-quarters female. These observations do not settle the question of the polygamous or monogamous habits of the animal, although the chances appear to favor the former possibility. Solitary animals were sometimes seen, but the hermits were not always males. The natives assert that females go off by themselves when they are about to have babies and do not rejoin their groups for a couple of weeks. One lonely female observed by Nissen appeared to have had a baby recently, but the baby was not in evidence—hidden, according to the natives.

Nissen was impressed with the large proportion of immature animals in most chimpanzee groups. About half of the animals in any group seemed to be less than half the size of the largest in that group, and 25 per cent of the groups included infants which had to be carried. It is thus possible that a single group is composed of one large polygynous family, with occasionally some grown-up sons still clinging to the family tree. About 75 per cent of the chimps were white-faced, but the black-faced individuals were always mingled with them, apparently regardless of age and sex. Most animals appeared to be in good condition, although a number of females were lean and a few adults of both sexes fat. No cripples, senile animals, or obviously diseased chimps were seen. Yet the chimpanzee catches cold in the wild, since Nissen heard coughing and sneezing on several occasions.

Chimpanzees wander about in a random fashion and possibly do not stay within the limits of a definite territory as do gibbons and howler monkeys. Nissen never saw a group remain for a day within the diameter of one mile. He followed one group from 5:30 A.M. of one day to 8:45 A.M. of the next day and then was too fatigued to continue without going back to camp. A summary of this long observation of a single group gives us the best picture of chimpanzee life in the wild which is now available.

A Day and a Night with a Chimpanzee Group

Nissen started out at 4:30 A.M., heard chimp cries an hour later, and located the group in another hour. He had to follow by crawling through the thick underbrush. Cries of the animals, feces, and trampled areas helped him in the trailing. Meanwhile, he was thoroughly bitten by ants. At 9:35 A.M. he saw 10 or more chimps feeding in a tree about 500 feet away. He watched them for 15 minutes, and followed when they descended and headed south. Twice they crossed a stream averaging 20 feet in width, in both cases over a log or stepping-stones where they could avoid wetting their feet. At 10:15 A.M. a chimp spotted the observer while the animals were feeding in a tree 75 feet away, and the band took up the trail again. Nissen had to wait for his porters and get some food, so that he could not resume the chase until 2 P.M. He located them at 5:20 P.M. They were walking along a slope, and one large female had her arm around a little one who walked at her side. Two pairs of adults passed each other at close range, going in opposite directions and paying no attention to each other. Ten fairly large animals were leisurely going uphill. At 5:40 P.M. 9 of the chimps came down the hill again. The largest was leading, but no infants or very young animals were in the band. They were in single file, but spread out during the slow descent. Here and there they stopped to eat leaves from low shoots. They seemed to be suspicious of the presence of the observers, although the latter were well hidden. One animal loitered behind, while the rest disappeared in the jungle. This large animal carried a branch of Naray pods, and would occasionally sit down, eat a couple, and then go on. He disappeared, carrying the branch in his mouth.

At 6:10 P.M. the first of the group ascended a tree in plain view, and the others soon followed it up into the tree. There were 11 or 12 of them. The first animal built a nest for itself in exactly 3 minutes, and the others followed suit, but sometimes laid off nest-building to eat. The nest-building went on until 6:50 P.M. Loud sounds of breaking branches and occasional mild "fear-pain" cries featured this activity. Nissen could see no infants in the nesting group. At 7 P.M. he heard several choruses of panting cries, started by one animal, with the others joining in. These good-night songs were not loud, but rather pleasing and harmonious. Nissen with one native spent a miserable, sleepless night on the spot.

Between 7 and 9:45 P.M. he occasionally heard single cries, either by chimps or green monkeys. It was windy and cold. Dawn came at 5 A.M. Soon the chimps began to move about, eat, and utter cries. The early risers descended to the ground at 5:15 A.M. and the two laziest stayed in bed until 6:45 A.M. The group moved off at about 7:10. Another group, which had evidently nested near by but out of sight of Nissen, also took up the trail. Under the trees where Nissen's group had nested were deposits of urine and feces. The 10 nests were 65 to 85 feet aboveground. Nissen followed the group for half a mile and then gave up at 8:45 A.M.

Chimpanzees get up early—in the dry season before sunrise, but,

YOUNG CHIMPANZEE IN COMMON SUSPENSORY POSITION

Photograph John Haeseler

YOUNG CHIMPANZEE IN ORDINARY QUADRUPEDAL POSTURE

according to native accounts, an hour or more after sunrise in the rainy season. They build nests in the dry season at dusk, but do not go to bed until dark. Nissen thinks that they dislike exposure to the burning rays of the sun. They are very careful to stay in the shade and spend a good deal of the hottest part of the day in resting. They may be in shady crotches of trees at these periods, but are oftener on the ground. They never have been seen by Nissen to occupy their nests during the siesta time. In the tree the resting animal may grasp an overhead branch or squat on a bough, leaning against the vertical trunk. On the ground chimpanzees are likely to make day beds in shady places by breaking off small trees or leafy branches. Occasionally they bend and twist small saplings to make canopies over the day beds. Usually, however, they pick shady places. Nissen doubts that chimps do much daytime sleeping. At night they make cries mainly when disturbed. The natives state that chimps have carnival nights when there is bright moonlight, and vocalize all night long. Nissen is skeptical about these jamborees.

LOCOMOTION

An exceptional kind of walking, apparently used when a chimp is going up- or downhill, is a crutch gait in which the weight is borne upon the forelimbs and the hind limbs are swung together between them. The usual gait on the ground is a slow walk or various forms of running and leaping. Both in walking and in running the animal moves in a slightly sidling fashion (i.e., the main axis of the body is at an angle with the line of progression). In the quadrupedal gait on the ground the present writer has noted that chimpanzees rest on the knuckles of their hands, but sometimes the knuckles are directed forward and sometimes outward. The toes are usually semi-flexed with the exception of the great toe, which is thrust inward at a wide angle. Chimpanzees never walk upon the knuckles of their toes so far as I have observed. Nissen is of the opinion that chimpanzees can move faster than men over uneven, underbrush-covered ground. The run of the chimpanzee is a sort of lope or canter; not very fast, according to what I have seen. These apes can walk up a tree without difficulty, even when the trunk is four or five feet in diameter. They usually back down, but Nissen says that they may come down head-first if the tree is one of small diameter. The more usual way of descending to the ground, if the tree has low-lying branches, is to walk out to the end of a branch until it bends down with the weight of the animal, so that he can step off or hang by his arms and make a straight drop. Nissen notes that chimpanzees do not ordinarily travel for any great distance through the trees. They get down and walk on the ground. Nissen has seen chimpanzees occasionally traveling from one tree to another for short distances. The jumps are outward and downward, the animal first swinging by the arms and then letting go at the end of a forward swing. I have had opportunity to watch the chimpanzee arm-swinging or brachiating in the cages at Orange Park. Usually progression from one part of the cage ceiling to another is achieved by alternate arm swings, performed very smoothly with full advantage taken of perfect rhythm and momentum. The horizontal movements seem to be performed more by body swing and thrust than by arm pull. Frank, a fine adult male, swings very rapidly along the open wirework cage roof toward the rear part, which is roofed with concrete. He ducks under this concrete part in his final swing, almost hitting his head and slapping his wrist hard against the concrete roof. He lands on the concrete floor with a smack, his legs flexed. Apparently the bent legs take up the shock. These semiflexed legs, upon which the chimp stands when in the erect posture, may not be very efficient for prolonged weight-bearing, but, with the prehensile feet, they are enormously springy and efficient in jumping. The chimp bounces up and down on his bent legs like a rubber ball. A chimp walks in the erect posture when it is carrying something, or when it wants to. The leg is never extended completely upon the thigh (i.e., the gait is always a bent-knee gait). The trunk is inclined slightly forward; the great toes thrust inward and make a wide-open angle with the long axis of the feet. The upright walk is waddling and slightly sidewise. I doubt that a chimpanzee could run bipedally or stand still in the upright position for any prolonged period without excessive fatigue.

Nissen thinks that wild chimpanzees spend about one third of their waking hours in trees. There is no evidence that chimpanzees swim. Whenever Nissen found a chimpanzee trail crossing a stream, it went over stepping-stones or natural tree-trunk bridges.

NESTS

The chimpanzee builds its nests in many kinds of leafy trees, but not in palms. The number of nests Nissen found in a single tree varied from one to 13. All the chimpanzees in a group do not invariably nest in the same tree, but they often do, and usually the nests are not widely scattered. The average height from the ground is 38.4 feet; the range 13 to 105 feet. The nests are made by breaking back and intertwining the branches, so that their leafy tips just reach the floor of the nest. The flat or concave nests have a circular to oval pattern and may rest on a crotch, or may be supported entirely by the intertwined, half-broken branches. The nest is lined with leaves, either growing on the broken branches or added by breaking off additional twigs. Nests are very smooth inside. The trick of the nest-building is to break branches at just the right spot to bend them for support. Sometimes branches 2 inches thick are broken for nesting. The number used is large. The larger nests, for big animals, are likely to be built among the larger branches. Most nests are placed so that the clear sky is overhead. An animal which visits and eats during nest-making may consume 25 minutes at the job, but a chimp working deliberately but steadily will complete the nest in 3 minutes. The chimp stands about in the middle of the place where the nest is to be and works at it from above. When it is finished, he stands or sits in it for a while, or may even leave it temporarily. The chimp sleeps lying on his back or on his side, probably with his legs and arms drawn up close to the body. Only one animal makes a nest or sleeps in a nest, with the exception of infants and very young animals which sleep with their mothers. It seems probable that a chimpanzee ordinarily builds a new nest every night, but Nissen has evidence that some nests have been reused.

Food and Feeding

By observing chimpanzees feeding and by examining trees and feces, Nissen was able to collect a list of 34 foods eaten by the chimpanzee during the dry season in a limited area of French Guinea. His inventory shows that 28 of the 34 foods are fruits, 3 stalks or stems, 2 blossoms, and one leaves. He thinks it possible that chimps also eat birds, rodents, eggs, etc., but has not seen any of them do it. Most of the diet is highly astringent and sour. The animals seem to prefer unripe food.

Nissen thinks that chimpanzees may spend between 3 and 6 hours per day in feeding, with 2 main periods of ravenous eating (early morning and late afternoon). During these hungry periods food is bolted rapidly and without much discrimination. When the animal is nearly satiated, it feeds lazily, rejects a good deal, and wastes large amounts. The food concentration is so low that a large bulk has to be swallowed.

Chimps sit, recline, stand, or squat on a branch and reach out with a free arm to pluck the fruit and convey it by hand to the mouth, or they may break off a twig with fruit on it and hold it to the mouth, eating from it directly, or the limb may be pulled and bent toward the mouth, where it can be stripped by hand or eaten directly. The feet are used to bend or break the branches, but Nissen never saw food conveyed to the mouth by foot.

Some foods are swallowed whole, some chewed and partly spit out; others are partly eaten and the rest rejected. An animal usually remains in one spot until all the food within reach is consumed. The ground below is littered with the debris of the messy feeding. Sometimes the animal group starts away before an individual has finished his meal. He may then break off a branch with fruit and take it with him.

Nissen saw only two chimpanzees drinking. Each crouched at the edge of a stream and lowered his head until he could suck (not lap) the water.

DEFECATION

Defecation probably takes place soon after rising, and never in the nest. The number of feces under a tree was carefully counted by our painstaking observer and found to correspond quite accurately with the number of nests. Elimination during the daytime is an irregular and individual matter. Nissen thinks that each animal defecates at least twice and probably three or four times daily. Hard feces do not occur, but most of them are firmer than those usually eliminated by captive chimps. Nissen noticed that, when a certain sugary and mealy fruit called Naray was available, the chimps, when first eating it, tended to have diarrhea, but soon got over it. Otherwise diarrhea was infrequent and, when present, could usually be connected with fright. Most of the fecal matter contained a good deal of undigested material —seeds, whole nuts, berries, fruit stones, etc.

It is a curious fact that this careful observer actually saw chimpanzees defecating only three times (quite contrary to the experience of Carpenter with the howler monkeys, which habitually let loose when directly above him). When defecating on the march, the animal keeps moving, but in a nesting tree seems to be careful to have the excrement drop to the ground.. Urination certainly occurs also in the morning. The urine may be almost colorless or dark brown, but never has a strong odor. These excremental details may not be pleasant to read, but they are most important to observe.

SOCIAL LIFE

Nissen's observations of social life among wild chimpanzees were very limited because of the difficulty of getting near the animals. He saw nothing which could be interpreted as the despotic domination of the group by any single large male, although he noticed several

times that the largest animal was leading the group—in one case a
female. He saw a good deal of playing among the immature chimpanzees—games of tag, wrestling, play-fighting.

Very young animals are usually carried by the mother. They cling
to her chest or abdomen; she does not hold them. At times the young
ride upon the backs of adults. In one case an adult male saw Nissen,
ran toward him, and picked up a chimpanzee baby which had wandered in the direction of the human observer.

Chimpanzee Noise-Making

Chimpanzees make a tremendous racket in the forest. A considerable part of this noise is produced by beating with hands and
feet upon hollow logs and the buttresses of trees. This drumming is
not rhythmic. Stamping on the ground is also frequent, but produces
vibrations rather than noise. Nissen classifies vocal sounds into five
categories: the excitement or panting cry in many variations of pitch
and intensity; the fear-pain cry—a high-pitched scream; barking;
whimpering or whining; an open, soft, abbreviated bark which he
calls "food-muttering." He guesses that 90 per cent of the noise is
produced when the animals are on the ground, but usually noise
ceases when a human observer is detected. Consequently, Nissen had
little opportunity to observe the chimpanzees making noises at close
quarters. He is strongly of the opinion that the noises not only are
expressive of emotion, but are also a rudimentary means of communication and signaling.

THE SEX CYCLE AND MATING

In the female chimpanzee the area around the external genital
organs which is called the sexual skin begins a series of periodic
swellings at adolescence. Similar swellings are observed in many Old
World monkeys, but not in man, nor (usually) in the orang-utan
and the gibbon. This swelling begins at a time when most of the
second dentition has already erupted and at ages apparently varying
between 7 and 9 years.[5] It is a prelude to menstruation, which may
not begin for several months or even a couple of years. The onset of
menstruation has been observed in chimpanzees at various ages, from
5 years (an estimate) to 9 years 9 months. In the macaque it begins
at 3 years, and in man at the average age of 15½ years, although there
are great individual, racial, and climatic variations.

The sexual cycle of the chimpanzee averages approximately 36 days,

[5] Schultz and Snyder 1935, pp. 193–205.

which is 6 to 7 days longer than that of man and the macaque.[6] The cycle ordinarily begins with a 3-day bleeding period, followed by 5 or 6 days in which the sexual skin is quiescent. It then begins to swell up, reaching a maximum in about one week. On the twenty-sixth day the swelling begins to subside. The period of greatest fertility in the chimpanzee seems to lie between the sixteeth and twentieth days in animals with a 33- to 37-day cycle. During these few days the female is physiologically most receptive to coitus. Of 289 mating opportunities studied in the Yale primate laboratory, 75 per cent of the 175 resulting copulations took place within this 5-day period.

By collecting 23-hour urine specimens from 2 adult females throughout the sexual cycle and from 4 adult males, it was possible to assay the excretion of certain hormones.[7] In the females peaks of estrogen excretion coincided with maximal genital swelling and with the premenstrual period. The females excreted half as much androgenic substances as the males and somewhat more estrogenic. The amount of these substances excreted by the chimpanzees was intermediate between that excreted by man and by the macaque, but nearer the amount put forth by the monkey. No relationship between these excretions and sexual behavior was discovered.

Very careful observations of 545 experimental matings between chimpanzees have been conducted at the Yale Laboratories of Primate Biology, Orange Park, Florida.[8] The male and the female were put into adjacent cages and the door was opened so that they could come together. The period of observation was 15 minutes. If the male is interested, he may run forward to meet or to pursue the female, or may await her, making postures and gestures indicating a desire for sexual contact. Ordinarily, the female responds quickly by running to him and crouching low or flat upon the ground with limbs flexed and genitalia presented to him. The male reacts by moving forward to bend over her back, with his hands on her shoulders or sides or touching the floor. In this position the copulation is effected and lasts in various pairs from 5 to 30 seconds. If successful and satisfactory, it is likely to be followed by "manual, oral, or olfactory self- or mutual-examination of the genitalia, or by grooming." The female is the arbiter of this act. She welcomes it, tolerates it, rejects it, prolongs it, or terminates it, according to her own sweet will. The male is "suitor and servitor, not lord and dictator." Yerkes and Elder think that the preliminaries and rituals of sexual inter-

[6]Elder and Yerkes 1936b, pp. 119–43.
[7]Fish, Young, and Dorfman 1941, pp. 585–92.
[8]Yerkes and Elder 1936.

course between chimpanzees may be more varied and prolonged in a state of nature. These experimental matings in captivity are quick and businesslike. Occasionally the female avoids the male, while luring him on. He follows, slapping the floor. This may be courtship. The male, before he has access to the female, apparently recognizes instantaneously that she is in condition for mating. He therefore adopts an expectant attitude and generally is not disappointed. Postures, gestures, and vocal noises are evidently very meaningful to chimpanzee consorts. But matings are much affected by immaturity, inexperience, unfamiliarity, and uncongeniality. The female seems to learn her way round in sexual behavior prior to maturation, but the inexperienced male is awkward, puzzled, often futile in his sexual efforts and generally inadequate. The female, on the contrary, is from the beginning efficient and co-operative.

The female chimpanzees vary more in their sexual behavior than do the males. Certain females seem exceptionally subservient to the males and willing to mate at any period of the sexual cycle. One female at Orange Park, not inappropriately named May, was a coquette given to luring the men on. Another, Mimi, was extremely frigid; another usually timid and unwilling; while one seemed to be so highly sexed that the observers accuse her of nymphomania. Some males are highly selective and fastidious; others (perhaps younger and less experienced) are likely to accept consorts impulsively and irrespective of their suitability at the moment. The female took the initiative in 85 per cent of cases when the matings coincided with the period of maximum swelling; at other times of the sexual cycle in only 65 per cent of cases. However, it is clear enough that chimpanzee females are, in these matters, no shrinking violets. The female is especially eager and receptive at certain phases of her sexual cycle. At other times she may be unenthusiastic but submissive, or even persistent in her refusal. These variations are dependent not only upon the female's temperament and her temporary physiological condition, but also upon how much she likes or fears the male. One particularly strong, mature, experienced, and courageous female treated three male mates quite differently. She accepted all eagerly when she was in the proper physiological condition. When her desire was weak or waning, she bluffed and intimidated one of the males, acted casually familiar and confident of the self-control of another, and with the third was cautious and conciliatory and submitted to copulation when necessary. Both males and females display marked individual preferences and antagonisms.

Copulation does not ordinarily take place between chimpanzees when the female is menstruating, pregnant, or nursing an infant. At these times the female seems to lack sexual desire and does not attract the male. When matings are effected during pregnancy, the female may submit, but is likely to display discomfort, uneasiness, and nervous tension. In one case the ultimate outcome of such attempts was recalcitrant behavior and fighting on the part of the female.

PREGNANCY AND PARTURITION

The average duration of 11 chimpanzee pregnancies from the beginning of the last menstruation to parturition is 251 days.[9] If the pregancy is counted from date of impregnation (usually about the middle of the sexual cycle) to, but not including, the date of birth, the average duration of 13 chimpanzee gestations is 236 days.[10] This period is about 30 days shorter than that of man, but considerably longer than that of the macaque (163 conception days).

Menstruation ceases during pregnancy in the chimpanzee, as in man and the macaque. Certain substances have been discovered in the urine of man which led to the Ascheim-Zondek tests of pregnancy. These substances have been noted in the urine of the chimp and the orang during pregnancy, but they are not constant and the test is apparently unreliable for chimpanzee pregnancy. The genital swelling persists for a time during pregnancy, but then disappears. In the latter part of the third month of pregnancy in the case of Evo, a Johns Hopkins animal, her nipples became enlarged and slightly firmer. During the sixth month she was observed repeatedly to touch and to lick her nipples. By this time her abdomen was definitely enlarged, so that she could not get through a door built for smaller females and for exclusion of large males. Evo became violently ill on the 188th day after onset of her last menstruation and a week later had a miscarriage.

Another chimpanzee proceeded normally with gradual increase in weight, and successfully bore her baby. The first definite uterine contraction was observed at 5:15 P.M., followed by another in 15 minutes. The animal was restless and uneasy and kept exploring her genital region. She was given a couple of large, clean pieces of burlap and immediately arranged them as a nest. At 6:31 P.M. the mother assumed a crouching position and expelled a small quantity·of fluid. The delivery of the head required about 2 minutes after it was first visible in the vaginal opening. The mother lay on her side, supporting the head of

[9]Schultz and Snyder 1935, p. 199.
[10]Elder and Yerkes 1936a, pp. 409–21.

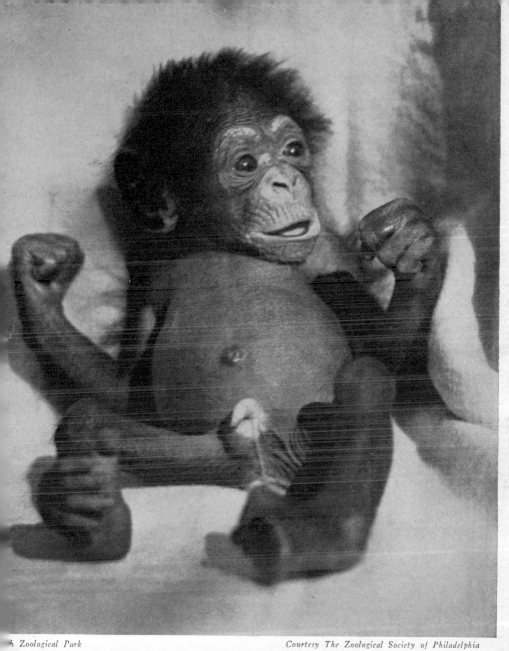

VERY YOUNG INFANT CHIMPANZEE

HUMANOID BEHAVIOR IN THE IMMATURE CHIMPANZEE

Photographs John Haeseler

the infant in one hand. At 6:35 P.M. the entire body was delivered in a single contraction, and the placenta was expelled 3 minutes later. The presentation was vertex, with the occiput anterior. Josie, the mother, first busied herself in licking up the fluids and at 6:41 picked up the infant, which she soon cuddled to her breast. The mother consumed the afterbirth within an hour after delivery. The infant was a strong, 2-kilo male, which was clinging firmly to the mother's hair a few minutes after birth. There was very little hemorrhage at birth but some postpartum loss of blood for 48 hours.

Elder and Yerkes, from whom the above account of Josie's parturition has been abstracted, summarize 14 single births and one twin birth. In one case the mother died of puerperal sepsis 15 days after the birth; in another the infant died about 24 hours after birth, probably from head injuries at or after birth. Most of the other births were entirely normal and labor was not difficult. The time of labor varies from 30 minutes to 5 hours. The placenta is usually expelled almost immediately, but one case of a retention for 30 hours has been reported. The mother ate the placenta in 8 of the 15 cases. This procedure is thought to be normal.

The chimpanzee mother loses a little weight in the first months of pregnancy, but at the end has gained on the average 5.33 kilos ($11\frac{3}{4}$ pounds). Since she loses 5.07 kilos after the birth, she comes out about even.[11]

Most remarkable is the consistent improvement of the female chimpanzee's disposition during pregnancy. An irritable, unfriendly, and disagreeable animal becomes gentle, affectionate, and co-operative. Whether this phenomenon has human parallels or contrasts the reader may decide from his own experience, if he has any.

MATERNAL CARE

The psychobiologists of Yale University have had ample opportunity to observe at the Orange Park laboratory how the chimpanzee mother does her job.[12] Two or three of the earlier observers of chimpanzee births in captivity have recorded what seem to be attempts of the mother artificially to stimulate respiration in the newly born infant by putting her mouth to its lips and blowing, or by sucking the tongue from the infant's mouth and then breathing deeply in and out. Such manipulation of the new baby has not been seen at Orange Park. The mother at once accepts the infant as her

[11]Grether and Yerkes 1940, p. 169.
[12]Yerkes and Tomilin 1935, pp. 321–58.

personal property and handles it freely, gently, and more or less skillfully, encouraging it to cling to her breast and abdomen. She gives much attention to the baby's toilet, grooming it with her lips, teeth, fingers, and nails, but not with her tongue. Much of her time is spent in removing from the baby's hair extraneous matter, loose particles, parasites, etc., and in cleaning wounds and abrasions. Some of the mothers go to such extremes in this task that they practically denude their infants of hair. One animal, Josie, was seen carefully plucking all the white hairs out of her infant's eyebrows. In one of 12 births of chimpanzees the mother was thrown into a paroxysm of fear by the sight of the fetus and the afterbirth and definitely refused to have anything to do with her baby, which had to be raised on the bottle.[13]

The infant usually locates a maternal nipple speedily, with or without the assistance of the mother, and begins to suck. When it actually begins to get milk from the breast is not certain—probably not for a day or two. Exclusive breast-feeding continues from 3 to 6 months, according to maternal behavior and other circumstances. Some mothers discourage or prevent their young from taking supplementary food during the nursing period. Taking food from the baby at

---

[13]In recent years at Orange Park it has become the practice to remove the baby from the mother as soon as possible, so that it will not become infected with intestinal parasites. Thus all the Orange Park chimpanzee babies are now bottle-fed. On April 16, 1941, I had the opportunity of observing some of the difficulties involved in this task of getting the infant from the mother. On the previous day, Wendy, the expectant mother, had given some signs of the imminence of the event. I had spent a good deal of the day in front of her cage, but nothing happened. On the morning of the sixteenth, the day on which I was to end my visit to the laboratory, I arrived somewhat later than usual, because I had been packing. To my disgust I found that Wendy had had her baby about half an hour earlier. Drs. Nissen and Finch were at the cage making observations and preparing to attempt the removal of the infant. One does not merely walk into the cage and grab it. One does not walk into cages of full-grown chimpanzees, anyhow. Wendy had the baby in her arms and was trailing the long umbilical cord and placenta on the floor. Each chimp has a drinking fountain in the outdoor cage, and the water had been turned off so that Wendy could not drink and was getting very thirsty. Nissen induced her to come to the bars of the cage and offered her a large cupful of a mixture of water, grape juice, and Nembutal. Drinking this draught would eventually put her under, so that the cage could be entered and the baby taken. Wendy took a good mouthful of the mixture and immediately spit it out and threw the cup with the rest of it on the floor. She retired to the back of the cage in apparent disgust, taking the baby, of course. I think that Dr. Nissen said that the Nembutal Mickey Finn had been successfully administered to her when she had her last baby, but it was obviously "no go" this time. The next method attempted was to get the animal to stay up against the bars long enough so that a good, large dose of the drug could be injected with a hypodermic syringe. During the several hours of that morning Nissen and Finch worked patiently at this task, but had not succeeded when I had to leave at noon. I subsequently learned that the job was successfully accomplished after lunch.

this stage may be due to maternal greed or perhaps to some biological urge to safeguard the milk supply by seeing that the demand made upon it is constant. However, after a few months the mother usually encourages the infant to eat supplementary food and the youngster becomes adept at thwarting Mother's attempts to get food away from it. If a chimpanzee baby is left with its mother, it will keep on nursing, more or less, for 2 or 3 years, although it may be, and probably is, nutritionally independent of her milk supply, since it can eat anything she eats. A varied milk, cereal, fruit, and vegetable diet is provided at the Orange Park laboratory and chimpanzees thrive on this from the age of 6 months on.

The mother starts playing with her baby at an early stage, and by the end of the year the baby has taken over the initiative in these frolics. The mother begins by tickling and gently biting the infant, to induce it to smile and otherwise contort its face. Then she pushes, pulls, and drags it, and the infant responds vigorously. Later crawling, striking, climbing, sliding, tumbling, rolling, and chasing are added to the infantile repertoire. Some mothers play with their babies a great deal and others very little. A number of the maternal attentions are definitely for the purpose of teaching the youngster certain activities. This teaching begins about the third month. The earliest of these lessons is a stretching exercise in which the mother lies on her back, holds the feet of the baby against her abdomen or chest with her hands, and pulls it into an erect position with her feet, as if trying to show it how to stand up. I saw Wendy doing something of this sort to her baby when it was a couple of hours old.

The baby, immediately after birth, clings to the hair of its mother's abdomen with hands and feet, perhaps with one foot in each of the maternal groins, supported or moved now and then by the mother. The baby at first has the ability only to cling. After a while it makes vague and weak efforts to climb up the abdomen and reach the breasts. The mother shifts it about now and then. After the first couple of weeks it gets much more vigorous and mobile and has to be shoved away from the breasts instead of being assisted toward them. The abdominal position of the infant "in arms" continues to about the fifth or seventh month. Thereafter, when the infant wants a ride, it clings to a maternal leg or arm, as to the trunk of a tree, or climbs upon the mother's back and rides jockey-fashion. Most of the young chimps observed by Yerkes prefer to ride a leg or an arm rather than to sit upon the back. They continue to scuttle back to the abdominal position when frightened.

A part of the chimpanzee mother's job is to teach the baby to stand, crawl, walk, and climb. Chimpanzee mothers either belong to the conservative, careful school of educators or are "progressive." The former type patiently and carefully encourages the baby to stand up by holding it erect and allowing it to pull itself up, clinging to her hair, first within the circlet of her arms, and gradually without such help and protection. The progressive variety pays little or no attention and lets the infant get along on its own, as best it may. The brat is allowed to "express itself." When it has learned to stand up, with or without support, the careful mother is likely to carry it over to the side of the cage, which, at Orange Park, has a 2-inch-mesh wire netting. She may place its hands on the vertical wall and then withdraw, leaving the youngster standing or clinging to the vertical surface. Under such circumstances the baby invariably begins to climb upward. When it reaches the roof and gets "stuck," it begins to cry, and the mother promptly comes and takes it down. This climbing practice takes weeks before the young chimp is able to climb sideways and backwards, as well as up. A still later stage of more difficult climbing is negotiating the horizontal ceiling, first by clinging with all fours, later by swinging from the arms alone. Mothers use gestures and vocal noises in this tuition, as well as directing and assisting by holding the baby. One mother was too fat and lazy to climb the ceiling herself; consequently, her children were retarded in learning this activity.

The chimp baby learns to walk first on all fours, and then on its hind limbs. The mother may take the youngster by one hand and half lead, half drag it. It follows on three extremities as best it can. Or she may crouch down in front of it and coax it to creep or walk to her. If the legs are not used properly, she may place a large hand under the small body and raise it from the floor, encouraging a standing walk on all fours. Crawling precedes walking during the time when the legs are too weak to support the weight of the body. Yerkes and his colleagues have noticed that the chimp, when first walking, places palms and soles flat upon the ground and only some weeks later begins to walk on the knuckles of its fingers and with partially contracted toes. Age of quadrupedal walking seemingly varies with the individual baby, as in the case of man. The range mentioned is from the fifth to the twelfth month. Bipedal walking begins in the second half of the first year and seems no more difficult for the chimp than the four-footed gait. Indeed, Yerkes thinks that the facility in bipedal locomotion may vary inversely with age.

Chimpanzee mothers get to understand their babies thoroughly. They are able to forestall their needs and to interpret correctly every infantile posture and movement. Yet the mother who is having her first baby is bewildered, uncertain, and clumsy in comparison with the experienced mother. The baby makes various kinds of noises: whines, screams, barks, shouts, whimperings. The mother seems to interpret these more by their abruptness, pitch, and volume than by type. She responds differently in many cases to the same kind of call. Her cautious and protective attitude toward the infant is marked at first, but gradually relaxes, although she is always ready to rush forward and defend it if any danger threatens. The infant is relatively slow in learning to respond to the mother's signals and direction. Maternal vigilance gradually relaxes as the child becomes more and more independent. Finally the youngster seeks her only when danger threatens.

Some chimpanzee infants acquire the thumb or great-toe sucking habit. The Yale primatologists say that bottle-fed chimps are invariably thumb-suckers. Fin, a 3 year old male, whom I watched for many hours, habitually sucked his right thumb. Sexually significant behavior of an infant toward its mother, or vice versa, is stated to be rare among chimpanzees.

Yerkes and Tomilin say that the "chimpanzee is a peculiarly rugged individualist, whose stage of socialization and its fruits should teach sociologists, economists, politicians, even statesmen and philosophers of the genus Homo, many helpful lessons."[14] Primatology ought to be included in a "liberal education."

Mona was the only one of 5 chimpanzee mothers who rocked her infants when they were fretful. Yet she rarely groomed her babies and almost never exercised them. She had twins and refused to let them cling to her except when absolutely necessary. Her method of tuition seemed largely negative, and she was the only one of the mothers who went in for corporal punishment. She was rather impatient and irritable. Josie was an unconventional mother who did everything to encourage infantile independence—for example, by placing her baby in climbing positions at times when the more conservative mothers were restraining the baby from trying. She carried her baby "every which way," back to belly, as well as belly to belly, over one arm, by a leg or by an arm. Yet she was gentle and cautious, though seemingly unconcerned. Yerkes says that she did not "indulge herself" at the expense of the infant's development. He seems to approve of this "progressive" mother. Another mother, Pati, is described as a perfect conservative, who always managed her baby according to the textbook descriptions. Some chimpanzee mothers are gifted teach-

[14]Yerkes and Tomilin 1935, p. 340.

ers and others are not. The same qualities which make for success in human tuition are required for the chimpanzee mother. It is possible that they are found more consistently in the ape. Of course, ape mothers cannot resort to child psychologists for advice. This is probably fortunate for young chimpanzees.

GROWTH

The baby chimpanzee begins to erupt its milk teeth in its third month and has a complete set of baby teeth by the fifteenth or sixteenth month. The second set of teeth begins to erupt in the chimp during the third year of life, as contrasted with the latter part of the fifth year in man. At the beginning of the eleventh year the chimpanzee has its full set of permanent teeth, whereas in man the wisdom teeth are usually not fully erupted before the age of 20. The chimpanzee is adult at 11 years.[15]

For the first 27 weeks of fetal life the growth curve of the chimpanzee apparently follows very closely that of man, but there is evidence that, during the last part of intra-uterine life, the chimpanzee fetus increases much more slowly than does the human fetus. At birth the chimpanzee weighs on the average only 1,888 grams, as contrasted with 3,300 grams, which is usually given as the mean birth weight for man.[16]

The adult female chimp averages 40 kilos in weight and the male 50 kilos. Thus the female chimpanzee at birth has reached about 4.75 per cent of adult weight, as against 5.5 per cent in the case of the human baby. The rate of postnatal growth has varied so widely among the chimpanzees studied up to this time that no standards can be established. The adult female chimpanzee is less inferior to the male in size than is woman to man.

As the chimpanzee grows, its trunk becomes more slender; its relative shoulder breadth decreases, and, in the female, the hip breadth increases slightly. The lower limb of the chimp grows somewhat more rapidly than the upper, and the forearm more rapidly than the arm. Chimpanzee hands and feet grow more slowly than the trunk and become more slender with advancing age. The thumb of the fetal chimpanzee is relatively longer than that of the adult. The head of the chimpanzee also decreases in relative size during growth. The cranial

[15]Schultz 1940a.

[16]Grether and Yerkes 1940, p. 187, record 1.86 kilos for birth weights of 4 males and 1.91 kilos for 5 females. The figure above is the weighted mean of these 9 records.

capacity, which is a rough measure of the size of the brain, is 46 per cent of adult capacity in the newborn chimp. At the age of 2 years capacity has attained 85 per cent, and at 4 years 94 per cent. Cranial capacity has reached its full development in 6 years. In man at the same age the cranial capacity is about 90 per cent of its ultimate size. The face of the chimpanzee increases enormously during growth, especially in length, and becomes steadily more overbalanced frontally on the spine. The cephalic index, or the head breadth expressed as a percentage of head length, decreases in the chimpanzee from fetal to the middle of juvenile life and then increases again, probably because of the thickening of the temporal muscles, which are attached to the sides of the head and work the heavy and projecting jaws. There is no such late increase in the same index taken on the dried skull, which drops from 83.7 (round-headed) in infancy to 74.6 in the adult, who is long-headed or dolichocephalic. The face of the chimpanzee also broadens prodigiously during growth; the bony ridge over the eyes increases tremendously, and the orbits (the bony sockets of the eyes) move forward from a position under the frontal part of the brain to one anterior to it. In the fetal period the eyeball of the chimpanzee is so large that it bulges out from the orbit, but, by adult years, the orbit is big enough to accommodate four eyeballs. A similar change can be seen in the relation of the human eyeball to the orbit during growth. The ear of the chimpanzee also decreases in relative size during growth.

The cartilaginous caps, or epiphyses, on the long bones of mammals are pushed apart by the shafts of the bone during growth. Ultimately, these cartilaginous caps are ossified (or turned to bone) and, at the cessation of growth, they become fused to the shafts and the lines of juncture are obliterated. In the skeleton the fusion of epiphyses then denotes the termination of growth, and various epiphyses are united to the shafts at different ages. Thus in man the earliest to fuse is the lower epiphysis of the upper-arm bone, or humerus, which generally unites during the fifteenth year. Other epiphyses fuse at different ages up to the twenty-fifth year, when all have united. In the chimpanzee epiphyseal union also begins at the lower end of the humerus, but in the seventh year. Apparently this growth process is complete in the chimpanzee between the eleventh and fifteenth years. The sutures, or lines of junction between the bones of the skull, are obliterated much earlier in the chimpanzee than in man, probably because brain growth and facial growth are completed at a more tender age.

Analysis of the growth curves of chimpanzees indicates that the rhythm is only roughly similar to that observed in man: (a) An infantile period of rapid but diminishing growth to about the age of 4 years. (b) A prepubertal growth phase which is marked in male chimpanzees but not in females. It reaches its maximum in males in the eighth year and achieves a poorly defined maximum in females in the seventh year. It is at this age that the male definitely secures the lead over the female in weight. (c) A terminal growth phase which drops off rapidly from the eighth year to zero in the twelfth year in males, but may continue into the thirteenth year in females.[17]

Puberty in the female chimpanzee is reached at ages ranging from 7 years 4 months to 10 years 2 months and does not seem to coincide so closely with maximum growth rate as it does in girls. Actually, the present evidence indicates that female chimpanzees, in failing to overtake the males in size and weight in the earlier pubertal spurt which is found in the human species, show an important divergence from the human pattern. Chimpanzees, like human beings, grow more rapidly in the fall and winter than in the spring and summer. At the year of most rapid growth the rate of maturation of the chimpanzee is almost twice that of man.

The terminal growth phase in the chimpanzee ends much earlier than in man. Boys go on growing until the age of 20 to 21 years and girls to the age of about 18 years. The peak of pubertal growth which is reached in chimpanzees about the seventh year in females and the eighth year in males is attained in girls at about the thirteenth year and in boys some two years later.

The Infancy of Alpha

Drs. Carlyle F. and Marion M. Jacobsen raised a chimpanzee baby by bottle during her first year of life, aided and abetted by the whole staff of the Yale Laboratories of Primate Biology at Orange Park, but especially by Dr. Joseph G. Yoshioka.[18] If there is any human baby which has been reared with such scientific caution by a flock of Ph.D.s, and whose first year has been recorded in such exhaustive detail, I should like to hear of it, but I should still be more interested in Alpha, the girl baby chimpanzee. Her mother died of childbed fever, which is not as unfavorable a comment upon the obstetrical ward of the Yale Laboratory as it would be if it had happened in a human lying-in hospital. For the first 8 months of her life Alpha divided her time between the laboratory and the Jacobsen residence, but in the latter place no effort was made "to humanize" her. Alpha's first 8 weeks were spent in a bassinet, and then she graduated to a crib, until she

[17]Grether and Yerkes 1940, pp. 190–91.
[18]Jacobsen, C. and M., and Yoshioka 1932.

was ready for an inside living room. Her companionship for the first 9 months was almost limited to human beings. Let us pass over her feeding formulas and her dietetic regimen, together with the accounts of her teething, how she liked spinach, and when she had diarrhea (not that these facts are either unimportant or uninteresting, but space is limited). We may also omit the accurate record of her physical development, including x-rays of bone ossification. Alpha's initial diffused and generalized body responses were gradually replaced by responses more localized and more specific; her bodily temperature regulation became more constant and more efficient under different physiological conditions. Her pulse and respiration decreased in rate and increased in stability—became better co-ordinated. The deceleration in sleep and acceleration in activity became more marked.

Here are some phases of motor development as exhibited by human/chimpanzee infants, based upon the work of Shirley on 25 human infants and of Jacobsen, Jacobsen, and Yoshioka on the chimpanzee Alpha.[19] The figures in parentheses denote the ages in weeks at which the human/chimpanzee babies attain the various stages.

Progress toward creeping
    (a) Lifting head when on stomach, chin free (3/3)
    (b) Lifting head when on stomach, chest free (9/5)
    (c) Knee pushing or swimming (25/7)
    (d) Rolling (29/8-10)
    (e) Rocking, pivoting, worming along (37/11)

Progress toward assuming upright posture
    (a) Lifting head when on back (15/5)
    (b) Sitting alone momentarily (25/12)
    (c) Sitting alone (31/13)
    (d) Standing, holding to furniture (42/15)
    (e) Pulling self to standing position by means of furniture (47/15)

Progress toward walking
    (a) Walking with help, led by person (45/17)
    (b) Standing alone (62/20)
    (c) Walking alone (64/25-29)

It may be seen that the chimpanzee is very precocious, but it should be remarked that Alpha did not creep forward and that, when she walked, she walked on all fours.

If the reaching, grasping, and manipulatory behavior of this infant

[19]Jacobsen, C. and M., and Yoshioka 1932, p. 50.

be compared with that of the human infant, it is found that the early patterns coincide in that, firstly, objects are looked at but no attempt is made to reach them; secondly, reaching and manipulation take place without grasping; and, finally, grasping occurs. The mouth, used early in attempts to reach objects, continues to play a larger part in the chimpanzee's life than that of the human infant throughout the first year. Both use a squeeze grasp, but Alpha did not develop an effective thumb–finger-tip opposition during the period of observation. The short, weak thumb of the chimpanzee may account in part for these differences.

Alpha's vocal responses included a screaming, fear-temper cry— the only vocalization during the first 8 weeks; a soft chimp bark, ninth and tenth weeks; a whimper occasioned by mild fear or discomfort (such as soiled diapers), twelfth week; lip-smacking (seventeenth week). All these cries were used in part for social responses. Her only response to human vocalizations included a soft bark in answer to simulated chimp calls, and refraining from biting the furniture at the command "No! No!"

Emotional responses included fear, anger, timidity, and mild excitement. Fear was first expressed by clenching hands and feet, drawing up arms, wrinkling the face, retraction of lips from teeth, and screaming. At first these expressions of fear amounted practically to a body spasm and were elicited very easily by handling, sudden noises, jars, etc. Later on they became much modified and were supplemented by withdrawal of a part of the body or flight. Alpha did not defecate when frightened, as do older chimpanzees. She was not afraid of a non-poisonous snake, although mature chimpanzees are terrified of snakes. Nor did she fear a house dog and a human infant. She was timid and exploratory rather than fearful in the face of strange objects.

It is often difficult to distinguish anger from fear in chimpanzee behavior. Anger was occasioned by lack of attention, being pushed away when she wanted to get into a person's lap, when spoons or cups were taken from her, when she was forced to submit to measurement. When angered or frustrated Alpha would frequently resort to thumb-sucking. Mild excitement was generally denoted by a soft bark. There was no smiling, babbling, laughing, or cooing. The mild bark was the nearest approach to the pleasure in human association expressed by the human infant. Alpha indulged in these soft barks when taken up, when protected, and when enjoying play with a human companion.

Alpha did not play much during the first 2 months, but sucked her thumb and her big toe. She then began exploring, scratching, feel-

ing the sides of her crib, and using the index finger for tactile examination. She was particularly interested in feeling the noses and
teeth of her human attendants. Eventually this exploratory play
involved tearing newspapers, pulling off spectacles, examining and
biting the furniture, playing with grass, nuts, vegetables, picking
up seeds in her mouth, dropping them, retrieving them, etc. This
type of play continued for a year. She began to organize her play
with reference to an object or person as early as the twenty-sixth
week. Thus, she tore some pages from a magazine, laid them down,
came back and placed them on her head several times. She often used
papers in this manner for ornamentation, but she did no nest-building.
At times she would direct her play toward an observer, climbing in
and out of his lap, rolling about his feet, jumping off chairs, radiators,
or other pieces of furniture in such a way that some part of her body
came into contact with the observer. A good deal of play was in the
nature of exercise—crawling through the rungs of chairs, jumping up
and down, banging a swing against the solid side of the cage. Her
play with a pet dog was largely aggressive and threatening. Grooming and toilet play began suddenly when she noticed a scab on the
back of an attendant's hand and examined it with fingers, lips, and
tongue.

Alpha's responses to human beings were first limited to approaches
and withdrawals, then threatening, swaggering, chest-beating, wrinkling the face, and patting or gently striking the person's face or hands.
Ultimately she became quite dependent upon human attendants,
clung to them, and whimpered or showed temper when separated
from them. Her short contact with a 13-month-old human infant
showed interest, mild aggressiveness, and gentleness. The human
infant led in their rather poorly organized efforts to play with kitchen
utensils. Somewhat later Alpha was put into a cage with another
female infant chimpanzee, Dula. At first she attacked and bit Bula
and in general intimidated her, so that they were separated. Some
weeks later, after they had been in adjoining cages, they were again
put together. Alpha again was aggressive, pushed Bula into the corner, took away her noon cracker, and by late afternoon had her so
cowed that she only needed to point her finger at Bula to make the
latter retreat up the side of the cage. Ultimately, Bula was allowed to
eat in peace, and eventually the worm turned and Bula fought back
and successfully resisted Alpha's aggressions. In the course of time
the two animals became much attached to each other. When one was
in distress the other would embrace and comfort her, and they actively
resisted separation.

To complete Alpha's first year of training, she was put through the tests of mental growth designed by Gesell of Yale for the preschool human child. In tests of postural control or locomotion she was equal or superior to the human child. In the simpler prehension tests she was neither retarded nor accelerated. In the more complex tests, such as throwing objects to the floor and putting a cube in a cup, she was definitely retarded. All subsequent tests, such as tossing a ball into a box and scribbling, were failed completely. In simple tests of eye-hand co-ordination Alpha was equal to the human child and perhaps a little superior. She did not succeed in tests involving imitation of the examiner, except in the simplest items. In play behavior she passed a few tests, but broke down in all the situations which required "exploitive use of the materials."

On the whole, she passed many tests at the earlier level, but toward the end of the year had reached a point where she made little progress. Lack of language was not her difficulty, in the opinion of the observers. Drs. Jacobsen and Yoshioka come to the conclusion that Alpha and the human infants are not "sisters under their skins."

OLD AGE AND LONGEVITY

The mature chimpanzee ceases to be active and playful and becomes sluggish and serious. In the wild the old male may lose his position in the family group and become solitary. Possibly, aged individuals become morose, ill-tempered, and dangerous, but data on senile chimpanzees are very meager. We know that the skeletal age changes ordinarily observed in man also take place in the chimpanzee. The bony crests on the skull and the ridges for muscular attachment on the bones become more prominent; the crowns of the teeth wear down; certain pathological and degenerative processes may be observed. The coats go gray, but never, as far as I am aware, white. Frequently the hair on the body becomes more sparse. From middle age onward some chimpanzees probably become heavier and others thinner, according to state of health and individual constitution. Mona, the oldest chimpanzee at Orange Park, with an estimated age of 29 years, is by far the fattest and heaviest animal in the colony. Jack, the oldest of the males, whose age is thought to be about 21 years, is somewhat emaciated and looks very old. However, when I saw him in the spring of 1941, he had been very ill and had lost appetite and weight.

Zuckerman gives 11 years as the average length of life in captivity of 20 chimpanzees and 26 years 2 months as the maximum. Yerkes thinks

USE OF HUMAN UTENSILS BY YOUNG CHIMPANZEE

INTERDEPENDENCE OF YOUNG CHIMPANZEES

that 50 years is a conservative estimate for the potential life span of a chimpanzee, although the average age of death would be much lower.

WHAT CAPTIVE CHIMPS EAT AND HOW THEY EAT AND ELIMINATE

Chimpanzees in captivity flourish on diets which include as staples cooked mixed cereals, milk, and raw green vegetables, such as lettuce, carrots, cabbage, potatoes; fruits, peanuts, and cod-liver oil (in small doses). A solitary animal eats in a cleanly, leisurely fashion, unless ravenously hungry or surrounded with an excess of food. In the latter case the chimp is likely to be messy and wasteful.

If there is competition for food, the animals are prone to gobble. They are skillful in manipulating food with hands and with teeth, picking out seeds from fruits, or spitting them out of their mouths. The lower lip is often protruded like a shelf and food taken in it is examined visually and with the fingers.

A disagreeable chimpanzee habit, said to be common to all adults, is "regurgitation" or the voluntary vomiting of undigested food, which is then lapped up and reswallowed. I am not aware that this habit has been observed in wild chimpanzees and it is apparently uncommon in infants and adolescents. An even more disgusting habit of chimpanzees is coprophagy (the eating of their feces). This practice is observed occasionally among captive animals, but it may not be characteristic of wild animals.

Both vomiting and defecating take place when the animals are frightened or greatly excited, as in fights between males and females. The prudent onlooker does not venture too close to the bars of a chimpanzee cage without keeping a weather eye on the lookout for the nasty tricks which they occasionally play with their bodily excretions. Spitting at persons outside of the cage is apparently a favorite practice, especially with the females. At Orange Park, if one approaches within a range of 3 or 4 feet, the chimpanzee inside is likely to sidle quietly over to the drinking fountain, take a good mouthful, and spit it at the observer with excellent aim. I noticed one female who would get a mouthful, swing along the top of the cage from back to front, bring up with a bang against the front netting, simultaneously ejecting the mouthful of liquid, thus utilizing the momentum of her swing to increase her spitting range to something in the neighborhood of 10 to 12 feet. When the chimpanzees do this repeatedly to the scientific observers who are trying to work with them, it is found expedient to punish them by turning a hose into the cage and sousing them. Young chimpanzees do not spit. Very rarely a chimpanzee may defecate in his hand and throw the excrement at a human being outside of the cage. The aim is likely to be good.

Captive chimpanzees drink by applying their lips to the liquid, or to a tap, or by lifting a cup, saucer, bottle, or other receptacle to the mouth and drinking in human fashion. They easily acquire tastes for a wide variety of beverages. A baby chimpanzee early learns to hold its own nursing bottle.

SOCIAL RELATIONS IN CAPTIVITY

Companionship Preference and Dominance

Dr. Vincent Nowlis has made a very fruitful study of companionship preference and dominance among a group of 5 pre-adolescent chimpanzees, all within 20 months of each other in age, and all between the ages of 4 and 6 years.[20] Two were males, 2 females, and the other a eunuch. A test animal was allowed to approach either of 2 stimulus animals and have contact with it through a grill of iron bars. The test lasted 3 minutes and preference was recorded according to the larger amount of the time spent with one or the other animal. Each chimpanzee was tested for preference of all others. The animals saw each other only during the tests and, in the first series of tests lasting 6 weeks, each chimp made 20 choices between each of 6 pairs. In the second series each animal chose 32 times, and the five were isolated only in the daytime. Dominance was tested by pushing peanuts through a trough into the cage and seeing which animal got them. Another method involved teaching the animals to climb through a small opening into a top part of the cage. The animal which got there first was taken out, released from school, and put back into living quarters. The animal which got left remained for a while in the cage. The result was that a regular order of dominance was established which was consistent between the various pairs of animals for both the food competition and the escape problem. In any single pair the same animal virtually always got all or almost all the food, and also escaped first.

In the food-sharing experiment the test animal was given 20 peanut kernels and a chance to share them with one or the other or both of 2 other animals. Food-sharing may take place in three ways: one animal helps itself to the other's food by reaching through the cage; the animal which has the food passes some on to the other without having been solicited; the second animal succeeds in getting some of the food by begging, whimpering, whining, beckoning, stamping, or threatening. Food-sharing occurred in only 16 per cent of cases, and the usual amount was only one or 2 of the 20 kernels. A dominant animal never shared with a subordinate. The 2 most dominant animals received between them 73 per cent of the food shared, and the 2 most subordinate subjects passed on 76 per cent of the food shared. Number 1 dominator never shared food and No. 2 only 4 times—all with No. 1. The tail-ender in dominance rating never received any shared food, and the next to the last in dominance received food only 5 times— all from the most downtrodden individual. The most effective way of getting food was by solicitation, not by proud, impassive waiting.

In the matter of companionship preference, size and age seemed to be of no importance, and dominance of little importance except in the case of the No. 1 dictator and the tail-ender. Two of the animals were twins who had been together constantly from birth. The female twin always preferred her brother, and in the first series this preference was reciprocated by him. In the second series of tests she had to take second place in favor. Most of the social behavior (87 per cent) in the preference tests took the form of grooming or play-fighting. Each animal had a perfectly consistent preference order, but the general preference rankings of the 5 animals were variable, except that the castrated male was always last. There was no relationship between dominance and preference nor between food-sharing and preference. The preferred animal is usually the one with which the subject engages most often and most congenially in grooming or in play-fighting. When the animals were tested in a series after 23 hours of isolation, preference seemed to be connected with grooming and that was the most frequent behavior. After only 8 hours of isolation, play-fighting was the preferred activity. Usually the 2 chimpanzees preferred by any third animal were the most congenial groomer, on the one hand, and the most satisfactory fighting partner, on the other. Ordinarily, the favored groomer and fighter are one and the same chimp.

Crawford, while carrying on tests of dominance by means of food competition in all possible pairings of 6 female chimpanzees, also observed the behavior of the various pairs in cages when no food was offered for competition.[21] The subordinate animals did more grooming of their dominant partners; otherwise no relationship between social and non-social behavior and dominance in food-getting was discernible. The same observer found that dominance in food compe-

[21]Crawford 1942b, pp. 267–77.

tition might be predicted from the behavior of the animals just before the tests. The animal which enters the cage of the other animal, attacks or bluffs it, and is groomed by it, is likely to prove to be dominant.[22]

FOOD-SHARING, HUNGER, FOOD HABITS

Nissen and Crawford, in a study of food-sharing by adolescent chimpanzees, have classified transfer of food or food tokens according to three modes of behavior: independent acquisition, begging, and unsolicited passing.[23] Small pieces of food, or tokens which could be exchanged for food, were given to one or both animals in the same or adjacent cages. Six subjects, grouped into 8 pairs, were observed for a total of 117 half-hour periods. Begging and responsiveness to begging occurred much more frequently in animals who were well acquainted and friendly than in comparative strangers. Some individuals were much more given to begging than others. Two chimpanzees did more than 90 per cent of all the begging recorded for the six. Unsolicited passing seemed to be unrelated either to begging or responsiveness to begging. Tokens were more readily transferred than actual food—probably because the tokens could not be cashed in immediately, whereas food could be consumed at once. Hunger seemed to have no particular effect upon food-sharing. Sales resistance to begging seemed to be cumulative to some extent. No cases of barter were observed, but a good deal of teasing was noticeable.

The studies of Nowlis have indicated that usually the amount of food-sharing is closely related to dominance and that the former can be somewhat accurately determined by the latter. Following up these investigations, the same observer has tested the effects of comparative degrees of hunger and satiety upon dominance as indicated by competition for food.[24] For this study 18 chimpanzees were used in 20 different combinations. Three degrees of hunger were set up: (1) satiation—in which the animal was stuffed with bananas and milk an hour to a half-hour before the experiment, until it would eat no more; (2) regular feeding; (3) deprivation—withdrawal of food up to 65 hours, with water always available, and with 10 small pieces of food twice daily offered in the experiments. All possible combinations of these degrees of hunger between pairs were studied. When both animals were kept at the same level of hunger, there was practically no variation in dominance (as expressed by the dominant animal's

[22]Crawford 1942a, pp. 259–65.

[23]Nissen and Crawford 1936, pp. 383–419.

[24]Nowlis 1941b, pp. 91–115.

taking all, or nearly all, the food), whether they were on regular rations or fasting. When the dominant animal was satiated and the subordinate animal was hungry, the amount of food secured by the latter rose quickly to more than half of the test food. There was reversal in control of the food chute (down which the test food was rolled into the cage). Upon further experimentation it was determined that the variation in the success of the subordinate in getting food seemed to be little dependent upon the extent to which it suffered from hunger, but was principally controlled by the degree of satiety of the dominant animal. Only a completely stuffed dominant was likely to permit the underdog to take the food. Regularly fed or unfed dominant animals frustrated the attempts of the subordinates to get at the food, no matter how hungry the latter were. However, when the dictator was completely satiated, the amount of food obtained by the subordinate varied with the acuteness of the pangs of hunger of the latter. After regular rations were resumed, all the original dominance orders were immediately operative. This experiment of Nowlis seems to have wide applications outside of chimpanzee society. One presumes that it is the first scientific demonstration of that agelong policy of wise wives in the management of their husbands: "Feed the beast!"

One of the most ingenious series of experiments with chimpanzees performed by the Yale group involved the substitution of food tokens for actual food as rewards for success and incentives for work. These food tokens were disks which could be inserted in a slot machine, which then yielded up one raisin per slug. The animals were first taught to use this vendor, sometimes called the "chimpomat."[25] With some training they readily performed work to obtain disks which were immediately exchangeable for food, and continued to work even when they were not allowed to make the exchange until after a group of tokens—10 to 20—had been secured. The tokens were obtained by the solution of standard learning problems accomplished in a room separate from that which contained the chimpomat. The chimpanzees readily differentiated between differently colored tokens—some which would yield food and others which would not. Immediate rewards of actual food were, of course, the most efficacious stimuli for the performance of work; next to food the food tokens, and the non-food tokens last. Work was done better and more rapidly when the food tokens could be exchanged for food at once than when they had to be held until after a group had been collected. One might expect this order of efficacy to hold for some human beings—especially children.

[25] Cowles 1937.

After a while the chimpanzees showed a decided reluctance to put the non-food tokens in the slot machine. Apparently they had become disillusioned.

Fletcher carried out an elaborate series of experiments in which chimpanzees pulled a carriage baited with banana slices of various sizes against different resistances, provided either by gravity or by the appliance of an electric brake.[26] The animals easily distinguished between the sizes of the incentives and did more work, more quickly, and with greater perseverance, the larger the food stimulus. If the size of the food incentive was kept constant and the resistance increased, the efforts of the animal to do the work gradually fell off to zero. If the food reward was increased and the resistance maintained at the same level, the responses of the animal usually went up to 100 per cent. In any session, however, responses tended to drop off through fatigue, satiety, frustration, and other causes. Each animal tended to develop his individual method of pulling and adhered to it. Some were more efficient and more persistent than others.

DOMINANCE AND SEX APPEAL IN FEMALES

The dominance of female chimpanzees in food competition is greatly affected by the phase of their sexual cycle in which the animals happen to be. Between mature females the ordinarily dominant animal tends to yield privileges, even to the extent of reversing dominance relationship, when the subordinate animal is in the phase of genital swelling. When the dominant chimpanzee herself is in this phase of sexual receptivity, she may encourage her companion to assume the role of the male and to mount her, simulating copulation. Either the subordinate or the dominant animal may play the male when her partner is in this condition. In some other mammals (cow, sow, guinea pig) the individual in oestrus mounts her companion, but in the chimpanzee the reverse obtains.[27] When a mature female is caged with an immature animal of the same sex, the older and more experienced animal is generally dominant, but when in the genital-swelling phase she may yield to the subordinate and solicit sexual attention. Between immature females dominance is usually a settled matter, but may be shifted quite independently of sexual phase, owing to factors of temperament and personality.

Crawford made a large number of trials of dominance in food-getting between 13 different female chimpanzees in 16 pairings and found that the subordinate usually obtained more food in the genital-

---

[26]Fletcher 1940.
[27]Yerkes 1939, pp. 115-36.

swelling phase of her cycle. At this time the ordinarily subordinate animal sometimes appeared to increase in aggressiveness and self-confidence.[28]

In mated chimpanzees the male, if dominant, ordinarily yields privilege or right to the sexually acceptable female in her period of genital swelling and maximum receptivity. The behavior of a sample pair of mates, summarized from the description of Yerkes, will illustrate the typical situation.[29]

Jack and Josie were both mature, vigorous, sexually normal, and experienced chimpanzees. They were well acquainted and congenial, both moderately self-confident and self-assertive. In their experiment the male obtained most of the food before and after the period of female maximal swelling, whereas during that period the female controlled the food-getting situation. In the beginning of the female's cycle Jack assumed control of the food chute and Josie accepted the situation, although she often tried to lure him away by play. Once she tried to distract him by pretending to attack another female in an adjoining cage. When he came over to watch the fracas, Josie took his place at the chute, but he returned and gently but firmly elbowed her aside. A few days later Josie got to the food chute first and was allowed by Jack to take food once, after which he replaced her for the other 9 trials. When Josie's genital swelling was about halfway to its maximum, she asserted herself by taking control of the chute and refusing to leave it, in spite of the male's sexual advances. She repelled the latter. Jack was evidently very resentful and rushed about the cage, jumping against the ceiling and banging about the auto tire suspended from a chain. Josie was alarmed, but stuck to her place before the chute. On one occasion Jack came up and struck her, but even then she did not yield and he went away restless and dissatisfied. She went to work at the food calmly and steadily, while he wandered about the cage, seeking distraction. Occasionally he approached her, seeking sexual contact, but was repulsed. However, Josie did retain priority during the initial phase of her sexual swelling. In a day or two Jack took over and refused to·yield, although he now let her eat his discarded banana skins. When Josie achieved her maximal swelling, she also obtained full control of the food situation, for, upon the setting up of the apparatus, she offered herself to the male, was accepted, and,after·copulation was allowed to take charge of the chute and obtain all the food, while the male sat quietly by and sometimes begged for a share. Jack then made no effort to dislodge Josie. Both

[28]Crawford 1940, pp. 483–513.

[29]Yerkes 1940, pp. 147–86.

animals seemed calm, confident, and content. The taking of food by the female was apparently her accepted right. This female dominance continued during maximal swelling until the experiment was interrupted in the period of oestrus, in order that Josie should not become pregnant. It was resumed after Josie's swelling had begun to subside.

When they again joined each other, the animals displayed no sign of sexual interest and Jack at once assumed his masculine prerogative of controlling the chute. After a few days Josie took her place at the chute, but was lured away in play and then gently and tactfully elbowed aside. Occasionally Jack allowed her a piece of banana skin.

In the case of young, sexually inexperienced males, experiments indicated that the shift of control from the female to the male at detumescence was delayed for a day or two. Again, inexperienced or timid females lacked the assurance which is necessary for self-assertion at the time when the female would naturally obtain dominance through her sexual status. One female, Nira, although apparently normal, persistently refused to mate with any male, but, nevertheless, was accorded food dominance during the period of maximum sexual swelling. Three of the females—Lia, Pati, and Wendy—were unusually courageous and domineering and secured the physical mastery and the control of the food situation over their mates. Two of these won their victories by being physically disagreeable or nasty to their mates, the other by seductive wiles. All of them managed to retain food dominance in the period after they had ceased to be sexually desirable.[30]

Differences in personality are a very important factor in determining the dominance between mates. The females are, in general, less generous than the males and display a wide range of self-assertiveness. One male, Pan, was unusually selective in a sexual sense, and would accept a female for copulation only when her cycle phase suited him perfectly. Usually he was self-centered, indifferent toward females, and not disposed to be friendly. Consequently, the various females were relatively unsuccessful in taking food dominance away from him. He would not ordinarily play with them or yield to their wiles. However, one female, Josie, by the skillful use of techniques of petting and grooming, succeeded with Pan better than the others. Says Yerkes:

That the female is, chameleon-like, a creature of multiple personality, is clear from our observations. . . . With Pan, Dita took no liberties, claimed little by way of right or privilege, while with Bokar she took end-

[30]The author hopes that these revelations will not be utilized for shaping the conjugal policy of any female reader of this book.

less liberties and laid claim to everything! She was the subdued, self-effacing, unassertive female in Pan's presence, whereas with Bokar she was self-confident, expressive, friendly, playful. . . .

Techniques of social control are numerous and frequently employed. Sex difference is notable. The male characteristically demands, commands, and as necessary physically imposes his will, unless he be the subordinate mate, whereas the female cajoles, requests, begs, and as necessary uses to achieve her aims various forms of sexual allure, physical play, and petting. The behavioral pictures of masculinity and femininity are sharply contrasted, for manifestly the values of the sexual relation differ fundamentally. For the male that relation is marked by impulsiveness, directness, immediacy, and appears an end in itself; for the female, indirectness, delay, and prolongation of interest indicate that it is a means to varied advantages and is so habitually used.[31]

Yerkes does not feel that either sex of chimpanzee can be described correctly as "dominant." The deciding factor is not sex but personality. In any situation social control may be taken by either sex. Often the smaller and weaker individual, irrespective of sex, manifests superiority by reason of greater courage, self-confidence, determination, and persistence.[32]

There is a difference in sexual receptivity between male and female chimpanzees which Yerkes notes to be most important in influencing the social behavior of these animals. During the period of maximum genital swelling the capacity of the female for primary sexual activity is almost unlimited. She is able to accommodate numerous males. By contrast, the male is "readily satiated, fatigued, or wholly exhausted even by one female." The result of this difference is that the female has an incomparably greater ability to trade upon the sexual relation than has the male, and the natural result in such an intelligent and highly adaptive animal is prostitution.

RAPE AND SEXUAL PERVERSION

The superior strength of the male chimpanzee makes it possible for him to rape females irrespective of their sexual phase, receptivity, and willingness. The several careful studies of sexual behavior made by various observers in the Yale Laboratories of Primate Biology do not seem to suggest that violent rape is often committed by the male. Sokolowsky describes this phenomenon in captive chimpanzees in German zoological gardens,[33] but possibly the chimpanzee had been

---

[31]Yerkes 1940, pp. 183–84, 186.

[32]Yerkes 1941, pp. 175–99.

[33]Sokolowsky, Alexander, "The Sexual Life of the Anthropoid Apes," *Urol. Cutan. Rev.*, 1923, p. 614. Quoted by Yerkes, R. and A., 1929.

modified by the German cultural environment. The troup consisted of a large adult male, some younger females, and a young male. The adult male was very dominant and dictatorial. He demanded repeated intercourse every day with his females and drove off the young male with bites and blows if he attempted to approach any of the females sexually. When the old male felt so disposed he would jump down from his perch and force a female to submit to his sexual advances, no matter how vigorously she might resist. I gather from the observations reported at Orange Park that the female may violently resist the advances of the male and successfully repulse him, but that, when he gets really serious, she is likely to submit rather than risk injury. On the whole, one gets the idea from the literature that the female is usually very well able to take care of herself in sexual relations, but, of course, her independence or submissiveness in this relationship is dependent partly upon her own personality and partly upon the temperament and physical vigor of the male in question.

Homosexual activities are not infrequently observed among female chimpanzees, as when, in the period of maximum swelling, one of the animals may encourage her female companion to mount her and simulate copulation. Yerkes reports a case of one of the most resourceful and determined females, Wendy, who mounted her male mate, Bokar, in the copulating position, apparently as a means of trying to induce him to surrender to her the control of the food chute.[34]

Masturbation is said to be practiced by nearly all chimpanzees. Fin, a 3-year-old male, commonly masturbated with either hand or foot when clinging by the other three extremities to the wire netting of his cage and watching the observer. Females are stated to masturbate by rubbing the clitoris against the wire netting. One female was observed repeatedly to back against the push button of the drinking fountain, thrusting it into her anus, and thereby getting a trickle of water down the vulva.

THE SENSES

VISION AND VISUAL PERCEPTION

Köhler wished to discover whether the chimpanzee, like man, perceives depth and distance more readily and accurately with binocular vision than with one eye alone. A chimpanzee which had previously been taught to fit two sticks together to make a longer implement for raking in a banana was timed on performance of this task, using each

[34]Yerkes 1941, p. 189.

eye separately and both eyes together. His time for binocular vision was 2.1 seconds, for monocular vision with right eye 3.4 seconds, and with left eye 5 seconds. In a second experiment the chimpanzee looked through a hole in a screen at a grape which was dropped either before or behind a screen dividing the chamber into two parts. Solution depended upon the chimpanzee's going to the right compartment after watching the grape drop. With binocular vision the animal succeeded in 84 per cent of trials, with monocular vision in only 53.3 per cent.

Köhler also ascertained that a chimpanzee could identify the larger of two boxes when it was placed in relation to a smaller box so that its retinal image was actually smaller. He found out that a chimpanzee trained to discriminate between a black and a white surface could continue to choose correctly when the illuminations were radically changed so that the direct sunlight fell upon the black surface, causing it to look lighter than the white surface. He discovered that a chimpanzee taught to choose light gray in a series of grays of increasing darkness would pick dark gray when the latter was associated with black. This seemed to prove that the animal could respond to relative, or structure-function, values of a stimulus.

Mrs. Kohts, a Russian investigator, worked with one chimpanzee, using a simple method of matching samples. This animal could discriminate between chromatic and achromatic colors, between different volumes and surfaces, color combinations, alphabets, and pictures. He distinguished 30 different chromatic colors, even when mixed up 20 at a time. He could also distinguish between 13 geometric figures of equal area, 10 solids of different shapes, 4 different shapes of ovals, 5 of polygons, etc. In size he could get down to 5 mm. differences in thickness when 5 objects were presented, and was correspondingly successful with lengths, widths, and heights. These discriminations were made very quickly, but the animal found them most tiring. Mrs. Kohts could not teach her chimp to count.

Köhler, however, claims that the chimpanzee cannot distinguish a part from the whole if they are in contact—that, for example, a table placed in a corner against the two walls is passed by as an immovable object when the animal is looking for something portable.

Color Vision

Early studies of chimpanzee vision have shown that these animals can be taught to discriminate between pairs of mixtures in the red-blue continuum and in the red-yellow continuum and that a chimpanzee can be trained to match color samples. In a number of studies color discrimination has been used in the stimuli provided for certain learning tasks. Walter F. Grether of the Yale Laboratories of Primate Biology has advanced knowledge in this field by more detailed and exact spectral studies.[35] The apparatus involved the use of stimuli to food rewards in which the spectral light could be adjusted to various wave lengths. First, the animals were taught to discriminate between spectral yellow and darkness. After they had mastered this problem, the transition to hue discrimination was made. Small hue differences were distinguished by the chimpanzees after 250 to 500 trials. Four laboratory chimpanzees were tested, together with 4 human beings— 2 children and 2 adults. The results indicated that the thresholds of discrimination in chimpanzees in the yellow and red regions of the spectrum are roughly twice as high as those of adult human beings, whereas in the blue-green region the differences are negligible. The three spectral points at which the tests were made were: 640 mu (red), 589 mu (yellow), and 500 mu (blue-green).

Earlier work of the same observer upon Old World rhesus monkeys indicates that these animals have approximately the same hue discrimination as chimpanzees, but for cebus monkeys there is a markedly anomalous hue discrimination which is evidence for two-color vision. The color vision of chimpanzees and rhesus monkeys seems to be at an evolutionary position just short of human vision. In a further experiment relative to color-mixture proportions, it was found that the proportions of red (640 mu) and green (560 mu) required to match yellow were virtually identical for chimpanzees and human beings. Spectral limits were also determined for light-adapted chimpanzees and human beings by finding the wave lengths at which discrimination between spectral color and darkness became impossible. Results indicated that the chimpanzee spectrum is at least as extensive as that of man. Although the chimpanzee hue discrimination is slightly inferior to that of man in the long-wave end of the spectrum, the similarity of hue-discrimination curves for man and chimpanzee indicates that it is highly probable that chimpanzee color vision is basically like that of man—trichromatic. Grether also measured saturation thresholds at 17 spectral points by finding the proportion of spectral color mixed with white needed to produce a discriminable hue. The saturation minima for chimpanzees are about 5 mu lower than for human beings. At this lowest spectral saturation there was found to be a radical change in primary hue, evidenced for chimpanzees by a spontaneous reversal of discrimination habit. At this level human subjects reported a shift from reddish to greenish hue. The probable

[35]Grether 1940b, pp. 167–92; 1940a, pp. 394–403; 1941b, pp. 419–27.

interpretation is that for chimpanzees the crossing point of the red and green excitation curves is shifted a little toward the shorter wave lengths, consequently making chimpanzee color vision slightly resemble human red-green color blindness.

Grether has also found that simultaneous color contrast and simultaneous brightness contrast are of approximately the same magnitude in chimpanzee and man.[36] The animals were trained to choose by pushing against one of two 3-inch square stimulus areas, each within a separate background. After they had learned to discriminate these areas by color or brightness the areas were made identical but the backgrounds were changed so as to give contrast. The chimpanzee choices then clearly showed the influence of simultaneous contrast.

USE OF TOOLS

HANDEDNESS

Dr. Glen Finch of Yale attempted to find out whether chimpanzees use one hand in preference to the other, how pronounced such hand preference is in individuals, and how right-handedness and left-handedness are distributed among these animals.[37] He used 30 chimpanzees and devised a variety of test situations in which the animals secured pieces of fruit through the 2-inch-square apertures in the wire netting of their cages. Hand use for each subject was tabulated in 800 manipulations. Of the 30 chimpanzees tested 25 showed marked handedness, equally distributed between right and left hands. Each of 18 chimps used the right or left hand in more than 90 per cent of trials. Eleven chimpanzees used the right hand, 14 the left hand in more than 80 per cent of trials.

WEIGHT DISCRIMINATION

McCulloch trained 5 young chimpanzees to lift the heavier of two weighted boxes, identical in size and shape, in order to obtain rewards.[38] The threshold of differences in weight at which responses were 75 per cent correct averaged 9.2 per cent of the lighter, 80-gram weight. These discriminations are comparable with those found for adult human subjects. A weight-sorting test for children at the 9-year level in the 1916 Stanford Revision of the Binet Scale requires a 25 per cent difference as the finest level of discrimination. It seems probable

[36]Grether 1942, pp. 69–83.
[37]Finch 1941a, pp. 117–18.
[38]McCulloch 1941, pp. 507–19.

that chimpanzee children may compare favorably with human children in discriminating weights.

Use of Implements

Chimpanzees skillfully build nests for themselves by breaking off and interweaving branches, but it is not known whether this practice is instinctive or due to individual adaptation or tuition. The use of sticks, stones, and branches as weapons is not well attested by reports. It probably occurs. All captive chimpanzees easily learn to use sticks as implements with which to draw in or knock down food, and some have been observed to break off branches and use them for this purpose. One of Köhler's chimpanzees succeeded in constructing a serviceable long implement by jamming a smaller stick into a larger tube, and having once learned to fit them together, did so repeatedly and easily. This same animal, when wishing to fit into the end of a tube a board which was too wide for insertion, chewed at the end of the board, biting off splinters to make it fit. He chewed and fitted repeatedly, but did not succeed in sharpening the end of the board far enough up to secure a firm fit of its pointed end into the mouth of the tube.[39]

A chimpanzee that is familiar with the use of a key to unlock a padlock may attempt to find a substitute to fit into the keyhole. The use of sticks as levers is quickly learned. Bundles of straw are twisted or doubled to form ropes. Poles are used with great facility for climbing and jumping. The imitative utilization of human tools is so extensive that it requires little or no comment.

Box-Stacking

One of the favorite earlier methods of testing ape intelligence was to suspend some lure, such as a banana, out of the animal's reach and observe its ability to utilize various objects or instruments whereby to secure the prize. One simple procedure involves the placing in the cage of a box which can be moved to a position underneath the lure, so as to enable the animal to get the fruit by climbing upon the box and reaching or jumping. Apparently all chimpanzees can solve this sort of problem with comparative ease, although individuals vary in the rapidity and precision with which they place and utilize the box. More elaborate problems necessitate stacking one, 2, or 3 boxes on top of each other in order to build a platform high enough to be used as a take-off for jumping at the prize. Casual but very interesting experi-

[39]Köhler 1925, pp. 136–38.

ments of this sort were carried out by Yerkes and Köhler in the pioneer days of studying ape behavior. The latter observer is particularly successful in describing these tests in an absorbing manner and in speculating brilliantly upon their significance.

In 1929 Dr. Harold C. Bingham of the Institute of Psychology, Yale University, standardized this type of experiment by using boxes of certain sizes and weights, setting up the problems in definite ways and definite relations in a specially devised experimental room. The results of such rigorously controlled tests are more reliable but considerably less readable than the accounts of the old masters. All 4 chimpanzees with which Bingham worked solved problems involving the placement of one cubical box, 2-box stacking, upending an oblong box, 3-box stacking, roundabout box-stacking (piling boxes underneath a rope, climbing the rope, and then proceeding along a horizontal beam to get a banana), upending plus stacking. Two chimpanzees managed 4 box stacking and a problem involving the upending of an oblong box on a cube. The original object of experimenters in setting up this sort of a test seems to have been to determine whether or not anthropoid apes behave with "insight." This term implied a planned behavior, a survey of the situation before acting, and a more or less purposeful and methodical way of going about the solution of problems, in contrast to trial-and-error, random movements such as are supposed to be characteristic of the lower animals. In recent years the view that an indefinable something called "insight" characterizes the behavior of primates in contrast to that of lower mammals has been subjected to a good deal of destructive criticism.[40] It is not that primates fail to exhibit this sort of rational behavior, but that cats, rats, and other animals also manifest it, along with inattentive, trial-and-error procedures.

In spite of these objections, and irrespective of the meaning and distribution among mammals of "insight," a great deal may be learned from the observation of animals using boxes for the attainment of a goal. The versatility of the animals in solving the problem, the clumsiness or facility with which they build and place structures, the precision of their building, and the rapidity with which they improve by repeated trials continue to command the interest of the person who wants to learn the possibilities of animal performance and is unconcerned with the validity of psychological concepts. Köhler, for example, as a result of watching box-stacking tests, states that "there is practically no statics to be noted in the chimpanzee."[41] He backs up

[40] Zuckerman 1933, pp. 119–29.
[41] Köhler 1925, p. 154.

this generalization by pointing out that the chimpanzees seem unable to distinguish between a stable structure and an unbalanced pile of boxes which will topple over immediately, and that an animal standing on a box supported by two others, at each end, like pillars, may attempt to pull out one of the supporting boxes to add it to the top of the structure, or may try to lift up a box on which it is standing, thus attempting the traditional feat of lifting oneself by one's bootstraps. Again, a chimp may attempt to balance a box diagonally, or set up a ladder vertically with no lateral support. Such interesting conclusions are subject to the criticism that they are usually based upon a limited number of observations involving the capacities of a few animals. Thus, Bingham points out that the difference between Wendy and Pan in stacking problems "is approximately the difference between an understanding of vertical building and absence of such understanding."[42] Pan merely pushes or pulls boxes together until they form some kind of supporting contact. Wendy uses favorable methods in handling boxes, adjusts herself and the boxes preparatory to lifting, and corrects unstable structures by straightening them. Often she makes a visual survey of her pile of boxes before attempting to climb upon them. These observations indicate that the "absence of statics" may be an individual matter among chimpanzees.

SELECTIVE TRANSPORTATION

One of the tests devised by Bingham involves what he calls "selective transportation." A square, close-meshed wire cage, 6 feet by 6 feet by 3 feet high, was provided with a small aperture at the bottom of the middle of each side. A banana was suspended inside from a rod which could be moved along slots in the top of the cage. These slots crossed each other at right angles and terminated above the windows or apertures. In order to get a banana, a chimpanzee had to climb on top of the cage and move the rod along the slot, either in a straight line or around a right angle, so that the banana could be reached from the single window which was open. The different test chimpanzees solved problems with this apparatus with varying facility.[43] Bingham felt that the experiment showed "ideational" behavior in the chimpanzees, as indicated by their tendencies to make initial visual inspections of the problems, to abandon futile methods, pause, and then renew activity along fresh exploratory lines, to respond rapidly to new discoveries by sudden action and change of facial expression. He considered also that a significant feature of the adap-

[42]Bingham 1929a, p. 53.
[43]Bingham 1929b.

tive behavior was the careful correction of mechanical errors when the rod overran the proper corner of the channels, the consistent orientation of animals toward the goal, diagonal pulling when a roundabout problem involved the necessity of moving the rod with the suspended lure around the corner made by the intersection of the channels. "Fluent solutions," made smoothly after close visual or tactile exploration, appeared to him to be evidence of "planning behavior."

Co-operative Behavior

Dr. Meredith Crawford of the Yale Laboratories of Primate Biology confronted a pair of young chimpanzees with the task of dragging up to the cage bars, by means of two ropes, a box weighing approximately 400 pounds upon which were placed pieces of fruit.[44] The horizontal pull required was 180 pounds—far too much for either of the animals to pull alone. He first decided that the problem had to be broken up into different stages in order to get each of the animals to obtain the food reward separately. So he taught each of them to pull the box in alone by a single rope when it was weighted lightly. Animals as low as rats easily learn to do such tasks. Crawford himself helped in the learning process by pushing the box and shouting "Pull!" at the animal. Thus he provided a secondary reinforcement. After a while he merely pretended to push and help. In the next stage the box was fully weighted and Crawford himself pulled on the second rope, calling out "Pull!" as before. Then both animals were set at the task. At first their pulls were not synchronized, so that the observer had to help by giving the verbal command, thus inducing them to work at the same time. The first evidence of true co-operative behavior appeared when the more eager of the two animals would sit in position to pull and watch the other, so that when the latter pulled independently, the former could pull also and achieve co-ordination. It was then noticed that the watching ape began to solicit its companion to pull, by whimpering, touching, and hooting at him.

I have a vivid recollection of watching one of these co-operative pulling tests by young chimpanzees when I visited the Yale Laboratory at New Haven a few years ago. The impressively large and heavy packing case rested on the cement floor some distance in front of the cage. Thick ropes, one attached at each end of the box, led into the cage. The pair of young chimpanzees co-operated magnificently. Each would seize his rope, brace his feet against the front of the cage, and watch the other animal intently. Without exchanging any vocal

[44] Crawford 1937.

signals, they would give co-ordinated and mighty tugs on the ropes, and the heavy box would slide toward the cage the distance of their arm pulls. Then each chimp would reach for a new hold and a new pull. They could scarcely have worked more efficiently if one of them had shouted "Heave ho!" as the signal for the tug.

INTELLIGENCE

MULTIPLE-CHOICE EXPERIMENTS

A type of problem frequently set for various animals by psychologists investigating their intelligence involves the selection of a certain box in a row, or a specific door in a series, for correct solution. Such problems are called "multiple choice" settings. The experiments of Kenneth W. Spence of the Yale Laboratories of Primate Biology sufficiently exemplify the results obtained from this type of work.[45] Originally, Yerkes' multiple-choice method had for its purpose the detection of reactive tendencies and their roles in solving problems involving spatial relations, the question of the operation of "ideational" processes, and the arrangement of different types of animals in the order of their success in solving increasingly difficult problems. Spence summarizes the results of multiple-choice experiments conducted by various observers upon different animals. End-box problems are solved by the learning of a simple position habit in such a zoological congeries as chimpanzee, monkey, orang-utan, pig, white rat, cat, and crow. Nor does there seem to be any relationship between speed of learning or performance in the control series and position in the zoological series. A middle-box or middle-door problem was solved by a small European songbird called the siskin, and flunked by 4 chimpanzees, one monkey, and 2 pigs. The alternate-end-door problem was solved by 2 pigs, one of 2 monkeys, and one only of 4 chimpanzees. One of 4 chimpanzees was able to solve a second-door-from-end problem, in company with 3 monkeys, 2 pigs, a skunk, and a marten. An orang-utan and 2 white rats also failed this test. These results are not very encouraging for the theory that the hierarchy of animal intelligence conforms to zoological resemblance to man.

Spence in his experiments used 17 chimpanzees, ranging in age from 2 to 22 years. Three children (chimpanzee) utilized in the work were the offspring of mothers who also participated in the tests. Actually, the younger chimpanzees appeared to learn more rapidly

[45]Spence 1939.

than the adults. Animals accustomed to experimentation learned more rapidly than the unsophisticated. Spence used 11 small nickel-plated brass boxes arranged equidistantly on a platform. This platform was pushed up to the netting of the cage.so that a chimpanzee could reach through and open a box. In the learning series the chimpanzees were allowed to open all boxes until they found the correct one containing the food. In the control or test series they were permitted to open but one box. If it happened to be the wrong box, the apparatus was immediately withdrawn. The baiting was done out of sight of the animals. Fifteen of the 17 subjects learned the middle-box problem to the extent of running all 12 trials of an experimental series correctly. The other 2 chimpanzees would have met this criterion had not their training been interrupted. This middle-box problem proved to be by far the most difficult of the various problems set. By arranging several settings of the same problem (i.e., in the case of the middle-box problem, boxes 1, 2, 3, 4, 5, or boxes 3, 4, 5, 6, 7, etc.) Spence found out that 5 of the 17 chimpanzees adopted a generalized method of solution, probably by position, so- that they solved all the various settings of the same problem simultaneously. The other 12 subjects learned each setting separately and in novel settings achieved only chance successes. Frequently observed was the tendency of an animal consistently to choose some particular box, usually the one nearest. Systematic response in which the successive boxes were tried, one by one, was noted in some problems. Apparently, the circumstances preceding a correct choice are likely to- become a part of the stimulus in repeating the solution. A chimpanzee which has achieved a successful solution after going to the back of the cage and climbing up the netting is inclined to repeat that procedure in subsequent trials. (Compare human superstitions, such as wearing a certain tie, or performing a certain ritual, when previous successes have been associated with that article or that action.) Some animals, having apparently solved the problem and made a large number of correct choices, will suddenly go wrong, persistently picking a specific incorrect box. This circumstance hardly favors the interpretation of "insight" in learning.

Yerkes tried a number of motivational incentives to see whether they would facilitate chimpanzee learning in multiple-choice problems.[46] These included various negative measures for discouraging incorrect answers, such as confinement in an incorrectly chosen box for a short period, electric shock, deprivation of reward, and such

[46]Yerkes 1934.

positive inducements as increase of food reward. These rewards and punishments had little or no effect upon performance, probably because the problem was changed from time to time.

DELAYED-RESPONSE TESTS

An enormous amount of ingenuity, patience, and careful recording of accurate observation has been expended by psychologists upon the so-called "delayed response" tests, which are really a measure of the animal's ability to retain what it has learned and to exercise the correct choice after an interval (generally short) between seeing the setup of the problem and attempting its solution.

Before summarizing the results of a number of these tests, as published in technical psychological literature, I shall describe a few trials in a series of experiments which I was privileged to watch at the Yale Laboratories of Primate Biology in Orange Park, Florida, on April 11, 1941. Naturally my observations are those of a quite untrained and naïve observer. This study was carried on by Doctors Nissen and Nowlis of the scientific staff of the laboratory. Three adult females were used—Pati, Mona, and Lia. Each animal was in a separate outdoor cage. A bowl of food was put on the ground in front of the cage and about 10 feet away, but in full sight of the animal. One of the experimenters walked over to the bowl of food, picked up a piece, and put it in a box which he carried in his hand. He then walked out of sight round the back of the cage building where he was joined by the other observer. Both of these then appeared around the end of the building, marching side by side in step, and each holding an identical food box. When they reached the cage of the testee, they left-faced and advanced to the bars, each holding out his box in his right hand. The chimp's problem was to reach through the netting and open the box which contained a reward. Sometimes Nissen baited and carried the reward box, and sometimes Nowlis. From time to time they shifted their positions so that the one experimenter would not always be on the same side when facing the cage. While I sat back against a neighboring building, some 20 feet away, and watched, Pati achieved 7 successes out of 8 trials, Lia 7 failures out of 8 trials, and Mona 4 out of 8 right. The experiment was at that time on the second or third day of trials. On the previous round Mona had succeeded in 4 efforts, Lia in 5 or 6, and Pati had done very badly indeed. On this day Pati, who was very successful, appeared to me to be the most concentrated and purposeful of the three animals. Mona, a sluggish, obese creature weighing 176 pounds, seemed to be rather indifferent, although she was described as the most greedy.

Lia, who was having a hard time, appeared to be very nervous. She kept picking at a gunny-sack coverlet which she had in the cage, wandered about distractedly, whined, moaned, and seemed much upset and frustrated. Nowlis said that he thought that she achieved her remarkable string of failures by avoiding each time the person who had frustrated her last. (I gather that the test was designed to attempt to get the chimpanzees to respond by remembering personalities.) While this marching and presenting of food boxes was going on for a considerable period, I found myself distracted several times by some activity of chimpanzees in other cages, so that I forgot which of the two psychologists had baited the box, and when they both appeared around the corner I had to think back and try to remember which would be the right choice. I told Nissen about this, and he asked me how I tried to figure it out. I said that I attempted to revisualize the last baiting: whether it had been done by the very tall Nowlis (about 6 feet 3 inches) or the shorter Nissen. The latter was rather disgusted with me and said I should have made my choice on the basis of personalities rather than by size. I suppose the results of this particular experiment are not yet available, but we shall have them in formidable statistical elaboration, in due course. I thought it was a good experiment, most interesting to watch.

A day or two later I watched Dr. Glen Finch doing a somewhat different delayed-response experiment with another female chimpanzee (I think it was Bimba). Finch had a wheeled apparatus with a retractable platform on one end and a screen, hiding the observer, on the other. On the end of the platform were two food boxes, one of which he would bait in sight of the animal. One of the boxes was white and the other black. He would then retract the platform inside the hood, shuffle the boxes (out of sight of the animal), and, after a short interval, thrust out the platform within reach of the chimpanzee, with the two boxes side by side. If she picked correctly, she received the reward, otherwise the platform was withdrawn. As I watched, Finch began to get quite excited, because Bimba ran off something like 17 consecutive successful choices. He had to remain concealed while the choice was made, although he could observe through a slit in the screen. Since I was sitting back and somewhat to the side, the wire meshes of the cage interfered with my seeing exactly how Bimba chose, and I began to get a little suspicious. I therefore obtained Finch's permission to move to the side of the cage and closer. I then noticed that before she made her choice Bimba squatted down close to the meshes and got her eyes down to the level of the bottom of the food box. I called Finch's attention to this procedure and we examined the boxes closely. They were so constructed that the top, front, and sides were hinged to the back and could be lifted to expose the piece of fruit. A very small crack between the front and the bottom of the box, when the latter was closed, made it possible to see whether or not the box was baited. The question arose then as to whether Bimba's string of correct solutions depended upon peeking or smelling. The box with the banana in it was identifiable to me by smell. These circumstances seemed to cast doubt upon the validity of Bimba's delayed-response activities, but at the same time to reflect credit upon her versatility, intelligence, or whatever you want to call it. I mention this incident to illustrate the difficulties which beset the psychological observer in his attempts to study chimpanzee "responses." I have no slightest doubt that the results of published experiments are all that the observers claim for them and that the woodpiles are devoid of niggers.

We may now attempt a succinct summary of the results obtained from delayed-response tests made upon chimpanzees. There are two general types of such response tests—those which are spatial (i.e., involve the selection of a clue which is that of location or position in a series) and those which are discriminational (such as selection by color clues, by identification of a personality, etc.). Chimpanzees do much better with positional or spatial clues than with those which are non-spatial. They learn by the former method much more rapidly and achieve higher scores with shorter delays in choice.[47] Chimpanzees, by dint of repeated trials and reinforcements, can establish discrimination habits (as, for example, based upon color stimuli), but these non-spatial clues are very inadequate or present great difficulties when they are used in delayed-response tests. It is thought that delayed response involves the necessity of some implicit or symbolic response to the stimuli which can occur when overt response is blocked. These symbolic responses may be something in the nature of ideas or representative processes. If these occur, the animal is able to make some sort of critical association which later permits an overt response. It appears that such symbolic representations can be made by chimpanzees in the case of positional clues, but are difficult if not impossible in tests depending upon visual discrimination. Human beings apparently solve delayed-response tests with equal facility, whether the clues are positional or non-positional. It seems probable that they use language responses in making the necessary associations of a symbolic nature. Since subhuman vertebrates other than chimpanzees also are more capable of coping with problems which involve the use of

[47]Nissen, Riesen, and Nowlis 1938, pp. 361–86.

spatial rather than non-spatial clues, it seems probable that symbolic mechanisms pertaining to spatial relationships are phylogenetically older than those applying to other types of stimuli.[48] Spatial clues are perhaps more important for subhuman animals.

PATTERNED-STRING PROBLEMS

Köhler's early observations stressed the fact that chimpanzees cannot distinguish between the convergence of strings to a point of contact and actually crossed strings. Subsequently, various investigators have tested primates on patterned-string problems which require the animal to pull the correct string in variously elaborated patterns in order to get a reward. Finch tested 8 chimpanzees on 11 patterned-string problems and found that 7 of them were able to solve all of them, including 2 problems which had been failed by a number of monkeys tested by previous students.[49] The chimpanzees proved to have superior ability to the monkeys in profiting by experience. The results of Finch's study indicated that chimpanzees were able to compensate for the illusory effect of converging-diverging string problems, contrary to Köhler's earlier contention.

MEMORY

Various experimenters have recorded the chimpanzee's ability to recognize persons who were objects of especial liking or dislike, over periods varying from a few days to several months or even longer. A rather crude experimental method of testing the span of an animal's memory is to bury some food while the animal is watching, immediately remove the animal, and then bring it back to the vicinity after an interval of time to ascertain whether, when turned loose, it will go to the spot where the food is buried and dig it up. Köhler found that chimpanzees readily remembered the location of buried food after an interval of 16½ hours. Yerkes and Yerkes, working systematically with 4 chimpanzees, found that a 48-hour delay was approximately the limit of the memory span within which the animals went directly to the spot and dug up the buried food.[50] However, at longer intervals, up to 96 hours, the more gifted animals remembered that food had been buried somewhere in the locality and went around digging for it, but in the wrong places. The females were definitely superior to the males in these memory tests. The same observers tested memory of

[48]Nissen, Riesen, and Nowlis 1938, pp. 382, 383.
[49]Finch 1941b, pp. 83–90.
[50]Yerkes, R. and D., 1928, pp. 237–71.

food-containing boxes of certain colors and found it convincingly displayed after delays of 30 minutes. Köhler was successful in getting chimpanzees which had learned to discriminate between colors to repeat their feats of discrimination with very few errors after vacations of 13 to 18 months.[51]

TEMPERAMENT AND EMOTIONS

* Infant chimpanzees are relatively helpless and dependent and consequently insistent upon parental attention or human aid. This insistence may be fretful and complaining, or cheerful. In childhood they are restless, playful, and generally good-natured, but they get more serious and businesslike as adolescence approaches and play activities are replaced by acts which enable them to get a living. The mature chimpanzee is a grave animal which tolerates no nonsense and is inclined to be morose and suspicious. Individual differences in temperament among chimpanzees are perhaps as great as in human beings. Their register of emotional expression covers a much wider range, since they use their entire bodies, not merely their facial muscles. They jump up and down, fling themselves around, and wave their arms and legs in extravagant gestures to express either joy, anticipation, impatience, or anger. They also emit a variety of sounds and indulge in facial contortions and grimaces. However, they neither laugh nor weep, according to the scientists, although ladies who have raised pet chimps insist that they do both. Authorities agree that chimpanzees are much more emotional than orang-utans or gorillas, more inclined to be sanguine rather than melancholy, much more good-natured, friendly, and co-operative, rather than aloof and self-centered, as are often gorillas and orangs.

In a single emotional category chimpanzees show, according to Yerkes, a range "from slight uneasiness through shyness, timidity, apprehension, and fear to terror." Strange, large animals, loud sounds, and anything unusual will startle the chimpanzee. Yerkes and Yerkes tested 29 chimpanzees of various ages in their fear responses to a badminton shuttlecock, a rubber dog, a rubber tube, a small tortoise, and a kind of harmless legless lizard which is called a glass snake.[52] The animals' responses were rated on a 9-point scale. Infants were generally less responsive than children and adults, both positively (seeking) and negatively (avoiding). In each group the maximum positive response was to the shuttlecock and the maximum negative

[51]Köhler 1925, pp. 287–88.
[52]Yerkes, R. and A., 1936, pp. 53–66.

PROFESSOR R. M. YERKES IN 1926, WITH (*left to right*) WENDY, BILLY, DWINA, AND PAN

response either to the tortoise or to the glass snake. Younger animals sought the toy dog, but older chimpanzees, which presumably knew live dogs, avoided it. The snake was more markedly avoided than the tortoise by adults. Males seemed slightly more cautious and timid than females. The curious result of this investigation was that the animals appeared to exhibit little or no evidence of fear or avoidance response except as a result of experience. This experiment was prompted by a desire to investigate the alleged terror of snakes said to be characteristic of chimpanzees.

The chimpanzee upon whom fright is growing usually remains perfectly quiet, as if trying to avoid attention. Pulse and respiration increase and the hair stands erect as the animal holds itself tense and ready for flight.[53] Fear easily merges into anger, if the aggressor seems to show timidity and readiness to give ground. The hair lies down again and the chimp may beat upon the ground with hands and feet and even rush forward in a threatening manner.

It is a well-known fact that chimpanzees strongly resent being laughed at and are likely to "get back" by striking or other unpleasant behavior. Under these circumstances some chimpanzees will "fly into a rage." Jealousy is often shown when attention or preference is given to another chimpanzee. These animals may take strong and enduring dislikes to certain persons, on no provocation whatsoever. Yerkes reports a case in which a young male chimpanzee took an immediate and very intense dislike to a perfectly inoffensive and friendly man, possibly because the latter, at their first meeting, had to repel the animal repeatedly in its attacks upon his buttons. Whenever they met within the next few years (which was rarely), the chimpanzee screamed, shouted, rushed toward the man, and attempted to strike him, bite him, or seize him. He accompanied these aggressive movements with transient erection of the hair on the back, opening the mouth, and drawing back the lips, and with repeated urination and defecation.

Young chimpanzees often fall into tantrums, in which they throw themselves upon the ground, writhe violently, striking themselves against various objects regardless of minor injuries. Often they will beat their heads with their hands, contract their lips, bare their teeth, shout, or scream. Frequently vocalization is checked by a glottal cramp, so that the animal chokes. These childish fits of anger are very similar to those displayed by uncontrolled human children.

The chimpanzee undoubtedly has methods of expressing joy, contentment, happiness, and amusement, but the facial movements or

[53]Yerkes and Learned 1925, pp. 33–34.

other motor accompaniments of these moods have not been described. Confidence, friendliness, and affection are expressed by hand-stroking, patting, or snuggling. Kissing and hugging are frequently observed, the latter probably independently of human influence. Sympathy for ill or injured companions is manifested by gentle treatment and caresses.

Chimpanzees are given to strong mood changes—from cheerfulness and elation to depression and melancholy. A chimpanzee separated from its companions, punished by deprivation of food, prevented from playing, or made to work at a problem which is difficult acts utterly disconsolate and thoroughly "fed up with life." The death of an inseparable companion may occasion expressions of grief which are quite heart-rending and long-sustained, including moaning, tearing the hair, and plaintive cries, together with fits of listlessness and depression. There is no weeping, but plenty of mourning.

PATHOLOGY

DISEASES

Little is known of the diseases which attack the chimpanzee in the wild, but there is a good deal of information about the causes of death in captive animals. Respiratory diseases such as bronchitis, bronchial pneumonia, and tuberculosis claim many victims. Diseases of the digestive and skeletal system are also common. Among 34 animals which died in the London Zoological Gardens over a period of some 40 years, causes of death, in addition to those listed above, were ulcers of the tongue, typhoid fever, peritonitis, colitis, chronic arthritis. A post-mortem performed on an adult female chimpanzee which died last fall at Orange Park indicated nephritis as the cause of death.

Apparently all the microbic diseases of the human races can be transmitted to chimpanzees. Among these are syphilis, cholera, typhoid, bacillic and amoebic dysenteries, typhus, yellow fever, acute poliomyelitis, measles, scarlet fever, smallpox, trachoma, pneumonia, and influenza. Many studies have been made of the parasites in the blood and the intestines of the chimpanzee. Among the blood-inhabiting protozoa of man which have been found in the chimpanzee are trypanosomes (which cause sleeping sickness) and plasmodia (malarial parasites). Amoebae and intestinal flagellates indistinguishable from those of man are found in the chimpanzee and in other primates. Some of these amoebae cause dysentery and liver abscesses. The intestinal ciliates called balantidia, which seem to be acquired by human beings by ingesting cysts from pigs, also occur in the chimpanzee and in other primates. This protozoal parasite may cause a form of dysentery.

Undoubtedly, chimpanzees also suffer from various deficiency dis eases as a result of their being fed upon inadequate diets, or failing to get sufficient fresh air and sunlight. Dryness of the skin, loss of hair, and affections of the bones and teeth have been attributed to these causes.

Lice are not commonly found on captive primates, but those which occur belong to a family which is limited to man and the other primates. Vermin of the genus *Pediculus,* which infests man, have been found on the chimpanzee, the gibbon, and some monkeys.

MORPHINE ADDICTION

Morphine addiction had never been established for any infrahuman organism before Spragg's experiments upon chimpanzees in 1935–37 at the Yale Laboratories in Orange Park, Florida.[54] He studied the effects of small isolated doses in 35 cases of young chimpanzees. The doses induced a hyperesthesia of the skin which resulted in much scratching, together with drowsiness and general sedation lasting from 4 to 6 hours. Appetite was reduced for a longer period. The animals were rendered tractable and passive. Four young chimpanzee subjects were used for chronic-morphinism experiments. Self-inflicted scratching and hair-pulling resulted to such an extent that some of the victims were covered with scabs and almost denuded of hair. Weight loss took place for the first six weeks, after which weight was maintained or slowly regained. No serious disturbance of alimentary functions was noted. Initial temperature drops were soon corrected by the bodily heat-regulating mechanism. Restlessness and nocturnal activity were increased. Dilation of the pupils of the eyes was a constant effect, and this has been uniformly reported for other infrahuman species, although the reverse effect obtains in man.

On multiple-choice and delayed-response tests the postdose per formances were consistently superior to the predose performances after injections had been carried on for 6 or 8 weeks. Decrease of playfulness and "social withdrawal" were noted. Evidences of a definite and strong desire for the drug appeared in 3 of the 4 animals. (The other animal was given injections for 6 weeks only.) One of the animals was tested in various psychological problems to ascertain whether he would work better for a drug award than for a food

[54]Spragg 1940.

award. He did. In the case of males, morphine injections stimulated sexual functions and withdrawals of the drug depressed them. These are in contrast to the results reported for human beings and morphinized monkeys. In the female, morphine inhibited genital swelling and probably delayed the onset of the first menstruation. Complete withdrawal of the drug occasioned some physiological disturbance, but recovery from addiction was complete in 2 cases. The other 2 animals died before recovery—victims of diseases to which morphinism probably did not contribute. Spragg's conclusion is that morphine addiction is primarily a physiogenic phenomenon, and that a "societal" factor, usually present in human addictions, is not demonstrable for chimpanzees. These morphinized chimps craved the drug without knowing that they were addicted to it and that it was "habit-forming."

ANATOMY

A detailed description of the anatomy and physiology of the chimpanzee would require a sizable volume, in spite of the fact that neither is thoroughly known. In this general book on the primates some of the more important minutiae on the principal animals and groups are lumped together at the end of each section, after the example of the punctuation marks in the famous book of "Lord Timothy Dexter."

SKELETON

The skull of the chimpanzee has a relatively larger brain case and less projection of the jaws than those of the gorilla and the orang-utan. The temporal ridges in adults nearly meet in the mid-line of the vault, but there is ordinarily no sagittal bony crest as in the males of the other great apes. Nor is the occipital crest so marked. The cranial capacity of the chimpanzee averages 399.5 cc. in males and 365.8 cc. in females. The sutures of the vault are obliterated early in life, but may be tortuous in young animals. A fronto-temporal articulation usually occurs in the pterion region. Wormian bones may occur in the lambdoid suture. The zygomatic arches are not massive or strongly bowed; the glenoid fossae are shallow, with rudimentary articular eminences. Posteriorly, they are bounded by postglenoid processes which project down below the tympanic bones. There is no proper mastoid process, but merely a rough ridge. Styloid and vaginal processes are generally absent. The foramen magnum is situated far back upon the skull base. The relief of the skull base is low. The pterygoid plates are only feebly developed.

Supraorbital ridges are large in adults and there is a marked postorbital constriction behind the torus or bar of bone which surmounts the orbits. The malars are small and project little, either anteriorly or laterally. The

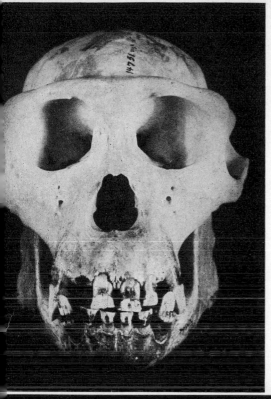

SKULL OF ADULT MALE
CHIMPANZEE

Photographs F. W. Orchard
Courtesy Peabody Museum

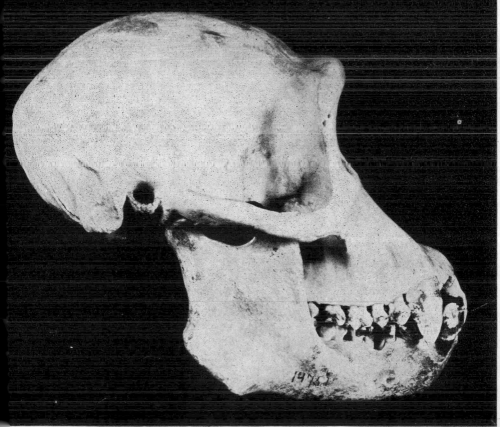

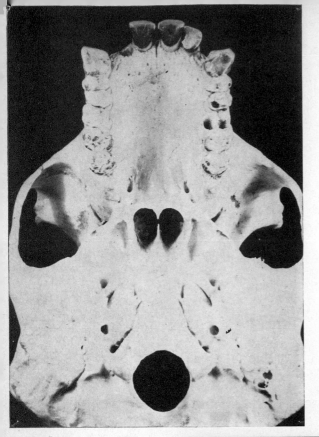

UPPER AND LOWER
DENTAL ARCHES OF ADUL*
MALE CHIMPANZEE

Photographs F. W. Orchard

Courtesy Peabod

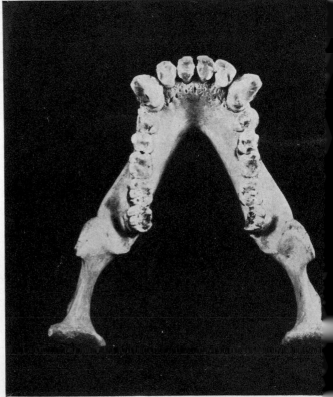

orbits are high and quadrangular with rounded corners. The outer sides are lower than the inner sides; i.e., the orbits slant downward and outward, following the slope of the supraorbital torus, which thins out laterally. The lachrymo-ethmoidal suture is narrow and may be replaced by a fronto-maxillary articulation. The interorbital space is small; the nasofrontal suture is low. The nasal bones fuse soon after birth. They have an hourglass shape, slightly arched transversely at the root, but flattened at the base, or even depressed into a median trough. The nasal aperture has neither well-defined side walls nor a sill. The sides and lower portions are formed by the premaxillae. Usually there is no anterior nasal spine. Frontal and maxillary sinuses are small. The alveolar parts of the maxillae are deep and anteriorly protrusive.

The mandible has a very broad ascending ramus with a sharply recurved coronoid process. The body of the mandible is not especially deep, but is sturdy and long. The symphysis falls away from the incisive border and there is no mental eminence. On the inside of the symphysis there is a pit or genial fossa, from which the geniohyoid and genioglossal muscles take their origins. At the base of the symphysis a shelf of bone unites the two halves of the narrow mandible. The mylohyoid ridge is faint or indistinguishable.

TEETH

The dental formula is that of man and all of the catarrhine primates ($I\frac{2}{2}\,C\frac{1}{1}\,PM\frac{2}{2}\,M\frac{3}{3}$). The upper median incisors are large and protrusive. The canine teeth are tusklike, but inferior in size to those of the other great apes. They are larger in males than in females. They interlock, so that gaps or diastemata in the tooth rows occur between the canines and the incisors in the upper series and between the canines and premolars in the lower series. The upper premolars are small and prominently bicuspid; the first usually has 3 roots, but the second only 2. Lower premolars are small, but typically anthropoid. The upper molars retain sharp V ridges of the primitive tritubercular pattern, but Gregory states that there is a poorly developed posterior ridge running from the enlarged hypocone to the metacone. They have 4 cusps. The lower molars have 5 cusps of the *Dryopithecus* pattern, but they are longer and narrower than those of man. The molar crowns are covered with enamel wrinkles and the cusps are low. The third molars are reduced and degenerate. The dental arch is U-shaped, but, especially in the male, wider across the canines than in the molar region. The size of the postcanine teeth is not superior to that found in many modern savages.

POSTCRANIAL SKELETON

Points of interest in the postcranial skeleton of the chimpanzee are noted in the general comparative treatment of primate skeletons found in Chapter XV.

Organs of Digestion and Absorption

The tongue of the chimpanzee is long and narrow, with fewer circumvallate papillae than are found in the tongue of man. The stomach is U-shaped and more horizontal than in man. The arrangement of the intestinal tract is similar to that of man. The appendix is 4½ inches long and the caecum 3 inches. The rectum and anal canal form a straight tube without any of the flexures present in man.

Organs of Respiration and Voice

In all apes except the gibbon there are air sacs communicating with the ventricles of the larynx. In the chimpanzee these lie under the platysma and consist of a central and 2 lateral parts. The former extends upward to the hyoid bone and downward to the lower border of the manubrium. The lateral part extends into the axilla. The left lung is usually divided into 2 lobes and the right into 3.

Urogenital Organs

The ovaries of the chimpanzee resemble those of man more than do the ovaries of any other primate except the orang. The uterus is small; the fundus rudimentary or absent. The urinary meatus opens in the middle of the anterior wall of the vagina. The labia minora are large, the labia majora very small. The clitoris is large and there is no hymen. The vulva and anus are directed backward. The long tapering penis has no pronounced glans. The lower part contains a fusiform bone. The seminal vesicles are large, coiled into tubes, and extend laterally beyond the bladder. The prostate is entirely retro-urethral.

Nervous System

The brain of the chimpanzee is larger than that of the orang but smaller than that of the gorilla. It is ovoid and the inferior surfaces of the frontal lobes are rostrated. The cerebrum overlaps the cerebellum to a variable extent.

CHAPTER II

The Gorilla Individualist

DISTRIBUTION AND HABITAT

THE GORILLAS are found in two limited equatorial regions of Africa, separated by an area of the Upper Congo basin which extends from 17° E. to 28° E.[1] The distance between the two groups of gorillas is about 650 miles. The western, coastal, or lowland gorilla is found, for the most part, in the Cameroons and the Gaboon. Its approximate northern limit is 6° N. to 6°7′ N., near the border of Southern Nigeria. Eastward its limit seems to be the Sanga River, a tributary of the Congo flowing southward at longitude 16°15′ E. On the southeast the limit follows the border of the forest, reaching the sea at the edge of the Belgian Congo, 5° S., 13° E. The range of the animal, according to Coolidge's map, does not reach the lower course of the Congo, but follows the border of the forest to the north and west of that stream after it is joined by the Sanga. Further, Coolidge states that along the coast the gorillas are usually not found for a distance of about 30 miles inland, since the forest begins some way back from the shore line.

The mountain gorillas occur in a narrow strip of the eastern Congo, a mountainous region west of Lake Edward and Lake Kivu, and extending south to the northern tip of Lake Tanganyika. This area appears to be about 250 miles long and 100 miles wide.

The habitat of the lowland gorilla is primeval forest with thick and almost impenetrable undergrowth. The area has been compared to a damp, moist greenhouse, into which the rays of the sun can hardly penetrate. The rainy season here lasts for 8 months. Torrential rains are interspersed with fogs, and the whole region, which extends nearly 1,500 miles from west to east, is indescribably depressing and melancholic. The mountain gorilla lives in a volcanic country dotted with extinct craters and cones and marked by lava flows of varying age. Primeval forest has overgrown the earlier volcanic deposits and the

[1]Coolidge 1936, pp. 492–98, 1929, pp. 362–63.

63

beginnings of vegetation overlie the recent flows. In this region the gorilla inhabits a mixed bamboo forest, ranging in altitude from 7,500 feet at the lower edge of the bamboo to more than 12,000 feet in the cold sub-Alpine zone.

DIFFERENCES BETWEEN MOUNTAIN AND LOWLAND GORILLA

In 1929 Harold Coolidge distinguished the mountain gorilla from the lowland gorilla in that the former has a longer palate, a generally narrower skull, thicker hairy covering, more black hair, and a fleshy callosity on the crest of the head.[2] Schultz later added many other distinguishing characters of the comparatively recently discovered mountain gorilla.[3] These include greater trunk length, higher-situated nipples, longer neck,[4] narrower hips, shorter lower limbs relative to trunk length, longer lower limbs relative to length of upper limbs, broader and shorter hands, great toe reaching farther distally and branching from the sole more distally, a less convex joint at the base of the great toe (indicating reduced opposability of the great toe to the other toes), shorter outer toes, usually webbed; higher face, narrower width between the eyes, smaller number of combined thoracic and lumbar vertebrae, absolutely and relatively shorter humerus (upper-arm bone), absolutely and relatively longer clavicle (collarbone) and ilium (pelvic bone), relatively longer radius (outer bone of the forearm), a peculiar concavity of the vertebral border of the scapula (shoulder blade).

DESCRIPTION

Size

The size of the gorilla has often been exaggerated, but sometimes underestimated. Harold Coolidge has compiled a list of measurements of gorillas taken either upon freshly killed specimens in the field or upon embalmed bodies.[5] In this list are included 7 adult male lowland gorillas and 12 adult male mountain gorillas, but complete sets of measurements are not available for all of them. In total length the

[2] Coolidge 1929, p. 375.
[3] Schultz 1934, pp. 51–61.
[4] Coolidge (1936, p. 488) says that the neck of the mountain gorilla is, on the contrary, shorter than that of the lowland gorilla.
[5] Coolidge 1936, pp. 479–501.

lowland gorillas ranged from 157.5 cm. to 182.9 cm. (approximately 5 feet to 6 feet), and the mountain gorillas from 161.9 cm. to 179.7 cm. (5 feet 3½ inches to 5 feet 10 7/10 inches). These few figures do not permit any conclusion in regard to difference in size of the two types. Reports of gorillas standing 7 to 9 feet are hardly credible, but large male gorillas may well exceed 6 feet in stature. Mrs. Belle Benchley states that the all-over body length of the recently deceased male mountain gorilla, Mbongo, was 77 inches (195.58 cm.). This measurement was obtained by adding the length of the torso from neck to crotch to the height of the head and neck plus the length of the extended legs.[6] The animal standing on his feet in life would have been some inches shorter, because the erect gorilla keeps his knees bent.

Total arm spreads in Coolidge's data range from 200 cm. to 271.7 cm. (78.7 inches to 106.9 inches). Mbongo's span across his back and between his middle finger tips was 97½ inches (247.6 cm.). Thus the span of the gorilla enormously exceeds its stature. Coolidge's chest circumferences of male gorillas range from 128.1 cm. to 157.4 cm. (50½ to 62 inches, approximately), but Mbongo had a chest girth below the nipples of 69 inches (175.3 cm.). Coolidge reports the weights of only 6 gorillas, all of the mountain type. These range from 293 pounds to 460 pounds. However, this authority states that Bobby, a mountain gorilla which died in the Berlin Zoo in 1935, at an estimated age of 10 to 11 years, weighed more than 584 pounds.

Roger Conant, curator of the Philadelphia Zoological Garden, has recently published statistics of the weights and estimated ages of gorillas now in captivity in the United States.[7] Mbongo, the obese but

WEIGHTS AND ESTIMATED AGES OF CAPTIVE GORILLAS

Males	Weight	Estimated Age	Residence
Mbongo*	618	14	San Diego Zoo
Ngagi	585	15	" " "
Gargantua	500	11	Ringling Circus
Bushman	473	13	Lincoln Park Zoo, Chicago
Bamboo	435	15	Philadelphia Zoo
Massa	360	11	" "
Sultan	80	5	Chicago Zoological Park
Females			
M'Toto	438	10	Ringling Circus
Susie	334	15	Cincinnati Zoo
Miss Congo	180	7	Chicago Zoological Park
Suzette	180	7	" " "

*Recently deceased.

[6]Benchley 1942, p. 379.

[7]Conant 1941, pp. 44–45.

still immature mountain gorilla male, died on March 15, 1942, at the estimated age of 16 years. The weight of 618 pounds was the last figure officially recorded for him, because in the last year of his life he was too big to fit properly upon the platform of the scale. His last weight fluctuated from 645 to nearly 670 pounds, according to the part of the platform upon which the greatest portion of his weight rested.[8] Mr. Conant tells me that it would be very easy to put an additional 50 pounds on Bamboo by allowing him to overeat. It seems improbable that wild gorillas ever get the opportunity of "digging their graves with their teeth."

PIGMENTATION

The youngest gorilla fetus on record, described by Duckworth,[9] was entirely unpigmented, being uniformly whitish in color. This specimen corresponded in development to human fetuses of the twelfth or thirteenth week of menstrual age. The next oldest specimen recorded by Schultz is roughly equivalent to a 15-week human fetus. Its only pigment is in the ears, which are of a light-brown color. A third fetus (fifteenth to nineteenth human week), studied by Deniker, was light brown, except face, palms, and soles, which were yellowish; the darkest pigment was on the back. Another gorilla fetus, considerably older, was less heavily pigmented. Reichenow's gorilla baby at the age of a month was still a fairly light chocolate-brown color. Certainly, the skin of young and adult gorillas is ordinarily black, but Schultz thinks that pigmentation begins earlier in the fetal life of the chimpanzee than in the gorilla. The iris of the gorilla eye apparently darkens with age. Famelart, quoted by Schultz, says that in one month the eye color of his infant gorilla changed from yellow to chestnut brown. The juvenile gorilla is said to have a medium-brown eye, while that of the adult is dark brown. The first hairs of the gorilla are also unpigmented and hair color changes with age, extreme graying in old age being typical.

ODOR AND SWEAT GLANDS

Various authorities, including Yerkes and Burbidge, say that the gorilla emits a peculiarly pungent and penetrating body odor, a little like rubber, according to one. Sweat glands are seemingly numerous and drops of perspiration may often be observed on the face and on the extremities.

[8] Benchley 1942, p. 379.
[9] Schultz 1927.

Hair

The first indications of hair on the gorilla appear on the eyebrows, lips, and chin—the same places as in human fetuses. In later fetuses the eyelashes have appeared and the eyebrows have reached a length of 5 to 7 mm. The hair on the scalp is fairly well developed and many parts of the body and limbs bear a short coat. In older gorilla fetuses, as in the chimpanzee, the hair on the head is much longer than that on the rest of the body. A fairly abundant coat of hair has grown upon the body of the gorilla, apparently as early as the third month of life, if we can trust the record of Reichenow. In the adults the hair is long and thick, more so in the mountain gorilla than in the lowland species. Coolidge says that the principal color of the mountain gorilla is deep black, with a gray or white area across the back. There is occasionally a sprinkling of gray or red hair on the crown of the head. The same authority states that the lowland or coastal gorilla has shorter and thinner hair, with no beard. This animal often grows very gray and sometimes has a chestnut patch on his head and neck. He may even be speckled with yellow. Some other authorities state that each hair is banded, the tip and the root being gray, while the rest is black. Evidently there is no little regional and individual variation. The rufous phase apparently crops out in both types of gorilla.

The scalp hair flows backward toward the neck, according to Sonntag, and forms a prominent crest along the center line of the skull from front to back. These hairs are erected when the animal is enraged and the crest is pulled downward and forward with the scalp. The same writer says that streams of hair pass down the sides of the head and include the ears, sometimes concealing them.[10] On the body the general direction of the hair is downward, but there are whorls over the shoulder blades and high up on the sides of the abdomen. The hairs on the leg are directed downward, but on the arms they converge toward the elbows. In the adult gorilla there is very little hair upon the face, palms, soles, and chest. The longest hair is found on the limbs and back, where it may attain 10 cm. or more.

Schultz has found that the gorilla alone of the anthropoid apes surpasses man in the density of hair on the scalp.[11]

Skull, Head, and Face

We must look at the skull of the adult male gorilla if we wish to appreciate the physiognomy of the living animal, since there is much

[10]Sonntag 1924, pp. 99–100.
[11]Schultz 1931, pp. 303–17.

more of bone and muscle involved in the structure of this massive head than in that of man. Man's skull is just a thin bony capsule covering a bloated brain, with a small face and jaws hafted to the front part of the base. This skull is overlaid with a thin muscular sheet on the vault. The only strong muscles are chewing muscles attached to the sides of the vault and face, and those at the back of the neck, supporting the slightly overbalanced head. The human masticatory and nuchal muscles are very small and feeble compared with those of a gorilla. Hence the brain case of a man looks like an overgrown eggshell. When we pick up the skull of the male gorilla, we are at once impressed by its great weight. Above the eye sockets is a tremendous transverse bar of bone, behind which the narrow and low forehead region is pinched in at the sides by the cranial walls to which are attached the thick temporal muscles. Down the middle line of the skull cap, beginning a little behind the meager forehead, is a vertical crest of bone one to 3 inches high, which meets a similar transverse crest extending clear across the back of the skull. Behind the massive arches of the cheekbones, which frame the sides of the face, are horizontal crests which meet the transverse occipital (or back-of-the-head) crest. Thus as you look at the gorilla skull from the top, it seems to be divided longitudinally into two compartments, or trays, by these partitionlike crests. The swelling curves of the actual bony envelope of the brain enclose a rather small cavity, and the outstanding scaffolding of the central crest reminds one of the false roof-combs on Maya temples, while the transverse occipital crest recalls the false fronts which used to be built up on little wooden shops in the West, to increase the apparent height of the façade. These muscular compartments to the right and left of the central crest are filled up to the tops of the partitions, and higher, by the huge lateral temporal muscles which furnish the power for shutting the jaws in chewing. The gorilla seems to have no back to his head, because the hinder part of the skull is flat and slopes downward and forward. To this occipital plane are attached massive neck muscles. Thus the back of the gorilla head is entirely buried in his neck. The vertex of the head seems to rise high in the living animal, but most of this cranial altitude is temporal muscle and bony crest, with a thickened callous pad surmounting the crest. This pad, which is made of connective tissue, is supposed to be characteristic of old male mountain gorillas, but probably occurs in both varieties and both sexes of each.

The bristly hair on the low gorilla forehead grows down to the great bar of bone which overhangs his cavernous eye sockets. His

MASSA, NEARLY ADULT MALE MOUNTAIN GORILLA

BAMBOO, INFANT MALE LOWLAND GORILLA

deep-set little eyes are very dark. Above the root of the nose and up the middle of the brow ridges are deep vertical wrinkles and across the insignificant nasal bridge and below the eyes are more coarse transverse wrinkles in the dead-black skin. In the middle of the place where the fleshy tip of the nose should be is a deep groove or furrow, on either side of which the nasal wings swell out and around the diagonal oval nostrils. These nasal wings or alae with the partition between them are shaped like a pretzel with its lower side merging into the bulging upper lip. The septum between the nostrils is ridiculously thin. The upper and lower lips of the gorilla are molded over a projecting muzzle. The mouth slit is bow-shaped and of great width, but there is practically no exposure of mucous membrane at the edge of the lips, which are thin and not outrolled and blubbery, as are the highly specialized and evolved lips of some races of men—notably the Negro. Deep naso-labial wrinkles run from the broad nasal wings down past the corners of the mouth. Below the mouth slit the lower jaw falls away in a hemispherical curve; there is no chin eminence. Actually, the face of the gorilla closely corresponds to the underlying bony structure, except the pretzel nose end, to which no clue is offered in the facial skeleton. The gorilla's face in repose has an expression which seems sad or pensive, not to say grim. It easily changes to one of indescribable ferocity.

The ears of the gorilla are small and close-set. In shape they resemble human ears, but the fatty lobe is either absent or merely suggested. The ears are really not much smaller than those of man, but they look tiny on the sides of the huge head.

When the gorilla opens his mouth, he displays truly formidable arcades of teeth. The upper incisors are massive, projecting chisels, the canines (or eye teeth) great conical, interlocking tusks. The palate is U-shaped with the greatest width at the front. The molar teeth are shaped much like those of man, but are far larger and have higher, sharper cusps.

The head of the gorilla appears to sit directly upon his high and relatively narrow shoulders, because the neck musculature is so massive that the neck itself is pyramidal rather than columnar. At the occiput, the great nuchal muscles slope into the back without transition, and at the sides merge gradually with the shoulders. The rounded masses of muscle which overlie the shoulder tips seem hunched up against the sides of the jaws. The shoulder is very high and the arm joint farther forward than in man, perhaps because the gorilla habitually hangs by his arms or uses them in quadrupedal progression. The collarbones are directed upward and backward rather than transversely as in man, whose arm is hung much farther out and down on the rib cage.

Extremities

The arms of the gorilla are nothing short of stupendous. They are, of course, very long—the forearm disproportionately so—but the total upper limb has not the exaggerated length of the gibbon and orang arms. In adult gorillas these mighty arms are generally clothed with long hair, which masks the details of their shape. The hand of the gorilla is very broad and relatively short—not long and slender like those of other apes. The thumb, though short and relatively small, is not so degenerate-looking as that of other apes. It is set farther forward on the hand than other anthropoid thumbs; yet it is not long enough to reach the basal knuckle of the index finger. The other four digits are thick and stubby. They are webbed up to the midde of the first phalanx or joint. The nails are black and more strongly curved from side to side than those of man, but they are not claw-like. The pads of flesh on the hands and the lines or folds of flexure are closely similar to those of the human palm. Great calluses on the middle knuckles show the effect of resting the body weight upon the bent hand in four-footed walking. It seems probable that the gorilla cannot extend and flex the four outer fingers of the hand independently. The fist closes and opens as a unit. The thumb can be rotated and opposed to the finger tips in some degree, but these movements have neither the range nor the precision of those of the human hand. In any event, the thumb is too short for perfect opposability.

The legs of the gorilla are thick, stumpy, and rather shapeless, but their contours are concealed by long hair. Relative to the arms and the trunk, the legs are very short, but far from slender. The foot of the gorilla is relatively broad and short like that of man. The great toe is a massive affair, set off on the inside like a thumb, but it is relatively shorter than that of the chimpanzee and springs from the sole much farther forward. Moreover, the heel is better developed and projected farther backward. The four outer toes are short and attached to each other by a web which extends up to the middle joints. The foot is a grasping organ, and the great toe can be opposed to the lateral digits. Nevertheless, the gorilla walks flat upon the soles of its feet and not upon the knuckles of the toes.

COMPARISON BETWEEN WRESTLING CHAMPION AND GORILLAS

To understand the differences in body build and size between man and the gorilla we may consider the table on p. 73, in which the measurements of M. Maurice Tillet, former heavyweight wrestling champion of the world, are compared with those of an adult male mountain gorilla and an adult male lowland gorilla. The measurements of M. Tillet were taken by my colleague, Dr. Carleton S. Coon, and those of the embalmed gorillas by Dr. Adolph H. Schultz of Johns Hopkins University.[12]

I want to make it perfectly clear that in comparing M. Tillet with gorillas I intend no disparagement of that excellent gentleman, who is my esteemed friend. M. Tillet was born in Rheims, the son of French parents. His father was a civil engineer. M. Tillet attended the University of Toulouse, was a forward on the All-France rugby team, and, subsequently, a petty officer on a submarine of the French navy. He is a man of culture, interested in science to the extent of being willing to allow his extraordinary physique to be studied by anthropologists. Of a naturally powerful build and a gifted athlete, M. Tillet has suffered an enlargement of the pituitary gland at the base of the skull. This gland is one of the principal agencies in regulating and stimulating growth. This endocrine disorder, called acromegaly, has the effect of producing excessive growth of certain parts of the body. If it occurs in an immature person, prior to the fusion of the caps or epiphyses with the shafts of the long bones, it causes gigantism, as seen in most circus giants and in the boxer, Primo Carnera. In the case of M. Tillet, the glandular disturbance apparently set in after he had attained his full normal growth. The general effect which it has had upon his physique is to enlarge and thicken his hands and feet, to elongate markedly and generally increase the size of his face, and perhaps also to add to the natural robustness of his bony framework and its muscular covering, with possibly some hypertrophy of the internal organs. But, whereas most acromegalics are poorly co-ordinated and physically weak, M. Tillet is probably one of the strongest men in the world and enjoys admirable health and the full exercise of his excellent mental powers. However, his body build, as well as his almost superhuman strength, make him the fittest human subject for comparison with the giants of the primate order. Upon first sight of M. Tillet, the observer is astounded at the size of his face,

[12]Data derived from Coolidge 1936, Table 4.

the tremendous breadth of his shoulders, the vastness of his torso, and the comparatively great length of his arms and shortness of his legs. As soon as one becomes personally acquainted with Maurice Tillet, his unusual physical appearance is forgotten in the charm of his personality, his sincerity, friendliness, and his store of interesting information.

M. Tillet was 36 years of age at the time these measurements were taken; we do not know the ages of the gorillas with whom he is compared, but they probably were younger. The Angel, as M. Tillet is called, stands 1,744 mm. (5 feet 8.7 inches) tall and weighs 276 pounds, very little of which is fat. The mountain gorilla was about 1½ inches taller than the Angel, but weighed 460 pounds. The lowland gorilla was a little more than one quarter of an inch taller than the Angel and of unknown weight. My guess at his weight, based upon his measurements and the comparative weight of the mountain gorilla, would be 400 to 430 pounds. Thus a gorilla of about the same standing height as the heavyweight wrestling champion of the world weighs almost half again as much. The lowland gorilla also has a combined head and trunk length which exceeds that of the Angel by 113 mm., or nearly 12 per cent, but the Angel's shoulders are only about one-quarter inch narrower than those of the gorilla. However, chest depth, chest breadth, and chest circumference of the lowland gorilla are enormously greater than those of M. Tillet, whose measurements are, nevertheless, tremendous for a human being. The gorilla's chest girth is nearly 17 per cent greater, his chest depth more than 21 per cent greater, and his chest breadth over 24 per cent larger.

When we come to total leg length, the Angel has an advantage of more than 15 per cent over the lowland gorilla, and the wrestler's foot, though shorter, is considerably wider. The long and massive arms of M. Tillet seem short and puny in comparison with the giant upper limbs of the lowland gorilla. M. Tillet's total arm length is only 71.6 per cent of that of the gorilla, and his forearm length only a little more than 66 per cent of that of the King of the Primates. The Angel's hamlike hands are shorter and narrower than those of the gorilla, but both have breadths that are approximately half of their hand lengths. If we had thumb lengths, those of the Angel would markedly exceed those of the gorilla.

M. Tillet, whose head dimensions are prodigious, nevertheless has a shorter and much narrower head than the lowland gorilla, but he slightly exceeds in both diameters the taller and heavier mountain gorilla. There is a good deal more of bone and muscle and less of brain in the gorilla's head dimensions than in those of M. Tillet. It is in the

BAMBOO, NEARLY ADULT, AGED ABOUT 15 YEARS

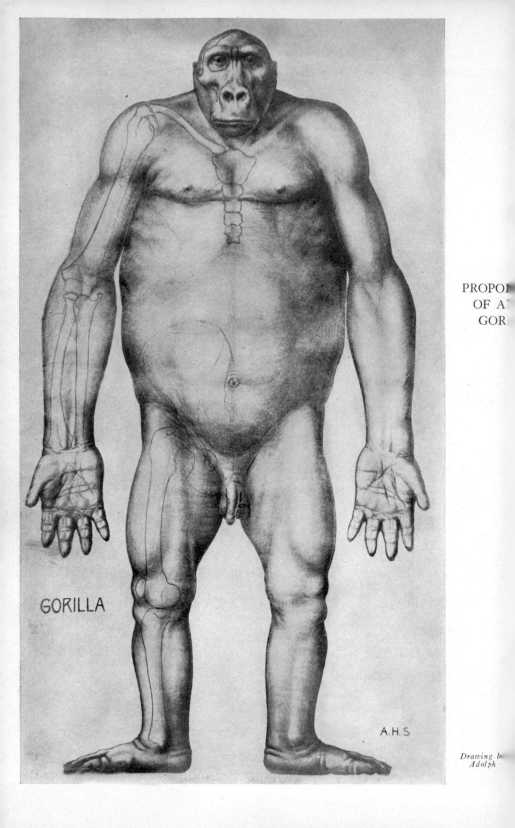

GORILLA

PROPO[...]
OF A[...]
GOR[...]

A.H.S

Drawing b[...]
Adolph

COMPARATIVE ANTHROPOMETRY OF AN ADULT MALE LOWLAND GORILLA, AN ADULT MALE MOUNTAIN GORILLA, AND M. MAURICE TILLET, "THE ANGEL," FORMER HEAVYWEIGHT WRESTLING CHAMPION OF THE WORLD

	M. Tillet*	Mountain Gorilla†	Lowland Gorilla‡
Age	36	?	?
Weight	276	460	?
Stature	1744	1778	1751
Head and Body Length	958	1086	1071
Shoulder Width	437	463	444
Hip Width	319	403	407
Chest Width	364	476	452
Chest Depth	285	329	345
Chest Circumference	1205	1488	1406
Leg Length	786	692	680
(Stature minus Sitting Height)			
Upper Leg Length	434?	416	389
Lower Leg Length	367	326	330
Foot Length	277	287	312
Foot Width	110	92	88
Arm Length	793	1096	1107
Upper-arm Length	326	466	479
Lower-arm Length	251	389	379
Hand Length	202	241	249
Hand Width	102	140	125
Average Diameter of Head	172.7	157	176.3
Head Length	219	217	224
Head Width	165	161	203
Head Height	134	94	102
Facial Height	179	190	190
Upper Facial Height	93	150	143
Facial Width	181	189	210
Nose Height	71	108	102
Nose Width	55	72	75
Ear Length	85 l.	52	60
Ear Breadth	42 l.	38	42
Upper-arm Circumference	394	?	483
Lower-arm Circumference	350	432 §	451 ‖
Upper-leg Circumference	610	699	737
Lower-leg Circumference	390	369	445
Cephalic Index	75.3 ¶	74.2†	90.7‡
Length-Height Index	61.2	43.3	45.5
Breadth-Height Index	81.2*	58.4	50.2
Total Facial Index	98.9	99.5	90.5
Upper Facial Index	51.4	79.4	69.05
Nasal Index	77.5	66.7	73.5
Span	2023?**	2760 ?§	2337 ‖
Span-Stature Index	116.0?	161.4?§	134.3?‖
Relative Sitting Height	54.9	61.1†	61.2‡

*Measurements by Carleton S. Coon.
†Columbia U. Anat. 2, Raven. W. Kivu, measurements by Adolph H. Schultz.
‡Columbia U. Anat. 21, Raven. French Cameroons, measurements by Schultz.
§Terv. Museum, measurements by H. C. Bingham.
‖Philadelphia 16981, Data from Coolidge.
¶Indices calculated by E. A. H.
**Reconstructed: 2 (arm length)+shoulder width.

height of the brain case above the ear holes that the human primate shows great and significant superiority. The lowland gorilla's head height is only 76.1 per cent of that of M. Tillet and the mountain gorilla's cranial altitude is only 70.1 per cent of that of the higher-browed human specimen. If we could measure the cubical contents of the skulls of the human athlete and of the two gorillas, we should undoubtedly find that the brain sizes of the latter were not more than one third of that of the Angel.

M. Tillet has the largest human face we have ever seen or measured, but it is much shorter and narrower than that of either gorilla, though closer to that of the mountain gorilla. Actually M. Tillet and the mountain gorilla are both long-headed and relatively long- and narrow-faced; their cranial and facial indices are nearly the same, but the lowland gorilla has a much broader head and a relatively shorter, broader, and absolutely bigger face.

The noses of gorillas are quite inhuman in shape and much longer and broader than the nose of the Angel, which is the largest we have ever seen or measured. Much of the facial length of M. Tillet lies in the depth of the chin and lower jaw, which is greatly increased in acromegaly, whereas the great length of the gorilla's face is in the upper jaw. The gorilloid chin is non-existent, and the depth of the lower jaw is small relative to the length of the upper face.

Two of the few measurements in which M. Tillet surpasses the gorilla are length and breadth of the ears. Gorilla ears are smaller than human ears, but M. Tillet has had his ears artificially enlarged and cauliflowered by being rubbed about in the wrestling ring. Also the Angel is past 35 years and, in man, ear dimensions increase through middle age. Nothing much is known about growth of gorilla ears after maturity. In one female gorilla ear size actually decreased during growth. Again, the gorilla has little or no ear lobe, while those of M. Tillet, in typical human fashion, are well developed.

The relative sitting height is the length of head and trunk expressed as a percentage of stature. In short-legged, long-bodied men it usually runs to 53 per cent, but the value found for M. Tillet (54.9) is very high. Yet the two gorillas have approximate values of 61.1 and 61.2 for this index. As roughly reconstructed, the span of M. Tillet's outstretched arms, from finger tip to finger tip, is about 2,023 mm. (79.6 inches) or 115.9 per cent of his stature. The span of the gorilla which is almost the same height as M. Tillet is 2,337 mm. (about 92 inches) or 133.4 per cent of his standing height.

Thus we have taken one of the strongest and most thickset of our contemporary fellow men and compared him with two adult male gorillas, of two different species, one of these being virtually the same height as our heavyweight wrestling champion. While this man is truly remarkable for the breadth, depth, and size of his trunk, and for his relatively short legs and long, massive arms, both gorillas far surpass him in gross size and in exaggeration of these proportions. The only measurements in which M. Tillet exceeds the gorilla are the length of his legs, the breadth of his feet, the size of his ears, and, most significantly, the height of his head.

The condition of the pituitary gland has caused overgrowth of the face and of the extremities which has brought M. Tillet's body form closer to that of a gorilla than it would have been had he not suffered this endocrine disturbance. The bones of the Neanderthaloid race, a fossil species which peopled the caves of Europe and Asia in the latter half of the glacial period, reveal body builds which are closely similar to that of the Angel. It has been suggested by Sir Arthur Keith and others that high activity of the anterior pituitary lobe determined these racial features. It seems possible also that gorillas owe their massiveness to hyperpituitarism, although, in any event, they would be very different animals from human beings.

POSTURE, GAIT, CLIMBING, AND HANDEDNESS

Satisfactory, systematic observations of the posture and gait of the gorilla have not been made, to my knowledge, in spite of the fact that a dozen or more of these animals have been kept in captivity for periods of several years. However, the main facts are well known. On the ground the gorilla habitually moves on all fours, walking flat on the soles of the feet, but resting the weight anteriorly on the middle phalanges of the flexed fingers. A less precise description of this position is "bearing the weight on the knuckles of the fingers." William L. Straus, Jr., of Johns Hopkins, has recently explained this use of the hand in pronograde walking in the three great apes. He studied the movability of the hands and fingers in several embalmed or recently deceased specimens. He found that the hand could be bent back (hyperextended or dorsiflexed) in the orang-utan, gorilla, and chimpanzee only slightly. On the contrary, in the gibbon (probably), in man, and in monkeys the hand can be bent back so that the palm is at right angles to the extended arm and the fingers can be straightened out so that palms and fingers rest flat upon the ground.[13] Human infants that walk on all fours, as exhaustively studied by Hrdlička,

[13]Straus 1940, pp. 199–207.

place the palms thus flatly and so do quadrupedal monkeys. In the large apes the dorsiflexion, or bending back of the hand, automatically causes digital flexion, or the bending of the fingers, because the long flexor muscles of the fingers are relatively abbreviated. When Straus straightened the hand of the gorilla on the forearm, the fingers could not be extended, although their flexion was somewhat less than in adult chimpanzees. It is thought that the rigidity of the wrist, as regards dorsiflexion, keeping the hand aligned with the forearm in hanging, permits suspension by the hands for long periods without the expenditure of great muscular energy. Since the gibbon can bend its hand back and is a most accomplished arm-swinger or brachiator, Straus thinks that it has become adapted to this form of locomotion differently from the orang, chimpanzee, and gorilla. He is inclined to conclude that the forearm of man is closer to that of a quadrupedal monkey, such as a macaque, than to that of any anthropoid ape, and to doubt that man's ancestors have passed through a brachiating stage. The dorsiflexion of the hand is, however, possible in very young chimpanzees, and apparently also in the gorilla.[14] Reichenow's young gorilla began to walk on the palms of his hands (apparently with extended fingers) but soon began to double the fingers. He then walked with the hinder part of the palm and the last joints of the fingers in contact with the ground. The final stage, quickly achieved, was to straighten the hand in line with the forearm and walk upon the middle joints of the fingers with the palm free.[15]

Marius Maxwell says that the mountain gorilla runs with the following succession of foot and hand impacts: right knuckles, left knuckles, margin of right foot pad, margin of left foot pad.[16] I do not fully understand this description. Maxwell says that this gait resembles a canter and that the forward progression of the body in the run is accompanied by a slight side swing, or a sideways twist of the hindquarters. Professor Yerkes states that he has observed this gait in the young chimpanzee, but never in the young gorilla. It is very difficult

[14]Straus says that Virchow claimed for the orang-utan a dorsiflexion of 90° when the fingers are bent. On p. 116 of my book *Up from the Ape*, 1931, is reproduced a photograph of an adult female orang in the Philadelphia Zoological Garden. This animal rests on the first phalanges of the second and third digits and the terminal phalanx of the thumb. All digits are flexed but the hand is also dorsiflexed at least 65° and, further, it is directed backward and outward rather than forward. The need for more careful observation of living animals is obvious.

[15]Reichenow, Eduard, "Contribución a la Biología de los Antropomorfos Africanos," *Soc. Espan. Hist. Nat.*, Madrid, vol. 50, 1921, pp. 345–47. Quoted by Yerkes, R. and A., 1929, pp. 448–49.

[16]Maxwell, Marius, "The Home of the Eastern Gorilla," *Jr. Bombay Nat. Hist. Soc.*, vol. 32, 1928, pp. 436–49. Quoted by Yerkes, R. and A., 1929, p. 406.

"BOBBY," MALE GORILLA,
AGED 10 TO 12 YEARS,
WEIGHT 584 POUNDS

h: Archives Berlin Zoological Garden

HE ANGEL," HEAVYWEIGHT
RESTLING CHAMPION, AGED 39
YEARS, WEIGHT 276 POUNDS

Photograph Zoological Park

Courtesy The Zoological Society of Ph-

BAMBOO, ADOLESCENT MALE LOWLAND GORILLA,
AGED ABOUT 14 YEARS, SQUATTING

to analyze such movements except with the help of motion pictures. As far as I am aware, this has not been done. Yerkes could easily outstrip Congo, the young mountain gorilla, in running. The chimpanzee can move much more rapidly. The same observer says that on occasion the gorilla uses the arms as crutches and swings the hind legs between them. No one seems to think that the gorilla is much of a jumper.

Everyone agrees, and nearly everyone who has watched a captive gorilla can attest, that this animal is able to stand erect with its feet flat on the ground and walk a few steps. The gorilla often stands up to beat its chest, to look around, or to reach for something. The knees are kept somewhat bent.

Mrs. Belle J. Benchley has made a few important observations upon posture, stance, and locomotion in the mountain gorillas of San Diego. In their earlier days they often walked erect, but this gait became less frequent as they matured and grew heavier.[17] When walking bipedally, they either clasped their hands behind their backs or let the arms dangle at the sides. They never went through the balancing motions characteristic of the gibbon and the orang. Again, in walking the foot is put flat on the ground. They do not shuffle and sidle as do the other large apes, but step forward with each foot in turn in a very human stride. They also squat on their heels with their feet flat on the ground.

Although the great toes are opposable and the foot can be used to grasp a rope, Mrs. Benchley does not think that the foot grasp is very strong. She has never seen the gorillas carry or lift objects with their feet.

Although the gorilla keeps the knees bent when standing erect, the legs are fully straightened as regards axis of lower and upper leg when the animal is moving on all fours. Because of certain anatomical peculiarities of the elbow joint (perforation of the bony septum between the coronoid and olecranon fossae of the humerus) the forearm of the gorilla may be hyperextended upon the arm, so that the angle of the two upper segments of the extended limit exceeds 180°. Some women can do this, probably for the same anatomical reason. One of the first things I noticed when I saw the Philadelphia lowland gorilla, Bamboo, was an apparent bending forward of the elbow rather than backward, when he was standing on all fours. Instead of knees pointed forward and elbows backward, both were directed forward. This hyperextension of the forearm may be advantageous in arm-swinging or brachiating. It looks very awkward in quadrupedal progression.

Thanks to captive animals and moving pictures we now know a

[17]Benchley 1940.

good deal about brachiating in all the apes except the gorilla. I can find no description of this arboreal locomotion, although it is generally assumed to be characteristic of the gorilla. There are some descriptions of young gorillas climbing trees or vines. They apparently walk up a good-sized tree trunk by applying the feet to the opposite sides and the extended arms and palms likewise.

The young mountain gorillas observed in captivity by Carpenter were slow, cautious climbers. It took Ngagi more than 2 minutes to climb a tree to the height of 20 feet and get a banana. Ordinarily, these heavy gorillas walked on top of the branches on all fours, but sometimes they walked erect, holding to a branch above them with their arms. They were reluctant to climb trees. However, they were good at swinging from one perch to another by a rope. The free end of the rope was carried between the chin and the chest. Carpenter saw these animals brachiating only twice. It is possible that heavy, full-grown gorillas rarely climb trees. However, Bingham and others have found plenty of gorilla nests quite high up in trees. These are generally assumed to have been made by mothers with infants and young ones. Perhaps only the lighter and younger gorillas make tree nests. Who knows? The general testimony is to the effect that all gorillas do, on occasion, climb trees.

No one seems to know whether or not the gorilla can swim.

The only reliable observations of gorilla handedness known to me are those of Yerkes. He found that his Congo was right-handed and left-footed. In reaching for food with a stick she used the right hand approximately two thirds of the time. When reaching for something with her feet she seemed to prefer the left. A lowland gorilla, called John Daniel, who was kept in captivity for some years by Alyse Cunningham, is stated also to have been right-handed. Two gorillas are not enough to establish handedness.

NESTS

All observers of gorillas in the wild agree that they build nests, but a conflict of testimony occurs in the matter of the location of the nests, whether in trees or on the ground. A full review of the evidence is offered by Yerkes and Yerkes, who conclude that the lowland or western gorilla sometimes builds nests low down in the trees, in addition to ground nests, whereas the mountain or eastern gorilla fairly consistently builds on the ground, or on low bushes.[18] These very cautious authors accept the statement of Von Oertzen that he found

[18]Yerkes, R. and A., 1929, pp. 412–16.

an abandoned gorilla camp in the Cameroons with 16 sleeping nests—
9 on the ground and 7 in the branches of umbrella trees at a height of
3 to 5 meters. He says that the nests were relatively small. One wonders about the possibility of confusing chimpanzee nests with those of
gorillas. In the same area Reichenow describes gorilla nests which
were always on the ground or in low bushes 3 to 5 feet above the
ground.[19] He says that the gorilla bends over all the standing plants
in a circular area 2 to 3 meters in diameter toward the middle, or
sideways, and weaves them together into a round, bowl-like nest, one
meter to $1\frac{1}{2}$ meters in diameter. He never brings to the nests plants
torn up from other places and he does not uproot the plants used in
the nests. Thorny plants are avoided in nest-making. The nests are
built similarly, whether on the ground or in the bushes above the
ground. They are made in the evening and deserted the next morning
after a single night's use. They are often dirtied with feces. Reichenow
has seen as many as 13 nests together, but ordinarily they are placed
in groups, 2 to 4 in a group, with the groups 8 to 15 meters apart.
Reichenow thinks that the single groups represent families and those
in the bushes aboveground, which are built with especial care and
cushioned, may be used by females with nursing infants.

A careful study of the nests and nesting habits of the mountain
gorilla was made by Harold C. Bingham in 1929.[20] The gorillas evidently made nests where night overtook them and they were not
reoccupied, except by chance. The nests were made in tall grass,
undergrowth, clumps of saplings, at the foot of trees, or under overhanging rocks, among the branches of fallen trees, in forks of trees
30 to 60 feet aboveground, in hammocks of vines between the branches
of trees, on tops of bamboos collected as a tepee some 10 feet aboveground, on heaps of dry vegetation covered with growing vines and
creepers 4 or 5 feet aboveground, etc. Most of the materials for the
nest were evidently gathered within the radius of the animal's reach.
The more substantial tree nests were supported in forks and constructed by bending and folding back branches so as to bring the
twigs and foliage into use in the nest. Branches were not entirely
broken from the trees. In two groups of sleeping places approximately
one third of the nests were in standing trees. One nest, to which
Bingham climbed, was 25 feet aboveground. It was supported mainly
on three incompletely detached branches, tips turned inwards,
branches crossed and crushed into a thick mass or table of vegetation.

---

[19] Yerkes, R. and A., 1929, p. 414, quoting Reichenow, E., "Biologische Beobachtungen
an Gorilla und Schimpanse," *Sitzber. Ges. naturf. Fr.*, Berlin, 1920, pp. 1–40.
[20] Bingham 1932.

Most of the weight was borne by a branch 3 inches in diameter. Usually the nests contained feces, contrary to the report of Nissen on chimpanzee nests in French Guinea.

Dr. C. R. Carpenter saw a young gorilla, weighing 40 pounds, build a nest in the St. Louis Zoological Garden in 1934. This animal was released to play in the park with two young chimpanzees. When they began to annoy her, she climbed to the topmost branches of a tree and began to build a nest. Small branches were pulled in and broken in the middle. These were held while other branches were pulled in and broken. In 3 minutes she had a crude nest which adequately concealed her from the ground. The San Diego mountain gorillas were bedded down on straw at night. Typically, they made nests of this straw in different corners of the room by pulling it in toward their bodies and tucking it around themselves.[21]

FOODS

Savage and Wyman, who first scientifically described the lowland gorilla, pronounced this animal a vegetarian and mentioned a number of foods eaten, including both sweet and sour fruits. Du Chaillu, another of the earliest writers on the gorilla, stated that the gorilla is a strict vegetarian and that he found in the stomachs of those he had killed only berries, pineapple leaves, and other vegetable matter. In the Cameroons the gorilla is fond of raiding the vegetable plots of the natives, especially abandoned gardens. Other writers, however, have claimed for the gorilla a carnivorous propensity. This view was notably upheld by Garner, the eccentric writer who professed to understand the language of chimpanzees. Of course, Garner emphasized the acidulous fruits and plants upon which the gorilla mainly subsists, but he stated that raw and cooked meat was also acceptable and that small rodents, lizards, and toads were added to the diet of this animal. Also Garner was informed that the gorilla robs birds' nests of their eggs. Yerkes and Yerkes think that accounts of the mixed diet of the gorilla in the wild are partly unreliable stories told by the natives and partly the result of mixing up information concerning the wild gorilla with the captive gorilla, which is easily taught to eat meat. Reichenow found that the intestines of wild gorillas were inhabited by species of infusoria which digest cellulose and, consequently, help their hosts to make use of plant foods. He says that these infusoria disappear in a few weeks from the intestines of captured animals and connects this change of intestinal flora and

²¹Carpenter 1937, p. 195.

BAMBOO STANDING

Photograph Archives of
Berlin Zoological Garden

ABOVE: Bobby;
BELOW: Janet Penserosa

Photograph John Haeseler

fauna with the propensity of captive gorillas for a carnivorous diet.

Until recently, persons who have attempted to raise gorillas in captivity have had little success, partly because of feeding difficulties, but perhaps more because of the susceptibility of the animals to infection, and because of their tendency to pine away and die in captivity from lonesomeness. Yerkes felt that the Burbidge gorilla, Congo, had too narrow a diet, since she accepted few foods and for the greater part of her stay in Florida subsisted upon baked sweet potatoes, baked bananas, and milk. Acorns, fruits, and other green vegetables she sometimes accepted but often rejected. Yerkes set himself to teach Congo to eat new foods and was successful up to a certain point. She died from acidosis, secondary to ileocolitis, probably as a result of reduction of her sugar tolerance by a predominantly carbohydrate diet.

The New York gorilla, Penserosa, was raised in infancy on a breakfast of milk, eggs, blood meal, and cod-liver oil. Her principal meal of the day consisted wholly of fruits and vegetables, especially bananas which were not quite ripe. Other fruits taken included oranges, apples, unpeeled potatoes (boiled or raw), lettuce, carrots, and rice pudding. Canned bamboo shoots from a Chinese restaurant were refused. The San Diego gorillas thrived on a diet of fresh, uncooked food and vegetables, with grains and seeds and an occasional crust of stale bread. The diets published by Mrs. Benchley indicate that these gorillas at the age of about 14 years were eating approximately 35 pounds of food per day, including a couple of quarts of milk and a few eggs twice or three times a week. The last-named foods were omitted during the summer. The daily diet consisted of about 10 pounds of citrus fruits, 10 pounds of bananas, preferably green, and the balance divided between carrots, potatoes, celery, corn, lettuce, apples, watermelons, and other seasonable fruits and vegetables. They ate practically everything except the skins of the oranges and grapefruits. Carpenter observed that they ate rapidly and chewed their food only a little. Corn was stripped from the cob with the teeth and hard foods were often soaked in water. These San Diego gorillas had a block of cattle salt which they consumed by wetting their fingers, rubbing them on the salt, and licking it off. They drank as much as two gallons of water daily. Usually they put their mouths to the water to drink, but when excited they dipped their hands in the water, raised them over their heads, and let the water run down into their mouths. They also dipped up water and drank from containers.

Like chimpanzees, gorillas often regurgitate their food, bringing it up into their palms or expelling it upon the floor and then swallowing it again. Gorillas usually stop to urinate in a quadrupedal posture, but defecation occurs casually, in any position.

GROOMING AND CARE OF WOUNDS

Carpenter states that gorillas do not groom themselves or each other as often as do chimpanzees; the tempo of gorilla grooming is slower and the mouth is not used so much. Mutual grooming is similar to that of other primates. One animal goes over the other more or less systematically, parting the hair and removing scabs and foreign articles with the finger and thumb of the right hand. One of the two San Diego gorillas, Ngagi, usually took the active part in mutual grooming. Small wounds and bruises were meticulously dressed by pulling away surrounding hairs, soaking in water, and putting the lips to the injured place. Both self-treatment and vicarious treatment of the other animal were observed.

VOCALIZATIONS AND GESTURES

Vocal sounds uttered by the San Diego gorillas, according to Carpenter, are limited mainly to series of low-pitched grunts. Under excitement these grunts are raised in pitch and intensity. The tempo and pitch of the grunts together with the changes in the behavior of the animal indicate that these sounds are important in conveying meaning.

The expression of the eyes is changed by raising and lowering the eyebrows and by the degree of eyelid closure. The lips are extremely mobile and expressive. Gestures are also important. These include not only chest-beating, but also rhythms of stamping and beating, and types of gait.

GORILLA FAMILY LIFE

Mr. George Schwab, for some 35 years a missionary in the Cameroons and an assiduous anthropologist and collector of zoological . specimens, has kindly communicated to me some of his unpublished information on the habits of the lowland gorilla.

Mr. Schwab thinks that the adult male gorilla maintains his position as the patriarch and head of his group as long as he is strong enough to defeat competing males. He is ultimately driven out and thereafter lives a solitary life. Mr. Schwab has seen a number of such lone males. Two or three of them at various times frequented the stations in which Mr. Schwab resided. Mr. Schwab also records the case of an adult female who was seen with a young male, about one-third grown, but unaccompanied by any adult male.

The size of the family group is best estimated from the number of beds or sleeping places. The largest number counted by Mr. Schwab in any one place was 14. He found this group sleeping place in a very dense growth of *Afronomum* plants, 6 to 8 feet high, in an abandoned farm. The plants had been broken and trampled down to make the sleeping places. Four were wider than the others, with bulges on the sides. These were asserted by the natives to be the places for children sleeping with their mothers. Two of the sleeping places, well to one side, were stated to have been for the subadult males. The natives swore to Mr. Schwab that they had had the group under observation from a safe distance. A narrow opening led into the trampled sleeping place. Across the opening lay a felled tree, over 2 feet in diameter. This trunk had some of the *Afronomum* plants upon it and was stated to be the bed of the father. It was so placed that any animal attacking the group would first have to deal with him. But Mr. Schwab has never known any animal to attack a gorilla. The brightest possibilities are leopards and pythons. Nor has Mr. Schwab ever been able to learn of a native who has come upon gorilla or chimpanzee bones in the forest, although, as he says, he has known some men "whose lives were one long prowling about in the forest." In this same part of the Cameroons was another group of gorillas stated by natives who had seen it to consist of 12 mothers, 4 children, 2 adolescent males, and the "father."

The following account of a gorilla family scene I quote directly from Mr. Schwab's written notes:

One day, while we were still at Metet, one of my hunters came excitedly to me, exploding so that the neighborhood could hear (as our neighbor's radio does several times a day, though he is a sizable distance from us) with "Let no one ever again tell me that gorillas are brave. I came on a family of them, several mothers busy gathering *Afronomum* seed pods. [Mr. Schwab has found quantities of these seeds in the stomachs and intestines of chimpanzees which he has examined.] The old father was sitting alone, watching a young one; a mere child it was. It climbed up a vine beside the old father. Every time it got up about as far as he could reach, he stood up and seized it by an ankle, pulled it down, and slapped it. The young one cried out as our children do when we do this to them, but with the voice of a gorilla child, not a man's child. I watched them for a time as this tormenting by the old father went on. One of the wives came and gave the old man some of the seed pods she had picked. He ate them. When I tired watching this family, I shot at the old man. He was holding the young one which he let drop as he gave a roar and ran away. Who says the gorilla is so fierce that no man can escape a wounded one? I could not even catch up with them as they ran through the forest. No, not even with the young one. The vines hindered me but not them. Fiercely courageous and fighters—the gorillas? Let no man again tell *me* that!"

MATING, REPRODUCTION, AND SEXUAL BEHAVIOR

Virtually nothing at all is known about the reproduction of the gorilla. The consensus of opinion is that a gorilla family is likely to include one adult male, several adult females, and immature animals of both sexes. The mating of gorillas has never been observed, nor is the sexual cycle of the female well known. So far as I am aware, Penserosa, the lowland gorilla female of the New York Zoological Society, is the only animal of the species who has been kept in captivity until she was old enough to menstruate. A female gorilla which was brought to Germany in 1897, at the estimated age of 4 years, was asserted by Grabowsky to show signs of sexual excitement regularly at intervals of about 4 weeks, but certainly a gorilla of this age would not have reached the menarche and there is no claim that she had done so.

In the first year of Yerkes' work with Congo, who may have been 5 years of age, this female mountain gorilla gave no signs of sexual development. The next year, however, in playing with a dog, the gorilla was observed to turn him on his side, raise a hind leg, and examine his genitalia.[22] She then turned him on his back and, stepping astride of him, assumed a copulatory position and made the appropriate movements. Next she threw herself upon her back and drew the dog down upon herself in what appeared to be a sex embrace. This was clearly sexual play. She much preferred male dogs to females, and on at least one other occasion Yerkes observed the gorilla going through the same sort of sexual play as that just described. The next year it was reported to Yerkes that Congo had formed the habit of presenting her genitalia, firmly pressed against the wire netting, when a man visitor approached her cage, and she was claimed also to have seized the hand of a man standing near the cage, drawn it

[22]Yerkes 1927b, pp. 520–22.

BAMBOO, ALMOST GROWN

in, and attempted to use one of the fingers for masturbation.[23] Yerkes has seen a female chimpanzee do the same thing. He himself noticed that Congo not infrequently tried to attract the attention of men standing near her by various forms of sexual presentation or exposure. On one occasion she threw herself on her back at Yerkes' feet, pressing her genital organs against him and trying to pull him down upon her, as she had done the previous winter with the male dog. Thwarted in this effort, she stood up on all fours and made the quadrupedal genital presentation, which is presumably the normal habit of female gorillas. During this standing presentation her body was quivering. This sexual aggression of Congo was both embarrassing and dangerous because of her enormous strength. Although she had not menstruated, Yerkes was of the opinion that she was approaching adolescence.

Dr. C. V. Noback observed menstruation in the New York Zoological Society's gorilla, Janet Penserosa, in March 1936.[24] The flow lasted 3 days. Before menstruation there was a definite turgid swelling of the labia majora. During menstruation the labia were shrunken and wrinkled. This gorilla at the time was at least 9 years old, but it may not have been her first menstruation.

GROWTH

Since no gorilla has been born in captivity, accurate knowledge of birth weights and infantile growth of this animal are lacking. The exact age of captive specimens is never known. Consequently, all records of gorilla growth (which are few enough) are based upon guesses as to initial age. Probably the youngest gorilla whose weight was recorded at time of capture was an animal described by Reichenow.[25] This male infant, Adán, was estimated to be about 2 weeks old at the time of his capture, since his navel had recently been covered with hair. However, this seems to be an inadequate basis for judging age. Adán weighed only 2 kilos (4.41 pounds), and measured 44 cm. from the crown of his head to the soles of his feet. Since a newborn gorilla undoubtedly loses weight, like the human infant, for at least its first 2 weeks of life, and only recovers its birth weight in 3 weeks or a month, it seems probable that the weight of Reichenow's gorilla must have been close to birth weight, or possibly a little less. Also the animal could scarcely have been more than a month

[23]Yerkes 1928.
[24]Noback 1936, p. 9.
[25]Reichenow, "Contribución," pp. 337–48. Quoted by Yerkes, R. and A., 1929, p. 448.

old, at most, and may have been less. It is sufficiently clear that the birth weights of anthropoid apes are considerably less than those of human infants. At 10 months of age Adán was 60 cm. tall and weighed 5.75 kilos (12.68 pounds). A number of young gorillas which have died on the way to America have been weighed and measured post mortem, but since the age of these specimens was not known and since they were probably emaciated by disease, the records are of slight value.

The next record pertains to a female gorilla, Janet Penserosa, who was received at the New York Zoological Park October 31, 1928.[26] This animal, with a baby female chimpanzee, had been in captivity at Duala, French Cameroons, for 3 months before being shipped to New York via France. Both of these primates were in terrible condition, suffering from dermatitis and severe colds. The gorilla weighed 17 ¼ pounds. She resisted an examination of her mouth, but 4 incisor and 2 canine teeth were visible when she cried, and Noback thought that she had a full set of milk teeth. Five months later a satisfactory examination of the mouth revealed that all milk teeth had erupted. If, as claimed by Reichenow, his baby gorilla cut the first lower incisors at the age of barely 2 months and the first milk molar toward the end of the sixth month, Noback's specimen might have been about 19 months old. On the basis of her dentition, another authority expressed the opinion that Penserosa was about 6 months younger than her estimated age. She gained weight for the first 2 months and then had bronchial pneumonia and a very close call. However, she pulled through and thereafter enjoyed good health. At the estimated age of 36 months Janet Penserosa weighed 19.54 kilos (43 pounds), and at 48 months 25 kilos (55 pounds). On March 3, 1930, at an estimated age of 36 to 38 months, Penserosa measured 86 cm. from crown to heel and 54.5 cm. from crown to rump. Her span was 122 cm. and at that time she weighed 42.7 pounds.

Congo, the young female mountain gorilla captured by Burbidge in the summer of 1925, was estimated to be between 4 and 5 years of age when first weighed by Yerkes in January 1926.[27] She weighed at this time 65 pounds, approximately, and was about 38 inches tall. A year later she weighed 128 pounds, and 13 months later, at the approximate age of 7 to 8 years, 160 pounds. Her standing height at the latter date was 50 inches, and her chest girth 42 inches. When Congo weighed 65 pounds she could pull 160 pounds on a spring balance with her feet braced. A year later, at a weight of 128 pounds,

[26]Noback 1930a, pp. 165–76; 1930b, pp. 117–51; 1931, pp. 75–104.
[27]Yerkes 1928, p. 5; 1927b, p. 385.

she could pull 240 pounds without much effort and without bracing her feet. Yerkes thinks she could have pulled 300 pounds—the limit of the spring balance—if she had really made a determined try. In her third year no pulling tests were made.

The two male mountain gorillas in the San Diego Zoo, Mbongo and Ngagi, were probably between 4 and 5 years of age when they arrived in California. One seemed to be 6 or 7 months older than the other.[28] Upon reception their combined weights only were taken, but subsequent consistent separate weighings indicated that one weighed about 125 pounds and the other 147 pounds. After 5 months' residence in the zoo, it was observed that both animals were shedding their milk incisors. In 1933, Mbongo, the smaller animal, weighed 172 pounds at the age of about 7 years; in 1936, 270 pounds; and in 1940, at the age of 13 years, 602 pounds. The other gorilla, Ngagi, which was the older and had an initial superiority of 25 pounds, weighed 205 pounds in 1934, and 539 pounds in 1940. When they stood erect these gorillas were estimated to have a height of about 6 feet. Ngagi, the lighter, is very broad-shouldered, but slender in the waist and hips, with a comparatively flat abdomen. His face is lean and he appears to be all muscle. The other animal, Mbongo, was grossly fat. He had a tremendously paunchy abdomen and no waistline. His crest wabbled on his head as he walked, like the hump of a fat camel. Owing to a foot injury, he was somewhat lame and less active than Ngagi. Seemingly, the crests of the male gorilla begin to develop at the age of about 8 years. White saddles on the back and gray hairs appear also during this adolescent phase. Since the estimated age of 11 years, Ngagi, the older animal, has apparently fully developed canines, but the tusks of the younger were not yet fully erupted at the time of his death.

Skeletal Growth of the Lowland Gorilla

Francis L. Randall has recently studied the growth of the lowland gorilla as shown in 456 skulls and 199 postcranial skeletons of assorted ages, the bulk of which are in the collection of Western Reserve University.[29] Dr. Randall has kindly permitted me to make a brief summary of his findings. Exact ages of these specimens are not known, but they can be classified in stages according to the state of tooth eruption, beginning with an infantile stage up to the complete eruption of the milk dentition, and running through to a sixth stage in which all permanent teeth are worn. Sexing the material in the

[28]Benchley 1942, pp. 377–80.
[29]Randall 1942.

first two stages is impracticable. Cranial capacity in the earliest stage (10 skulls) averages in combined sexes 432 cc. In males, Stage VI (95 skulls), it is 549 cc., and in females (56 skulls) 459 cc. The maxima are 685 for males and 580 cc. for females. The female reaches her ultimate cranial capacity much earlier than does the male—at the time of the appearance of the third molar.

In general, skull growth in the gorilla falls into two phases: that of the cranial vault and that of the face. The basic structure of the cranial vault is laid down at the completion of the eruption of the milk teeth, and subsequent growth of the brain case is due to secondary deposition of bone to form the crests, brow ridges, and mastoid processes. In male skulls growth during the first three stages (in III the second permanent molar is erupting) is predominantly lateral. Later it is longitudinal because of crest expansion. These phenomena are not so marked in the female. The cranial index increases in males up to Stage IV and in females to Stage V and thereafter decreases in both sexes. The changes are due to external growth and not to alteration in shape of the brain. The adult male skulls fall into two groups: a long-headed population with a mode at 76, and a broad-headed population with a mode at 84. There is the possibility of a third hyperbrachycephalic type. Geographical data suggest that the Cameroon gorillas are predominantly broad-headed and the Gaboon gorillas long-headed. Female series show feebler differentiation. A number of other measurements on the two groups (long-headed and broad-headed) show correlated differences. Females tend to be more brachycephalic than males.

Facial growth of gorillas is much more exuberant than brain-case growth. It is concluded much earlier in the female than in the male. In general, facial growth tends to stop in the female at Stage III, but continues to the last stage in males. Growth in both sexes is stable and closely correlated until the second permanent molar erupts. Then the male diverges markedly from the female, because the latter falls off in growth and the former spurts. The first suture to close is the internasal and the last the basilar. Marked overbites are a transitory phenomenon of Stage III and the first part of Stage IV.

X-ray assessments show that facial growth is due to an anterior deposition of bone around the orbital region and an inferior and anterior deposition below the orbital areas to accommodate the growing teeth. The mandible also grows inferiorly and anteriorly and is carried forward during the process. Facial growth is different in the two sexes. Ultimately, the male has a relatively longer face and a relatively narrower palate.

BAMBOO, FULLY GROWN

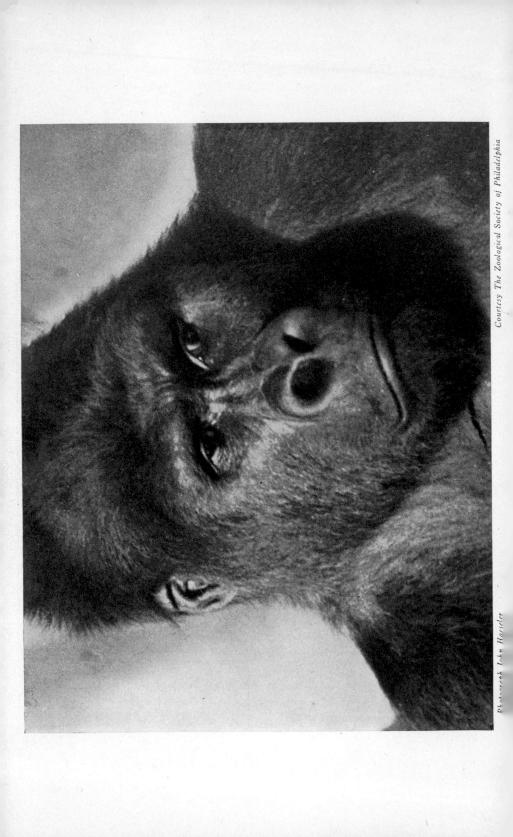

The growth of the postcranial skeleton in the lowland gorilla is also marked by an initial period in which there are relatively small sex differences metrically, and then a marked divergence after the appearance of the second molar, due to exuberant growth of the male.

INFANT BEHAVIOR AND DEVELOPMENT

Inadequate descriptions of the development and behavior of infant gorillas may be culled from the scanty literature. The Reichenow gorilla, Adán, at the estimated age of a couple of weeks, was "hazel"-colored—much lighter than his Negro wet nurse, but his skin rapidly darkened so that at the age of 3 months it was almost black. The body was at first covered with scanty black hair, except the face, which was bare. A reproduction of a photograph of this infant at the age of 2 months suggests that the face is bare, the head covered with bristly black hair, much thicker there than on any other part of the body. Reichenow reports that at the age of 2 months the hair had thickened all over the body and was especially heavy on the backs of the arms and legs. The hair began to grow on the face in the third month and a long tuft of brownish black hair which grew on the head was replaced by short black hair which grew down close to the brow ridges. The lower incisors were cut at the beginning of the second month, the upper middle pair 2 weeks later, and the first molar toward the end of the sixth month. Adán always rubbed his gums a good deal with his thumb before cutting his teeth.

At 3½ weeks Adán began to react to sounds by turning his head and at 8 weeks he could follow a moving object with his eyes. At the end of the third month he began to extend his hands toward his nursing bottle as soon as it came into his field of vision, but it is uncertain whether he distinguished persons before the seventh month. At 5 months Adán sat up by himself and began his first attempts at locomotion He would stretch out and grasp objects and pull himself toward them by bending his arm. At 7 months he could stand on his feet, provided that he could catch at something with his hands to support himself. When he began to walk in the eighth month, his legs were so bent that his rump almost touched the ground, and he supported himself on the palms of his hands. Then he began to double the last two knuckles of his hands so that they rested on the ground, together with a part of the palms. Some days later he began to walk, resting upon the knuckles exclusively, and at about the same time he began to climb.

A few other details of infantile development in the gorilla are furnished by the reports of Dr. Noback upon the New York Zoological Society's Penserosa.[30] She was first seen to climb a pole at the approximate age of 21 months, although she had been moving about awkwardly on all fours and climbing on a trapeze before this time. She was much slower and more serious and deliberate than the chimpanzee of approximately the same age who was her companion. While being fed, the gorilla made a low, soft, purring sound, as also described by Yerkes. When she was greatly excited, as, for example, if her companion were removed to another room, she opened her mouth, retracted her lips, and let out a long, high-pitched shriek, like an angry child. She and the chimpanzee usually woke up at about 6 or 7 o'clock in the morning and spent an hour or more wrestling and tumbling about. They behaved quite differently at feeding time. When the chimp heard the rattle of the pots and pans in the kitchen she would become restless and anxious, directing her gaze toward the kitchen and crying out. As soon as the keeper came in with the food, the chimpanzee would seize her pan of milk and her solid food and hastily consume them. The gorilla, on the other hand, would pay little or no attention to breakfast preparations and, even when her pan of milk was set before her, might ignore it, or merely glance at it, going about her own business, or perhaps beating her chest lightly. After a few minutes, however, Penserosa would lie down in a comfortable position, take the pan in her hands, and drink her milk slowly, making a purring sound. Often she had to be coaxed to eat. When the keeper brought bananas, the chimpanzee would jump up and down, scream, seize all the bananas and hoard them away in the corner of the cage. If the gorilla was given a banana, the chimp would take it away from her. However, if the gorilla was very hungry, she would fight and insist upon getting her proper share.

Out on the lawn Penserosa was more self-reliant than indoors. She would play about by herself quite contentedly, climb a small cherry tree, and eat leaves, buds, and bark. She seemed usually serious, but relaxed. The hot sultry days of the New York summer depressed her more than her chimpanzee companion, and she would lie still, pant, and drink large quantities of cold water. Apparently she sweated only on the face and under the arms. The cool, crisp, fall air exhilarated her and she romped about—indoors and out—clapping her hands, beating her chest, and dancing rhythmically. In November and December she was allowed to go out in the sharp air and enjoyed it. Her chimpanzee friend felt the cold. Both enjoyed playing in a snow-

[30]Noback 1930a, pp. 88–103.

storm, and the gorilla picked up small pieces of ice and ate them. The changes in temperature did not cause the gorilla to contract colds. Her first permanent molars appeared in her third year, although they do not erupt in man until the beginning of the sixth year.

Penserosa, when in a good humor, slapped her abdomen and rolled over and over on the floor. She frequently built a simple circular nest of straw and often, for diversion, rode on the back of the chimpanzee.

The skin of the face was black but of fine texture. On the rest of the body the skin was grayish where the hair was sparse, and light flesh color where it was thick. The hair coat was black with the exception of three white patches—two on the cheeks in front of the ears, and one in the anal region. The bristly pompadour on the crown of the head had some rufous and grizzled hairs, and there were some banded black-and-white hairs on the outsides of the thighs. X rays showed that the wrist bones of this female gorilla were present before the fourth year, whereas in human children they do not appear until the tenth to twelfth year. The skeletal development of the female gorilla thus appears to be precocious in comparison with that of man.

Janet Penserosa developed a partial paralysis of her lower extremities soon after her first menstruation at the age of 9 years. In 1940 she was purchased by Dr. J. F. Fulton for neurological studies and was killed at the closely known age of 13 years and 3 months.[31] At the time of her death she was fully grown and weighed 74.84 kilos (roughly 165 pounds). Some muscular atrophy of the legs had re sulted from the partial paralysis.

Schultz has recorded some interesting growth changes in this gorilla, who had been measured from infancy, and some notable morphological variations. Her trunk became relatively stouter and broader with age and the proportion between facial and brain-case parts of her head changed but little. Her ears became relatively and absolutely smaller. In 1929 this gorilla had small but clearly defined ischial callosities. These had become larger, thicker, and harder at the time of her death. When first examined by Schultz, Janet's second and third toes were of equal length, but at her death the second toe was the longest toe of each foot, a condition never before observed by Schultz in any of the great apes examined by him. Janet possessed not only an occipital bony crest on the skull, but a sagittal crest about 11 mm. high, a most unusual feature in female gorillas. She also had a crown pad of connective tissue about 2 inches thick, such as is

[31]Schultz 1942b, pp. 1–21.

commonly reported in old male mountain gorillas. Toto also has such a pad. All of Janet's cranial sutures were closed, as were also the epiphyses of limb bones and spinal column.

GORILLA BIOGRAPHIES

INFANCY AND CHILDHOOD OF TOTO

Toto is the young female lowland gorilla now exhibited as the future mate of Gargantua in the circus of Ringling Brothers and Barnum and Bailey. She was the only survivor of a group of nine gorillas, the others having been slain in a hunt in which Mr. and Mrs. E. Kenneth Hoyt participated. The data of the following account are derived from Mrs. Hoyt's recent book about this animal.[32] The point of view of the author is not that of a scientist, but rather of a woman who raised a baby gorilla, lavishing all the care and affection upon it that is customarily given by a mother to her own child. Mrs. Hoyt's attitude toward Toto is essentially maternal and sentimental, and she undoubtedly anthropomorphizes the gorilla. Nevertheless, the facts she reports are probably reliable, although some of her interpretations should perhaps be accepted with reserve.

The gorilla baby, thought to be about 2 months old and to weigh 9 pounds, was handed to her by one of the natives. The infant was biting and scratching at the chief's bare shoulder and uttering cries of terror. She at once quieted down when Mrs. Hoyt took her in her arms. Mrs. Hoyt made a flannel bellyband for Toto, wrapped her in a sheet, and put her in a basket. The feeding presented great difficulties. All the recommended formulas and the foods prescribed by naturalists were thrown up or caused dysentery. For a considerable period the gorilla baby was fed successfully at the breast of a Negress wet nurse. Two other gorillas, a male about 5 months old and a tiny female baby, were also added to the collection. Toto at once became jealous of the new arrivals and went into tantrums, making angry noises at them, slapping them, and attempting to bite them. After the wet nurse became unavailable, Mrs. Hoyt began to feed the gorillas on a mixture of canned milk and boiled water from nursing bottles. The little male gorilla had to be forcibly fed and soon died. The two females throve. During the trip to the coast the baby Toto began to crawl on all fours. By the time Duala was reached, the other gorilla baby, together with a 5-year-old female gorilla, Polly, had died of dysentery.

[32]Hoyt 1941.

In Paris the baby Toto contracted lobar pneumonia and was saved only by the use of an oxygen tent and all the medicinal care and nursing which modern science could give. Mrs. Hoyt never left her bedside until after the crisis of this illness had been passed. By this time the gorilla was more completely spoiled than any human child could be. Anything which annoyed her precipitated a temper tantrum. She was infinitely demanding. Mrs. Hoyt states that she had, and has, the most acute sense of hearing, so that her native attendant could not tiptoe from her room without her awakening and giving vent to indignant howls. She could hear this native, the softest-footed walker Mrs. Hoyt has ever known, crossing the tiled floor of the bathroom in his bare feet.

About this time Toto became increasingly interested in ornaments and would tear the necklace from Mrs. Hoyt's neck whenever she could reach it. Before she left Paris, Toto weighed 20 pounds, but Mrs. Hoyt does not state her age. During the voyage to Cuba, where the Hoyts had decided to settle, largely because they thought the climate would be suitable for Toto, the gorilla baby managed to break several chairs and to tear up most of the curtains in the suite on the steamer. In Havana Toto was given a room and a large baby crib, but she invariably crawled into bed and slept with her Negro attendant, Abdullah. At the age of 9 months (?) she began to walk upright, holding to Abdullah's hand. A picture of her in Mrs. Hoyt's book represents her first steps. The legs are flexed, the great toes abducted, and the outer toes curved. Evidently the weight is borne largely on the sole and on the web between the great toe and the outer toes. At this time she also began to cut her first teeth. She was much entranced by her mirror image, and Mrs. Hoyt describes her as delighted with her appearance and studying her one tooth in the glass with rapt attention. Again, she would get angry at her image and try to destroy it. Her playroom was a large, glass-enclosed veranda, fitted with small but very substantial chairs and tables and equipped with magazines. Mrs. Hoyt states that she would turn the pages, looking at pictures by the hour, stopping for a long time at any picture which especially interested her. However, she liked most of all to crumple and tear up newspapers.

Toto was terrified of the swimming pool when she saw Mrs. Hoyt going in to bathe. She screamed and attempted to pull her mistress out. The first time she was taken into a room equipped for her with ladders, swings, rings, etc., she ran up a 10-foot ladder and dived from the top. Mrs. Hoyt thinks she would have been killed had not Mr. Hoyt caught her. Mrs. Hoyt ascribes this recklessness to the fact that baby gorillas often drop or fall considerable distances to the ground in the African forest, but are not injured, owing to the thick carpet of leaves upon which they land. When Christmas came, the Hoyts had a decorated tree for Toto. Among the presents which she appreciated were hard-rubber balls, spinning tops, and white chalk. Toto is said to have become an expert at spinning the top after one lesson. She bounced hard-rubber balls upon the pavement and caught them deftly. She spent hours drawing hieroglyphs on the limestone walk with pieces of chalk. Some of these drawings came out to look like numbers, and when this happened, Toto's Cuban keeper, Tomas, would put his money on this number in the lottery. Mrs. Hoyt does not tell how much money he won.

We are told also that Toto was very fond of stealing pieces of ice out of the refrigerator for eating purposes, and also loved meat, especially when rare and bloody.

An iron crib was constructed for Toto with a cover of iron bars into which she could be locked. In one corner the mattress and springs were cut away and underneath this corner was placed a chamber pot. She kept her bed clean and dry at night, and in the daytime used the regular toilets. She was so fond of turning on faucets that the handles had to be removed throughout the yard and keys substituted. She was not allowed to drink tap water for fear of infection, but only Vichy water and carbonated beverages. Regular analyses were made of her urine and feces, although the laboratory staff never suspected that this work was being done upon the excretions of a gorilla baby. Tomas, Toto's Cuban keeper, taught her to sit at the table and eat with him. She learned to eat meat by receiving bits from his plate. She was especially fond of chicken, but would always strip the skin off the bones before eating the meat. She loved to crack the bones with her teeth and suck the marrow from them. Eventually she and Tomas received for meals individual trays containing the exact same amounts and kinds of food. This practice was necessitated by Toto's habit of snatching from the tray of Tomas any food which her own did not contain, whether she liked it or not.

By the time Toto was 3 years old she had become something of a problem because of her strength and mischievousness. She could turn doorknobs, unlock doors, and if the door was unlocked and the key missing, she would break off the knob. As she grew heavier, she developed the habit of crashing through doors by pushing against them with her shoulder. The Hoyts had a main stairway in their house with a broad marble balustrade which came down 20 feet, with two landings and marble posts at each. One day Mrs. Hoyt was terrified to see Toto run up the stairs and start a lightning slide down, astride the balustrade. Just as she was about to crash into a marble pillar, she turned and, seizing the post in her hand, swung her body off the balustrade, around the post, and onto the balustrade again, continuing her magnificent slide and ending with a swing upon the bottom post and a few rolls on the floor. Thereafter, this balustrade-sliding was her principal indoor amusement. When Mrs. Hoyt tried to prevent her sliding down the balustrade, Toto substituted rolling head over heels downstairs. So she was allowed the privilege of the banisters.

By this time it was felt advisable to construct separate living quarters for Toto. These consisted of a large bedroom, a living room, and an outside enclosure 40 by 80 feet, surrounded and covered with heavy iron bars. Usually she was not confined in this enclosure. She loved to lie in the shade on a bed of palm leaves which she made for herself, and often she would also cover herself with palm leaves, as she disliked intensely the glare of the sun and always wanted to be in the shade.

During this period Toto was eating various kinds of powdered baby food mixed with vegetables, arrowroot, rice flour, etc. She was fond of black-bean soup and ate all fruits in season. Especial favorites were mangoes, tamarinds, bananas, zapotes, and papaya. She liked to drink cocoa. She enjoyed climbing trees to pick fruit, but knew that the thinner branches would not support her weight and never ventured on them, but rather coaxed her attendants or friends to climb up ladders to get the fruit for her.

At this time Toto began to have periods of 2 or 3 days during which she was unruly, sullen, and even dangerous. These spells, according to Mrs. Hoyt, always occurred during the new-moon phase. This animal had not begun to menstruate and the account of her mood change at this time is suggestive. In these periods she would hide and defy authority. Since "she could understand Spanish as well as any Spanish child of her age," her mistress and attendants could not call out directions to each other when Toto was dodging them in the shrubbery. They had to use large placards with directions printed on them. Apparently Toto could read no better than any Spanish child of her age. She developed a habit during these spells of throwing handfuls of sand and gravel at her keeper, and worse, of pulling back one of the swings in her playroom and launching it suddenly at his head. An electric goad which gave her a harmless shock had to be devised for her control.

Toto had a lady friend next door, who used to come out on her balcony every day within sight of Toto, set the phonograph going, and dance for the gorilla child. Immediately, the latter would respond by stamping and pirouetting in perfect rhythm, "her face wreathed in the slightly foolish, childlike smile that is one of her most endearing expressions." Mrs. Hoyt learned to slip out of the playroom when Toto was approaching the climax of her dances, since she had a tendency to end up in an ecstasy of delight by tearing the clothes off her mistress.

Toto was fond of letting columns of ants run up her arm so that she could lick them off her fur and eat them. She also caught and ate mosquitoes. She had never seen a live lion, but exhibited every sign of repugnance and trepidation upon seeing a new lion-skin rug on the floor.

One aspect of gorilla behavior which I have never read in any other account, but which seems credible, is reported by Mrs. Hoyt. She says that the gorilla's head crest of bone and gristle is very tough and that it is used as the fulcrum of a lever for breaking things. Just as we break sticks across our knees, so the gorilla breaks branches by bringing them down sharply on the head crest, holding the ends with the two hands. Toto started this trick with folded newspapers, and ultimately did the same with heavy branches of trees or with anything else she wanted to destroy.

A little Japanese who worked about the Hoyt place was terrified of Toto and always tried to keep out of her way. One day Toto hid behind a bush, seized him by one hand, tucked him under her arm like a kitten, and began to climb the wall of her enclosure, using her other arm and two feet. Five or 6 feet above the ground she lost interest and dropped the Jap, then proceeded to the roof of her enclosure, where she stood upright, beating her chest and "grinning in pleasure."

At this age Toto's daily routine of feeding began at 7:30 in the morning with her culture bacillus in sugar water. At 8:15 she drank a quart and a half of milk with tapioca. At 10 o'clock she was given a large mug of orange juice which had to be carefully strained. At 11:30 A.M. she had eight bananas and cream cheese. At 1 P.M. she and Tomas had lunch on trays. This generally included chicken or steak. At 4 P.M. Toto had a quart and a half of milk with oatmeal, Pablum, or Cocomalt; at 6 P.M., two baked apples and a jug of milk. Between meals she drank all the water she wanted, indicating her thirst by looking at the water faucet and smacking her lips. In the morning she was lively and playful. After lunch she took a siesta on the roof of her house or in the hammock of her playroom. If she could get into the food storeroom she would leave the place a shambles. She was particularly fond of stealing eggs. In the afternoon she would often sit in a tree in the garden and play games, watching the passers-by. She liked to play in a sand pile with a pail, making castlelike shapes. She also enjoyed building blocks. When she went on one of her sprees and got loose, everyone would run for cover. Doors would be slammed and locked and windows barred. On such occasions Tomas often had a terrible time getting her shut up in the evening. In December 1937 Toto, while playing with Mrs. Hoyt, jumped into her swing, gave it a long backward push, and, rushing forward, bumped into Mrs. Hoyt, so that the latter fell backward and fractured both of her wrists. Somewhat later, Toto found the station wagon in the garage in her way, picked it up by the rear axle with one hand, yanked the car out, and then, although the emergency brake was set, dashed it forward against the garage wall, breaking the headlights.

This animal had now become so dangerous that it seemed desirable to transfer her to the circus, where she would be kept in an air-conditioned cage, and, ultimately, it was hoped, mated with the famous Gargantua. Finally, a quotation from Mrs. Hoyt's opinion of Toto may be of interest:

She has too much intelligence and initiative and too much human affection to fall easily into the submissive attitude of other domesticated animals, enough analytic self-consciousness to feel slights keenly, yet little or no ability to discipline herself and make herself adopt a role of social conduct. She is, as the Paris doctor said, a charmingly foolish child, yet with the physical strength of twenty men.[33]

Toto, at the age of about 9 years, is said to weigh 438 pounds.

Massa, Gargantua ("Buddy")

Massa, the younger of the two gorillas now in the Philadelphia Zoo, was received in 1931 by Mrs. Gertrude Davies Lintz as an infant very ill with pneumonia. This gorilla, supposedly of the mountain type, was considered a female by Mrs. Lintz, but has turned out to be a male. Mrs. Lintz had Massa for 4 years and is unable to think of "her" as other than feminine.[34] After Massa recovered from pneumonia, he was attacked by a disease resembling infantile paralysis. He was stunted and delicate. Mrs. Lintz found Massa a much more conservative, cautious, and constructive animal than any of her chim-

[33]Hoyt 1941, p. 235.
[34]Lintz 1942.

panzees. She felt that he attempted to observe and to understand, proceeding by trial and error. This animal was very affectionate and imitative. Mrs. Lintz always dressed her apes in human clothes and Massa was very fond of dressing up in finery borrowed from his mistress.

A year after she had acquired Massa, Mrs. Lintz became the owner of another baby gorilla, "Buddy," now called Gargantua. On the voyage from Africa a sailor had poured nitric acid over this gorilla and his face and chest were terribly burned. For many months he was under the care of a surgeon and dermatologists, and his sight was endangered. He recovered, but his face is hopelessly marred, his nose almost eaten away. That he survived at all was due to the care and nursing lavished upon him by Mrs. Lintz. Mrs. Lintz states that Gargantua, or Buddy, is a coastal gorilla. Both of these gorillas when young were very neat and precise in the use of their hands. Since in the yard they pursued caterpillars and small animals, Mrs. Lintz decided that they needed meat and began to feed them liver and ground beef, with good results. Eventually each ate a half-pound of liver daily. Massa gradually recovered the use of his paralyzed limbs by means of a rope-and-pulley exercise machine devised by Mrs. Lintz. Buddy was easily taught to walk erect, but it was difficult to get him accustomed to wearing human clothes, especially shoes. When dressed he always walked erect. He slept 10 hours a day and was fed every few hours on a mixed diet, mostly of fruits and vegetables, but including also cereals, milk, eggs, liver, and sweets. Both gorillas were very cleanly about their persons. Both were given oil rubs instead of baths, since tubbing in soapy water dried their skins too much. Mrs. Lintz says that the gorillas have a body odor very much like that of the Negro, but that chimpanzees, in her experience, have none at all. She also maintains, as does Mrs. Hoyt, that gorillas laugh out loud and shed tears.

In gorilla chest-beating Mrs. Lintz recognizes three forms indicative of different emotions: a full-belly beat with the flat of the hand in slow alternating slaps (contentment or well-being); excited rapid beats with both fists at once high on the chest (intense joy); very rapid and loud tattoo on the lower ribs with both fists tightly clenched (rage).

The unfortunate incident which led to Massa's incarceration in the zoo was the result of this animal's fondness for scrubbing a floor with a pail of soapy water and a brush. Massa was unaware of Mrs. Lintz's approach and the latter slipped on a patch of wet floor and overturned the pail of water on the gorilla. He was terrified and attacked his mistress, biting her and wounding her severely. Thereafter Mrs. Lintz could no longer dominate this young gorilla. He also became increasingly dangerous to other persons and most destructive whenever he could escape from his cage.

As both gorillas grew larger and enormously strong they had to be confined in cages, and eventually it was necessary to find homes for them in the zoo or the circus.

PLAY

The San Diego gorillas observed by Carpenter when they were about 10 years old played actively and vigorously, but seemed not to go in for "play-fighting."[35] Self-play included rolling, somersaulting, chest-beating, and manipulating feet, toes, and genitals. These animals have not been seen masturbating. Playing with bundles of straw, rope, and the garden hose were favorite occupations. Slapping water from a pool and letting it run into the mouth from the hose were fascinating diversions. One exciting game consisted of wetting the floor of the cage by splashing water on it from the pool and then running and sliding on all fours from one end of the cage to the other. Chasing was simple, but wrestling was far more complex and would be continued intermittently for hours. The apes stood erect, put their prognathous faces over each other's shoulders, and clinched in powerful embraces, each striving for a position of advantage which would enable him to bite his opponent in the nape of the neck. Prior to an attack and after it each would beat his chest with open hands. In play and wrestling, Mbongo, then the lighter animal, was always the aggressor. One ape swinging by the other on a rope might give him a vigorous kick as he passed. The chest-beating did not indicate anger, but rather a playful challenge or a display. Carpenter never saw these gorillas really angry.

DOMINANCE AND CO-OPERATION

One of the two San Diego gorillas, Ngagi, was consistently dominant in feeding operations and hogged the food. If the other, Mbongo, was fed first, he would run away when Ngagi approached, carrying as much food as possible with him. When they were fed in separate rooms, the dominant animal would run from one room to the other, taking his choice of the food, but he did not actually take

[35]Carpenter 1937, pp. 175–96.

food from the hands of the subordinate except on one occasion, when he snatched a peach. This was the only instance in which any ill temper or pugnacity was displayed.

Dominance was reversed in play and wrestling. The smaller animal, Mbongo, frequently got the better of it through harder and faster activity. Ngagi, the elder, seemed rather more sluggish and reluctant to engage. However, he was dominant in grooming.

Co-operative behavior was especially noticeable in grooming, but also in moving the 800-pound log which lay in the cage and in splashing water on the floor so as to make it slippery for sliding.

INTELLIGENCE

LEARNING ABILITY

Carpenter tried for a time to separate the two San Diego gorillas for experimental purposes. He found it impossible to do so. In order to separate them he had to coax one animal into the sleeping room and then shut the door. The animal quickly caught on to this maneuver and, if lured into the sleeping room by food, snatched it and immediately dashed out again. Once a gorilla had been coaxed into the sleeping room, the trap door between it and the outside cage had to be lowered, but as soon as Carpenter began to lower the door the animal would grasp it and raise it up again. The slightest movement toward the control chain on the door was the sign of an immediate attempt to escape. These gorillas easily recognized human individuals and made differential responses to them.

YERKES' GORILLA STUDY

Professor Robert M. Yerkes is the only scientific observer who has carried on extensive investigations upon the mentality of the gorilla. Beginning in the early part of the winter of 1926, Yerkes worked about 2 months for 3 successive years with Congo, a young female mountain gorilla which had been brought back from East Africa by Ben Burbidge in October 1925. Her estimated age at the time of arrival was 4 to 5 years. During the first 2 winters Yerkes experimented with Congo at the residence of Mr. Burbidge near Jacksonville, Florida. The third winter the gorilla was acquired by Mr. John Ringling, and Dr. Yerkes studied her at the circus winter headquarters at Sarasota, Florida. Unfortunately, Congo died less than one month after the termination of the third season's experiment. Her death was a very great loss to science, since Dr. Yerkes had established

most amicable personal relations with the animal and planned to continue the study of her mentality and behavior up to maturity.[36]

PERFORMANCE ABILITY

In the winter of 1926 Dr. Yerkes tested Congo for her capacity of
using sticks in four different problems, none of which she could solve
without teaching and assistance. She seemed to lack all ability to
employ a stick as an implement and failed to use it for reaching,
pulling, or striking, although she used it on her own initiative as an
aid to climbing. In the next winter Yerkes tried Congo again on the
same experiments and found that she succeeded promptly. For
example, a first experiment involved the necessity of her reaching
through the door of her cage and using a stick to draw in a banana
which was on a shelf and out of reach. The second year she solved
this problem without delay. A similar experiment required the use
of a stick to sweep within reach fruit on a platform outside the bars
of the cage. In 1926 she had been taught to accomplish this feat with
the greatest difficulty and she had used the stick with astounding
clumsiness and ineptitude. The next winter she succeeded without
any assistance. In this period she was able to master a problem which
involved poking a stick through a pipe to dislodge a banana, and she
evinced not only memory of former learning, but some indications of
ability to cope with problems which had previously been too much
for her. Yet, on the whole, she showed very little mechanical ability.
Hasp, padlock, and spring-snap devices were managed successfully,
but rather through trial-and-error fumbling than by the sort of activity
supposed to show insight. She was far inferior to chimpanzees in
such tests.

Box-stacking tests, which necessitate the piling up of boxes directly
below a food objective, were very hard for this young gorilla during
her first year and she achieved some success only by imitation and
tuition. The next year she was much readier and more skillful. She
was very good about remembering the use of the greatest dimension
of a box and of 2 boxes simultaneously, and showed considerable manual skill and judgment in the placing of the boxes. Her successes were
achieved quite independently. At least on one occasion she managed
a 4-box pyramid. Yerkes notes that adding a fourth box to a 3-box
experiment had the effect of creating for this gorilla an entirely new
problem.

During the tests of the first year very little was set or achieved in
the way of delayed-response or memory exercises. In 1927, however,

[36]Yerkes 1927a, 1927b, 1928.

Congo showed good ability in remembering the locations of buried food and the identity of the baited box among several boxes of different colors, after delays ranging from 3 to 24 hours. Up to 3 hours her success was good, even when the interval of delay was full of distractions. After a day, however, her memory was less accurate. Prior to Yerkes' experiments with Congo, successful delayed responses for animals lower than man had been limited to 5-minute delays. Thus, Congo compared favorably with chimpanzees and orang-utans in memory, although she was inferior to them in mechanical activities and in general adaptability.

In the third season of work with Congo, Yerkes repeated many of the simpler experiments of previous years and found that, in general, she retained her ability to succeed in those which had been mastered. However, her mechanical ability in handling hasp, spring-snap, and locked-box problems seemed not to have improved to any great extent. A simple roundabout type of stick problem was beyond Congo in 1927 and another was set for her in 1928. On a platform outside the grill of the cage a V-shaped arrangement of blocks was nailed with its apex directed toward the cage. Within the V was a banana which had to be secured by the use of a 36-inch broomstick. Congo tried very hard at this problem, but never got the idea of pushing the food back and then around the end of the V. Yerkes tried a similar problem with 4 young chimpanzees, the oldest of whom solved it successfully. The others failed, but made much better attempts at solution than did the gorilla. The chimpanzees were superior at this type of work, but it was evidently difficult for them also.

A new type of experiment tried in 1928 was the turntable selector. On a turntable outside of the cage, but within reach of the gorilla's arm, were placed some 6 food containers of different colors. One was baited within sight of the animal and, after a delay, she was allowed to turn the table until the correct box was immediately in front of her. In this experiment Congo, after practice, achieved as high as 80 per cent of successes and her prompt, correct, and definite responses were much more numerous than those of chimpanzees.

It became increasingly evident to Professor Yerkes as he worked with Congo in the last 2 seasons that her general adaptational ability was steadily increasing. At first the animal seemed to be bound to specific situations in her ability to adapt and could not transfer her training from one problem to another. Later on she seemed increasingly capable of generalizing her learning and of adapting it to new situations. In fact, this animal's memory seemed excellent, especially for persons. After intervals of 10 to 11 months, she had no difficulty in recognizing Professor Yerkes and greeted him in an undoubtedly friendly and familiar way, with a deep, throaty, grunting sound which previous experience had taught Yerkes to interpret as indicative of satisfaction. Ordinarily she would pay no attention to strangers.

IMITATIVENESS, CURIOSITY, INSIGHT

Young primates are usually considered to be wantonly destructive. Professor Yerkes has remarked that he has worked experimentally and in other situations with a wide range of primate forms, including marmoset, cebus monkey, orang-utan, chimpanzee, gorilla, and man. He thinks that, in proportion to its strength, the monkey may well take first place in destructiveness, although he is certain that the young chimpanzee and the human child are in a tie for a close second. Such destructiveness is probably incidental to manipulation and testing of objects which have for their purpose the acquainting of the organism with these extraneous things through tactile and visual perception. It is in some sense a manifestation of curiosity and a form of scientific investigation. A young chimp pounces upon new objects, tests them with every available sense, manipulates them, and shortly demolishes them, if possible. Yerkes was then astounded to find that Congo, the young female gorilla, in her first year of work "mostly confined herself to a demure and ladylike examination of unfamiliar objects." She would look at them, smell them, touch them, and taste them. If edibility were indicated, the appropriate disposition of the object would be made; if not, it was usually neglected. He never saw her wantonly destroy an object. He often tested her by placing within her reach various objects such as a corncob pipe, tools, and instruments, and he even thought of leaving his best hat overnight in her cage, but prudence forbade. He was quite confident that, if he thus risked his headgear, it would be recoverable in a recognizable form the next morning, whereas if left with a chimpanzee it would be unidentifiable in a few hours.

These considerations led him to ponder deeply the question of Congo's curiosity. He planned various experiments to elicit curiosity and found that she generally lacked it or suppressed it. Congo ordinarily displayed curiosity and interest only when she suspected something edible to be in the offing. One day when Professor Yerkes was writing up his notes, she came over, seized the page, tore it out, and made off with it. As soon as she was out of reach, she stuffed it into her mouth, but, finding it unsatisfactory, threw it to one side. Strive as he would, Dr. Yerkes could not get her to imitate him in manipulating objects, or in movements of the body, including opening the mouth, grimacing, etc. She was always watchful and interested, but completely negativistic. Copy-setting was peculiarly unprofitable. Almost his only success in such efforts was in teaching Congo to enlarge the range of her diet by eating other foods in her presence. When she did eat these new foods, she usually retired to some distance and turned her back on Yerkes, possibly because she was reluctant to let him witness the acceptance of his suggestions.

However, in the second year of Congo's work with Dr. Yerkes, she exhibited a remarkable increase in destructiveness and was as bad as any chimpanzee. Curiosity was a good deal more developed and played a much stronger role in the animal's adaptations to new situations. Yet Congo's curiosity remained far below the level of that of the average chimpanzee. She would not go far in testing, examining, and manipulating unfamiliar objects and often maintained apparent indifference in situations which might have been expected to evoke the most lively curiosity. Yerkes observes that her independent, aloof, and introverted temperament may have caused her to repress visible evidences of curiosity. He could not rid himself of the impression that, if the animal were out of sight and free from suspicion of being observed, she might behave differently. She was not much more imitative in 1927 than she had been in 1926. If Yerkes attempted to teach her by showing her how to do something, it merely stimulated her to keep trying more vigorously to do it her own way.

This animal was extremely independent socially, and appeared to be interested in persons mainly as sources of food or desired attention. During the first year of work she was consistently friendly, but not at all demonstrative. She was not very playful, although often she would respond to playful advances. With her dog friends she occasionally played very vigorously, but oftener paid little attention to them or was so rough that she discouraged them. Her play activities were most simple, including merely chasing or being chased, climbing, hide-and-seek, and foot- or fist-cuffing. She was very strong and rough, and given to climbing over persons and throwing her entire weight upon them. She displayed no originality or inventiveness in devising games.

Perhaps the most intense and consistent interest displayed by this gorilla was in her own mirror image. She attempted to touch it and kiss it repeatedly, felt round behind the mirror, actually went around it to investigate, and pounded upon the back. This interest endured throughout the two years of 1926 and 1927 upon the few occasions when the animal was given a mirror. It was very difficult to get the mirror away from her, once she had her hands upon it. Yerkes thought that she was searching for a companion.

One of the most impressive features of Congo's behavior in connection with tasks involving a food reward was her appraisal of the amount of food offered, the difficulty of obtaining it, and, apparently, the general worth-whileness of the effort. Often she would not work if the food offered was something she did not like or did not fancy at the moment, or if the amount offered was insufficient. In some cases she would make no effort at all for half a banana, but would work strenuously and persistently for a whole banana.

TEMPERAMENT AND DISPOSITION

The gorilla, as exemplified, at any rate, by the single immature female, Congo, is utterly different in disposition from an orang-utan or a chimpanzee. Toward her friends Congo was indifferently tolerant and consistently dignified. At first, Yerkes thought that she distrusted him, but afterwards he came to regard her attitude as one of independence or aloofness. She seemed to have a "superiority complex." She adjusted herself slowly but steadily to human environment and gradually became more tolerant of strangers. Yerkes felt her to be a markedly shut-in or introverted personality. As he knew her better, he came to feel that she was not so much shy and timid as self-sufficient, self-confident, and superior.

It was very difficult to elicit from Congo any emotional responses beyond withdrawal or avoidance. She accepted punishment stoically. Electric shocks brought forth no cries of pain, nor did disappointment in obtaining food stir her to sounds of anger or resentment. Such stoicism is in remarkable contrast to the emotional outbursts of the chimpanzee. Yerkes used to marvel when deprivation of a dinner within reach occasioned no more evidence of resentment than a frown or a growl. As a matter of fact, the penetrating observer soon came to suspect that Congo was, in truth, profoundly emotional, although she gave no overt sign. She was inexpressive to the highest degree. The most striking exemplification of emotional disturbance occurred in the first year of experimenting, when Yerkes attempted to place Congo on a platform scale. He accomplished this task with difficulty against resistance the first two times. The third time Congo attempted to bite him and made vigorous efforts to run away. Yerkes writes that he ought to have realized that the animal was profoundly disturbed, because she had never before tried to bite him, but he was so absorbed in trying to record the weight that he misunderstood the situation. When Congo got back to her cage, she exhibited unmistakable signs of relief from emotional stress and a physiological reaction which included temporary diarrhea. Yerkes thinks that he had never before done anything which had caused such extraordinary alarm to the little animal. Altogether, Congo was not a timid animal.

Congo was fond of rough play which involved pommeling and tickling and would retaliate wholeheartedly. Persistent chuckling and low throaty growls were probably the equivalent of human laughter, and in such situations a sound resembling purring was often made. Movements of the facial muscles were identified as smiles. The purring, which was similar to that of a great cat, was also an expression of pleasure in food or at the attentions of some human friend. Congo sometimes gave vent to a high-pitched whine in situations which indicated lonesomeness, mild discomfort, or dissatisfaction. Growls of resentment were infrequently heard. Gorillas also scream loudly and vigorously when extremely angry or terrorized, but Yerkes never heard this sound.

Beating on the chest with the two fists, or, less frequently, upon the ground, is a common means of emotional expression with gorillas. In the case of Congo, Yerkes says that not very much noise usually resulted, although she seemed to take considerable satisfaction in the activity. He received the impression that chest-beating indicated impatience, mild dissatisfaction, irritation, or merely the desire to startle or intimidate the observer. Mr. Burbidge informed Dr. Yerkes that wild gorillas also open their mouths widely and beat their stretched cheeks rhythmically with the palms of the hands. The same traveler states that gorillas relax the lower jaw and with both hands strike the chin, causing the teeth to knock together and make a clicking sound.

On the whole, Congo manifested such a stable emotional equilibrium and was usually so calm and placid that it was easy to miss the minor modifications of facial expression that may have indicated emotional shifts. Yet this animal was definitely moody and showed it by her attitude toward her work on different days. Sometimes she was hopeful, eager, and optimistic, at other times indifferent and apathetic. Yerkes suspects that Congo often disguised her true feeling, purpose, and intent. He suggests that she displayed a sort of "Harvard indifference." He believed her to be deep and given to the practice of craft and cunning, rather than naïve and stupid.

The San Diego gorillas were extremely amiable and tolerant of each other and of their life in captivity. They quarreled and fought much less frequently than do other apes and were evidently deeply attached to each other. Frequently they sat touching hands, and one or the other often patted his fellow gently and, apparently, lovingly. When they had been separated, as was necessary on several occasions when one of the pair had been ill or injured, they became very lonesome and miserable and lost weight. They disliked change and did not readily adjust themselves to new human beings, although they became friendly and attached to a few individuals with whom they had had long contact. They usually ignored apes in neighboring cages, but their indifference was probably simulated.

There were some marked differences in temperament between the two gorillas, and these remained constant over a period of some 9 years. The heavier of the two, Mbongo, was friendly, comical, and at times somewhat tricky. He was more buoyant, more lighthearted, and at the same time more easily depressed than Ngagi. The other animal, Ngagi, was naturally a leader and seemed to dominate over the younger but heavier gorilla and to watch over him and control him. Even when Ngagi was ill, he retained his dominance. When, however, there was an actual fight, Mbongo was the fiercer and the more clever.

Carpenter says that the adjectives used by Yerkes to describe the temperament of the female gorilla, Congo, which fit in the case of Ngagi and Mbongo are "good-natured, emotionally stable, and playful"; but "inexpressive, aloof, self-dependent and moody" do not fit the San Diego immature male gorillas. They were not sullen, ferocious, aggressive, or melancholic. Carpenter regarded them as fearless toward each other and toward man, deliberate and persistent in attention, somewhat sly and tricky, but contented and well adapted to each other and to their life in captivity. They showed decided stubbornness and powerful spontaneity, as well as considerable determination.

PATHOLOGY

Gorillas, according to general report, are remarkable for personal cleanliness. Captive animals are careful not to soil their beds and, in general, refrain from littering their cages. They are said usually to be free from parasites. Of course, if they are kept in filthy places and under unhygienic conditions, they cannot live up to their natural inclinations. Young animals are very likely to die of dysentery or other digestive disturbances. Gorillas are apparently very susceptible to respiratory diseases, such as influenza, bronchitis, pneumonia, and tuberculosis. Recent success in raising captive gorillas has been based upon rigorous precautions against infections, such as keeping the animals behind glass, and, in the case of the Ringling gorillas, in air-conditioned, glass-enclosed cages. The other factor of great importance is a properly balanced diet. Undoubtedly, many captive animals have been weakened by nutritional deficiencies and possibly endocrine imbalance set up by improper diets. Scurvy and the falling out of the hair probably result from these causes.

The amoebae which cause dysentery and liver abscess have been found in the gorilla; also an intestinal ciliate, *Troglodytella,* which belongs to a different genus from that found in man; and, further, the *Plasmodium* of malaria. As for external parasites, it is interesting to note that one genus of the Pediculidae, *Pthirus,* the crab louse, has been found only on man and the mountain gorilla. This louse is said to brachiate among the pubic hairs, but I am not ready to vouch for this statement.

Another disease which has been ascribed to the gorilla is nephritis, a kidney inflammation. Two gorillas, Massa and Janet Penserosa, seem to have suffered a partial paralysis of the lower limbs—possibly poliomyelitis.

Much stress has been laid upon the importance of keeping gorillas happy by giving them human or other primate companionship. Certainly, several outstanding successes in raising gorillas, and, before them, chimpanzees, have been due to the affection, care and solicitude lavished upon them by women. Mme. Abreu of Havana was the first person successfully to breed anthropoid apes (chimpanzees) in captivity. Miss Alys Cunningham, Mrs. Lintz, and Mrs. Hoyt have been responsible for the upbringing of Sultan, Gargantua, and Toto, the last two of whom have survived. Mrs. Benchley should be credited with the survival in good health, up to the present year, of both of the San Diego gorillas, and before they reached the zoo, it seems probable that Osa Johnson had a great deal to do with their upbringing. The feminine, not to say the maternal, touch may not be essential, but it has been most efficacious. Yet Bamboo, the splendid lowland gorilla in the Philadelphia Zoological Garden, has thrived for years without benefit of feminine care. I should doubt that a gorilla would pine away and die from loneliness and melancholia if it were protected from infection and given a proper diet, with plenty of exercise and fresh air.

On March 15, 1942, Mbongo, the younger of the two San Diego mountain gorillas, died at the age of almost 16 years, after an illness of 3 weeks. His death was due to a fungus (*Coccidioidis imitis*) which had destroyed his lungs and spread to his other organs. According to Mrs. Benchley, the disease, which is called coccidioidal granuloma, is prevalent among the agricultural areas of the San Joaquin Valley,

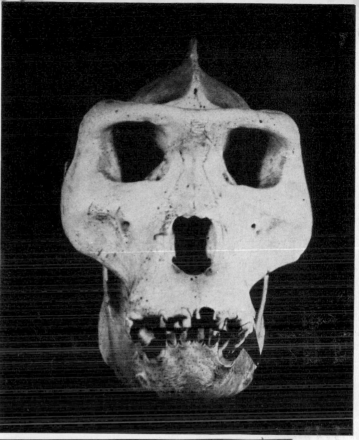

SKULL OF AN ADULT
MALE LOWLAND
GORILLA

Photographs F. W. Orchard
Courtesy Peabody Museum

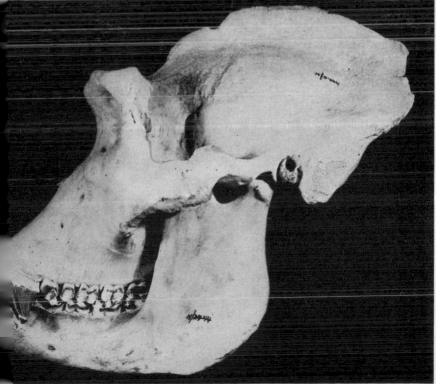

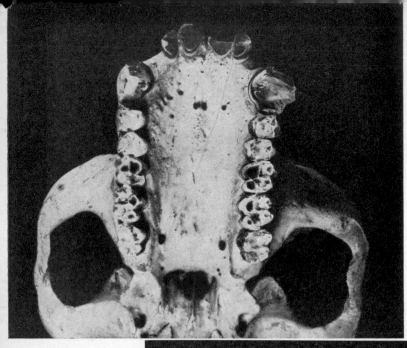

Photographs F. W.
Courtesy Peabody I

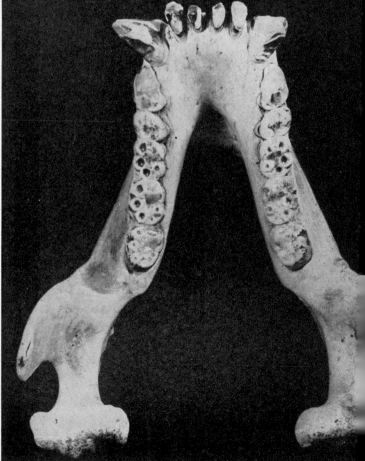

UPPER AND
LOWER DENTAL
ARCHES OF
ADULT MALE
LOWLAND
GORILLA

particularly among human beings, but also among cattle and some rodents. The disease seems to be contracted from soil or heavy dust which carry the spores. In proper media these spores proliferate rapidly and death occurs usually in a couple of weeks. Mrs. Benchley thinks that Mbongo may have been infected from a clod of earth caught in the hay used for bedding or thrown at the gorilla by visitors to the zoo.[37]

Randall found 3.3 per cent of skulls and 5.6 per cent of skeletons of wild lowland gorillas had healed fractures. These fractures represent 26 individuals. Interestingly, the fractures were confined to adult or nearly adult animals, in contrast to Schultz's findings on the orangutan. The most frequent fracture was of the nasal bones (7 cases). Fractures are much commoner in males than in females.

Bony growths of a pathological nature were observed in a considerable number of cases, usually in the aged individuals. Three individuals had bullets embedded in their bones, with signs of healing. Indications of arthritis were observed in a fair number of cases, mostly in the vertebrae.[38]

ANATOMY

SKULL

The skull of the gorilla is larger than those of the chimpanzee and the orang-utan, especially in the facial portion, and the sex differences are greater. In the adult male the temporal crests converge at the top of the frontal bone and form a sagittal crest which increases in height with age. Posteriorly, this crest unites with an almost equally large occipital crest. The massive brow ridges of the gorilla are more nearly horizontal than those of the chimpanzee, and they do not thin out laterally like those of the other African ape. The skull is much more constricted behind the supraorbital torus than that of the chimpanzee. The massive zygomatic arches delimit a huge temporal fossa in which the wing of the sphenoid is deeply channeled. As in the chimpanzee, there is usually a fronto-temporal articulation at pterion. The glenoid fossa is shallow and limited posteriorly by a large postglenoid process. This ape is the only one which possesses a real mastoid process, with a vaginal ridge on the tympanic bone and even a small styloid process. The foramen magnum is far back on the skull. The basilar process of the occipital is very long and the skull base is closed in, rather than opened out as in man. In the male skull the entire planum occipitale is occupied by attachments of the nuchal musculature and this occipital plane slopes from above downward and forward.

[37]Benchley 1942, pp. 378–79.
[38]Randall 1942, pp. 164, 167.

In the female the occiput is feebly convex. The average cranial capacity of the lowland male gorilla is 549 cc., and of the female 459 cc.

The orbits of the gorilla, below the massive torus, are high and square with rounded corners. They are not tilted. A fronto-maxillary suture is commoner in the interior of the orbit than the lachrymo-ethmoidal suture which prevails in man. The interorbital width is large. The nasal bones have a lanceolate projection upward which extends into the middle of the glabellar region. They are constricted at the root and there may be the vestige of a bridge, generally in the form of a slightly elevated crest. The nasal bones extend down well below the orbital borders and are very broad where they terminate at the top of the nasal aperture. The nasal aperture is bounded laterally by the swellings of the maxilla and premaxilla which enclose the roots of the massive canines. There is no real sill to the nasal aperture, but, far inside, the slight transverse crest may show in the middle 2 small tubercles which are homologous with the nasal spine. In skulls of young individuals the maxillo-premaxillary sutures may be seen at the sides of the nasal aperture. The malars are deep, but not markedly projecting. The maxilla is high and has very deep alveolar borders. The entire face is notably prognathous. The palate is long and relatively narrow, with the greatest width in the canine region. The posterior nasal spine is small, as are usually the pterygoid plates. The mandible is massive, with a very high, broad ascending ramus and a shallow sigmoid notch behind the high, recurved coronoid processes. The symphysis falls away at the incisive level. Interiorly, it has the usual genial pit and geniohyoid spine. Some comparative details of the postcranial skeleton will be found in Chapter XV.

TEETH

The great canines and converging dental arcades of the gorilla are regarded by Gregory as recent and rather swinelike adaptations for a frugivorous diet. These specializations are absent in young specimens and feeble in females. The incisors are relatively narrow, the upper premolars wide, and the anterior lower premolar somewhat like that of a baboon, with a sloping, well-worn antero-external face. The molars have high cusps and are uncomplicated by wrinkles of enamel. The upper molars are divided into larger anterior and smaller posterior moieties, but traces of the original trigonal pattern are visible in the 4-cusped form. The lower molars are long and have usually the 5 cusps of the fundamental *Dryopithecus* pattern.

ORGANS OF DIGESTION AND ABSORPTION

The stomach of the gorilla is more globular than that of man and the pyloric antrum is better defined. The gorilla has a good-sized vermiform appendix, which increases in size during life, contrary to the condition found in man. The large intestine, especially the ascending colon, is short.

The gorilla has a more primitive type of liver than is found in the other anthropoids.

ORGANS OF RESPIRATION AND VOICE

The gorilla, according to Sonntag, has a complicated group of air sacs which branch off from a central cavity. The left lung is usually divided into 2 and the right into 3 lobes.

GENITAL ORGANS

The external genital organs of the apes, unlike those of man, undergo a process of atrophy as the animals grow. In the gorilla the labia majora are vestigial and there is no mons veneris and no hymen. The penis has a well-developed glans, which appears to be almost cleft. The entire organ is narrow and tapering and contains a small bone. The spermatozoa of the gorilla most closely resemble those of man.

BRAIN

The brain of the gorilla is largest in volume of any primate below man and probably nearest to that of man in the character of its association areas. No ape has a complete Sylvian fissure, and in all a part of the island of Reil is exposed. All apes also have a large "simian sulcus" which sweeps across the hemisphere behind the parieto-occipital sulcus. In man the small sulcus lunatus corresponds to this "Affenspalte." The human brain weighs about 2½ times as much as that of a gorilla. In the adult gorilla the brain is about 1/150 to 1/200 of body weight, as against about 1/50 in man. The neopallium is relatively much smaller in the gorilla than in man, and the frontal lobes are rostrated.

CHAPTER III

The Reactionary Orang-utan

HABITAT

THE ORANG-UTAN LIVES only in the northern tip of Sumatra, in the province of Atjeh, and in the great island of Borneo to the east, in which it has a much wider distribution. The fauna of Borneo and Sumatra are more closely allied than are those of either of these islands and Java, which has closer affinities in this respect with the Malay Peninsula. However, fossil remains of the orang occur in the Middle Pleistocene beds of Java and in the caves of southern China. This ape must formerly have had a much wider range. In Borneo the orang inhabits a belt of low, forest-covered swamps, lying between the seacoast and the interior mountain ranges and extending around the western coast of the island. In this forested alluvial plain the distribution of the orang is not continuous, but patchy. In the Territory of Sarawak, for example, it is found along the rivers Batang Lupar and Sadong and their tributaries, but not along the Sarawak or Samarahan rivers. It also occurs sporadically on the south coast.

There is only one species of orang-utan and no important differences between the Bornean and Sumatran animals have been established. However, Professor W. C. Osman Hill thinks that the Sumatran orangs are larger than those of Borneo, that the foxy-red color of the coat and orange beard are especially characteristic of the Sumatran apes, and that the tendency to absence of the great-toe nail or to a vestigial condition of it is more constant in the Sumatran variety.

DESCRIPTION

SIZE

The average weight of 13 adult male orang-utans, according to Schultz's compilation, was 74.89 kilos or 165.2 pounds. The maximum weight of these animals was 90.72 kilos or about 200 pounds.[1] How-

[1]Schultz 1941c, pp. 57–110.

112

ever, 8 adult females averaged only 36.85 kilos or 81.25 pounds. Thus the male orang weighs more than twice as much as the female. Schultz points out that sex differences in weight vary among the primates to a surprising extent. The smallest females relative to males are found in the proboscis monkey, a primate in which the female equals only 49.1 per cent of male weight, and in the orang-utan, 49.2 per cent. At the other end of the scale is the South American spider monkey, whose sex-weight ratio is 108.7. High in the scale is the gibbon, 93.0, and the langur monkey (*rubicundus*), 92.8. The chimpanzee has a sex-weight ratio of 87.9 and man is about 81. Schultz quotes no figures for the gorilla. It is clear enough that the two Asiatic anthropoid apes—the gibbon and the orang-utan—are at opposite poles as regards sex differences, in weight, and in general bodily size. The female gibbon is virtually as large and heavy as the male.

The great naturalist, Alfred Russell Wallace, gave data on the stature of 9 adult male orang-utans and 7 adult females. He stated that, in the case of the former, height erect ranged from 49 to 50 inches. The largest specimen measured by Hornaday was 54 inches in height, but Hill has recently recorded the body length of a Sumatran orang as over 62 inches. Since the orang is an habitual quadruped, some students feel that estimates or measurements of its erect standing height are unnecessary. Yet the orang can and does stand and walk erect occasionally. Wallace reports that the span of one of these animals that stands a little over 4 feet is likely to reach 7 feet 8 inches. Hill's 5-foot 2-inch orang had a span of 8 feet 4 inches.[2]

Schultz, in his recent monograph upon growth and development in the orang, omits giving information on total body length of the 38 animals he has measured in the flesh. However, in an earlier publication he gives the average of 2 adult females as 1,135 mm. (44.68 inches) and of 3 males as 1,304 mm. (51.33 inches).[3] The tallest of these 5 animals had a total body length slightly under 135 cm. (1,349 mm. or 53.1 inches). The orang-utan, on the basis of these data, is a trifle taller than the chimpanzee and much heavier.

HAIR

The hair of the orang-utan is a reddish or yellowish brown, shading into something close to a real carroty or "bright-foxy" red.[4] It is longer

[2] Hill 1939, p. 453.
[3] Schultz 1933a, pp. 154–83.
[4] Hill's big Sumatran male orang had hair on the flanks 375 mm. long, and only slightly shorter on the shoulders and arms. The hair on the vertex, shoulders, and arms

than that of any other anthropoid, individual hairs being over a foot in length on the head and arms. Yet the hair of the orang is less dense than that of most other primates. Schultz counted the number of scalp hairs per centimeter on his adult orang, who seemed to have very long and abundant hair. He found only 158 per square centimeter. Man and the gorilla both exceed the orang, and probably the chimpanzee, in density of scalp hair. On the whole, the giant primates are sparsely covered with hair.

The hairs on the upper arm and forearm of the orang converge at the elbow. Direction of hair growth in other parts of the body is apparently variable. Wood Jones says that the frontal region is relatively hairless, but that the hair grows forward rather than backward. The face of the orang is naked, with the exception of the beard and sparse hairs on the lips, cheeks, and forehead. The palms and soles are also devoid of hair.

PIGMENTATION

Pigmentation of the skin begins early in the fetal life of the orang, even before any lanugo, or fetal down, is visible. In the youngest pigmented fetus the skin is light brown, darkest in the region surrounding the anus, on the ears, and on the nasal bridge.[5] In a fetus studied by Schultz, the highest possible age of which was a little over 6 months, the scalp was the darkest, being slate-blue in the region of the vertex. The lips were pale brown, much lighter in color than the cheeks and forehead. The palms and soles were light pink. In this specimen the hair on the scalp was coppery red, whereas on other parts of the body it was still straw-colored. In later fetuses the hair all over the body had become reddish brown. No feelers or sinus hairs were found in any of the orang fetuses examined. In the adult the skin color is brownish, apparently darkening somewhat with increasing age. Some areas are deep brown, purplish, or grayish. Also the skin surface has a rough, pimply aspect, resembling "goose flesh." Evidently, the orang usually does not attain the black skin color characteristic of the gorilla, the gibbon, and some of the chimpanzees, although Hill describes the general skin color of his Sumatran specimen as "bluish black."

The reddish tint to the hair and the reddish brown of the skin suggest an abundance of carotin.

was fiery red, on the lower back browner, deepening to a reddish chestnut on the buttocks and back of the thighs. The stiff, profuse beard was bright orange. This ape must have been one of the most impressive "strawberry blonds" on record.

[5] Schultz 1933b.

SKULL AND HEAD

Some brief description of the skull of the orang-utan is necessary for the understanding of the features which overlie it. The brain case is rounded, but the whole posterior portion is taken up by the attachments of the neck muscles, which extend up to a bony crest that crosses the vault from one ear hole to the other. Thus, in the flesh, the orang's occiput is buried in his neck, so that he appears to have no back to his head. You are familiar with the type of winter cap which has ear flaps tied together at the top when not in use. These tied-up ear flaps would represent in the orang the area of the skull vault covered by the huge temporal muscles. Exposed between them in the frontal region is a strip of moderately high forehead, the concave sides of which converge and meet near the vertex of the skull. Along the mid-line of the vault where the temporal muscles come together, a bony crest of varying height develops in the male orang. This fore-and-aft crest affords additional attachment for the thick and powerful temporal muscles and meets the transverse occipital crest which delimits the attachment of the neck muscles.

Thus the round brain case is covered with thick muscles, except a narrow frontal strip. The cranial capacities of 47 adult female orang-utans measured by Schultz average 336.6 cc. and the mean of 52 adult males is 416.4 cc.

The cranial capacity relative to body weight is about the same in orangs as in chimpanzees, when the animals are of equal body weight. However, the heavier the animal gets, the less is its relative cranial capacity. Thus 8 adult female orangs averaged 36.9 kilos in weight and had a relative cranial capacity of 0.93 per cent, while 4 female chimpanzees with average weight of 40.0 kilos had a relative cranial capacity of 0.88. In 7 adult male orangs average weight was 79.3 kilos, and average relative cranial capacity 0.56. The male chimpanzee, which is a much lighter animal than the orang, would show higher relative cranial capacity. Man's relative cranial capacity, as determined by Schultz on a series of 13 adult male Negroes, averages 2.06 and ranges from 1.54 to 2.74. Since these Negroes had an average body weight of 66.8 kilos, it is evident that man's relative brain size is far superior to that of the ape, irrespective of his body weight.

The facial skeleton of the orang is long, broad, and concave. The bony ridges which surmount the eye sockets are not extraordinarily large, but are eyebrow-shaped thickenings of the upper parts of the orbital rim. They do not fuse into a transverse shelf or bar, as in the gorilla and the chimpanzee. The forehead is much higher and more convex in the orang than in either of the other two great apes. These two facts are interrelated. A low, receding forehead does not provide sufficient resistance against the stresses of chewing originating in massive, projecting jaws. It must be reinforced by a bony buttress, which is provided by the bar of the brow ridges in the African anthropoids. But a high, vaulted forehead takes up these chewing stresses without the necessity of much additional buttressing. The orang has a high forehead and relatively small brow ridges.

All the anthropoid apes have very large orbits (sockets for the eyeballs). In the orang the orbits are almost circular, but higher than they are broad. Chimpanzees and gorillas have orbits approaching more closely quadrilateral forms. The orbits of the orang are so close together that the nasal root is pinched down to a point and the flat nasal bones are merely narrow parallel splints, which usually fuse together early in life. The nasal aperture is broad, but there is no bony bridge of the nose. The cheekbones of the orang are much more massive and bulge laterally far more than those of the gorilla and the chimpanzee. In fact, the orang has a somewhat Mongoloid facial skeleton. Below the nasal aperture the alveolar portion of the upper jaw, which lodges the teeth, bulges strongly forward, accentuating the concavity of the upper and middle face. In the adult male the massive canine teeth at the anterior corners of the palate delimit a pyramidal area by the relief of the bony sockets of their long, thick roots. These sockets converge above, enclosing the nasal aperture. The base of the pyramid is the alveolar border. The lower jaw is deep and massive, but falls away in the chin region like the sloping end of an old-fashioned bathtub. The enormous and heavy jaws with their big teeth dwarf the brain case.

When this bony skull is clothed with flesh, the orang has a square, flat face with eyes set shallowly in almost circular bony rims and a trough in the concave area where the bridge of the nose ought to be. Molded to the lower part of this square face is a broad and deep bulge, swelling out below the nasal opening and including the long upper lip, the mouth slit, and the deep but receding chin. In an infant orang this alveolar bulge looks like a hemisphere pasted on the lower third of the square face. In the adult female the bulge is almost square, but with the corners rounded. In the adult male it is a vertical oblong with rounded corners. In the adult male the wedge-shaped blinkers or cheek pads make semicircular, platelike flanges extending from the lower angles of the jaw to the crown of the head. These make the face look like a pancake with the eyes in the middle and the nostrils

ADULT MALE ORANG-UTAN

PROFILE OF YOUNG ORANG-UTAN

opening just above the jaw bulge which projects from the bottom of the rim.

EYES, NOSE, MOUTH, EARS

The eyes of the orang-utan have biconvex lid openings and appear small in adults relative to the great expanse of the face. Eye color is brown, but I can find no detailed description of the orang iris. Several concentric wrinkles or folds encircle the eye slit, and these are especially deep below the eyes. In the infant orang these wrinkles form on the inside corner a pseudo-Mongoloid or epicanthic fold.

The nose of the orang is so flat that it does not project above the facial level at any point except at the margins of the nostrils. The latter are obliquely placed, oval, and converging at their lower extremities. Because the outer nose is so sunken in the face, it needs no support on the sides and the cartilages merely stretch across the front. Hence the tip and wings seem undeveloped. The center of the tip is marked by a deep furrow which terminates just above the thin septum, or partition between the nostrils.

The upper integumental lip of the orang is greatly elongated and is marked by numerous vertical puckers. The wide mouth slit reveals only a thin line of mucous membrane. The lips are capable of being protruded into a trough or funnel.

The orang-utan has the smallest ear relative to head size of any of the higher primates. The ear is set close to the head and usually concealed by the long hair. Typically, the upper part of the helix or rim of the ear is deeply folded and the hinder margin moderately rolled. The antihelix (the inner fold which encloses the ear opening) is very prominent in the fetuses figured by Schultz. Wood Jones says that the orang ear is very similar to that of baboons, save that it is considerably more reduced, thicker, and fleshier.[6] There is ordinarily no trace of a lobule. Hill's huge Sumatran male orang had an ear only 38 mm. long and 21 mm. broad. The large external auditory meatus was lined with thick, glandular skin and provided with a profuse growth of long, red hairs which projected outward. The pinna, or external ear, itself had only a few short, bristly hairs.

TEETH

The front teeth of the orang have become enlarged and specialized for feeding upon fruits with heavy, tough rinds, especially the durian. The canines in the males are very large and probably have a defensive

[6] Jones 1929, p. 256.

function. As in other anthropoid apes, the molars have 4 cusps in the upper series and 5 in the lower series. However, the crowns of the molars are low and flat and covered with numerous fine wrinklings, which Gregory considers an advanced specialization. In the palate the greatest width is between the canine teeth in adults. The tooth rows converge posteriorly. Extra molars occur in about 14 per cent of 336 adult male orang crania, according to Schultz.

CHEEK PADS

A peculiar specialization of orangs—found usually only in adult males—is the cheek pads, which consist of enormous, lateral, wedge-shaped flanges made of fat and fibrous tissue and covered with naked skin. They seem to have little connection with the facial musculature. These cheek pads appear in all fetuses and young infants as symmetrical folds of skin extending from halfway between the ear and the eye down the middle of the cheek to the level of the mouth, or even farther. During late infantile and juvenile life these folds disappear, but reappear and develop rapidly in maturing males. In one adult male, which grew up in captivity, the cheek pads were fully developed within 6 months of the time when they were first noticed. In another animal the full development required 2 years. These cheek pads occur sometimes in females and are occasionally absent in adult males. When they are absent, there is usually some folding of the skin in the region where they ordinarily develop.

The function (if any) of the cheek pads is unknown. If the adult males fight among themselves or with other animals, these tough, warty flaps may be useful as defensive structures.

LARYNGEAL POUCHES

The male orang usually has an enormous throat pouch which can hold as much as 6 liters of air and may extend down to the bottom of the breastbone and into the armpits. It may be single, or divided into right and left portions. In the back this laryngeal pouch may extend over the shoulder blades to the occiput, or back of the head. These pouches open into the larynx above the vocal cords. They can be inflated with air and in this condition give the owner a goiterous appearance. Adult females have these pouches, but they are inconspicuous compared with those of the males. At birth these air sacs are small, but they develop quite rapidly during infantile life.

All anthropoid apes except gibbons have a greater or less development of these air sacs, but they are largest in male orang-utans. Various functions have been suggested for these structures. They may or may not act as vocal resonating chambers, but I am not aware that the male orang is especially vociferous. It has also been suggested that this air cushion underneath the·chin helps to support the heavy, overbalanced jaws. The most improbable idea is that this air pouch serves as a swimming bladder. Perhaps it would be of utility as a defensive structure.

GLANDS, SKIN, AND NAILS

In the adult orang-utan the nipples lie very high and are situated far laterally—just in front of the armpits. This condition is not so marked in the fetus as in the adult. The nipples of adult females may be very long and pendulous—38 to 46 mm. in length. Also the breasts of the nursing female may be large and similar to those of man, contrary to what has been observed in other primates. Schultz found that the diameters of the breasts in two freshly killed female orangs were 188 mm. and 214 mm.

In the middle of the smooth skin of the chest of a fetal orang, slightly above the nipple line, Schultz discovered a small, circular pit, which was evidently a natural opening. Upon sectioning this area and examining it under the microscope, he found this pit to be the opening of a considerable number of sebaceous glands clumped around and beneath it. He then investigated this feature and found it present in 24 of 29 males and 4 of 26 females. The pit gets smaller and the gland apparently degenerates in older animals. In fetuses the opening reaches a diameter of 2.5 mm.; the skin forms a circular pattern about it.[7] In juvenile animals a low, circular wall often surrounds the pit, which is the center of a dark-brown spot. The depth may reach 3.5 mm. In one living juvenile orang it was possible to feel beneath the pit the gland, about the size of a pea, and to squeeze a tiny drop from it.

Nothing comparable with this sternal gland has been observed in other apes and monkeys. Its function is unknown. Some marsupials have an accumulation of glands in a hairless region of the chest and sternal glands are found in some forms of bats. In both of these groups of mammals and in the orang the glands are more strongly developed in, or entirely restricted to, males.

Ischial callosities, which are found in all Old World monkeys and in the gibbon and siamang, occur in 8 of 78 orangs examined by Schultz, or about 10 per cent. More than one third of chimpanzees have such callosities. In the chimp these bare, horny areas are often strongly developed, but in the orang they are smooth, hairless, and thickened, but not really horny.

[7] Schultz 1921, pp. 194–96.

It is commonly stated that the great toes of orangs lack a nail, but this is not invariably the case. When the nail is absent the last joint or phalanx of the toe is also absent, fused, or vestigial. In a series of 68 orang skeletons examined by Schultz, the great toe has 2 phalanges in both feet in 37 per cent of cases, 2 on one foot in 4 per cent, and only one in the 3 remaining 59 per cent. This condition is found in the orang fetus, as well as in adults. Schultz has observed a family of captive orangs in which the father has nails on both great toes, but the mother and both babies lack great-toe nails.

HANDS AND FEET

The hand of the orang-utan is long and narrow, but relatively broader than that of the gibbon. The digits, relative to palm length, are also shorter than those of the gibbon. The fingers are strongly tapering and have only very small terminal pads. The nails are laterally compressed. The thumb is very small and springs from the palm far back toward the wrist, so that its tip reaches only to the middle of the palm. The index finger is shorter than the ring finger. The back of the hand and the fingers are covered with hair, which extends to the end of the middle joint of all the digits except the thumb.

The long and narrow foot of the orang is remarkable for its diminutive great toe and for the great length of the outer toes, which are as much developed as fingers. The great toe, though small, is relatively and absolutely bigger than the thumb. It is often devoid of a nail, is set far back on the sole, and when aligned with the long axis of the foot does not reach to the base of the second toe.. This big toe is carried nearly at a right angle with the sole, and it is, of course, opposable to the other digits. The heel is poorly developed.

BODILY PROPORTIONS

The chest circumference of the orang, according to·Schultz's earlier data, averages 854 mm. in combined sexes, which is about 33 inches.[8] For the chimpanzee and man the corresponding figures are, respectively, 796 mm. and 834 mm. The orang has a total leg length of 545 mm., the chimpanzee 577 mm., and man 882 mm. In arm length the rankings are reversed, with the orang at 924 mm., chimpanzee 789 mm., and man 773 mm.[9]

Chest circumference relative to trunk length is 148.8 in gibbons, 161.6 in man, 173.6 in siamangs, 176.1 in chimpanzees, 185.0 in the

[8]Hill's giant Sumatran orang had a chest circumference of 1,300 mm. (51.2 in.).
[9]Schultz 1933a.

YOUNG ORANG-UTAN

PROPORTIONS OF
ADULT MALE
ORANG-UTAN

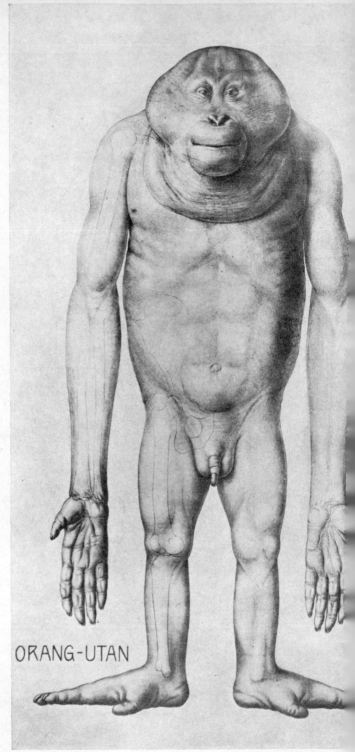

ORANG-UTAN

Drawing by Adolph H. Schultz

orangs, and 216.7 in gorillas. However, relative shoulder breadth in the orang is somewhat less than that of man, although slightly larger than that of the chimpanzee. The gorilla exceeds all other primates in this proportion. In relative hip breadth the orang falls somewhat below the chimpanzee and the latter below man. The gorilla is again supreme. The breadth of the chest, expressed as a percentage of its depth, is as follows: gibbons 118.2, siamangs 124.8, orang-utans 126.0, man 128.8, chimpanzees 129.0, gorillas 139.3. Thus the orang-utan has a relatively deeper and narrower chest than any of the other giant primates.

In relative leg length the orang-utan with 119.2 falls below all the other anthropoid apes. The gibbon (146.5) approaches most closely to man (171.0). In relative arm length the gibbon (237.8 per cent of trunk length) easily leads the rest of the primates, followed by the allied siamang (233.4). The relative arm length of the orang is 181.9, that of the chimpanzee 175.0, whereas in man this index drops to 150.1. The lowland gorilla differs markedly from the mountain gorilla in this index (183.6 as against 153.7). Arm length relative to leg length is only 87.7 in man. At the other end is the siamang with 177.5. The orang has an average of 169.6 for this intermembral index, and the gibbon 162.2. Gorillas and chimpanzees range between 136 and 140. The orang has a forearm which slightly exceeds the upper arm in length, while in the siamang and even more notably in the gibbon the forearm markedly exceeds upper-arm length. In the other giant primates the forearm is shorter than the upper arm. The anthropoid-human range is from 76.6 in man to 112.8 in the gibbon. The chimpanzee with 77.7 is virtually human in this proportion.

The foot of the orang relative to trunk length is the longest of all the higher primates (64.0 per cent). At the other end of the scale is the very stubby mountain gorilla (40.9 per cent). Man, with 48.8 per cent, falls a little below the chimpanzee (50.1 per cent) and the gibbon (52.7 per cent). Of course, the four outer toes of gibbons and orangs are greatly elongated, whereas they are shortened in man. The relative breadth of the foot in the orang does not differ significantly from that of man. Gibbons have the narrowest feet, while both the chimpanzee and, most markedly, the gorilla have comparatively broader feet. In relative hand length the orang is surpassed only by the gibbon. The mountain gorilla falls below man in this proportion, whereas the lowland gorilla and the chimpanzee exceed the human mean. Gorillas lead in relative breadth of the hand with man next, followed by the chimpanzee, the orang, the siamang, and the gibbon. Of all the higher primates man has relatively the longest thumbs and great toes, and the orang by far the shortest. This anthropoid has miserably short and degenerate first digits.

The orang-utan and the lowland gorilla push man very closely in relative head size, as expressed by the average of the cranial diameters in percentage of trunk length. Lowland gorillas and orangs are practically tied for first place in relative face length, with gibbons and siamangs at the bottom and man next to them. With the exception of gibbon and siamang, all the higher primates have relatively longer and narrower faces than man.

The head index or cephalic index is the breadth of the head expressed as a proportion of the length. In man we call the individual brachycephalic or round-headed who has an index of 82 or over. Below 77 is long-headed or dolichocephalic. Here are Schultz's figures, based in the case of man on 9 cadavers of assorted races, and upon even fewer of the various apes: mountain gorilla 74.6, man 78.3, lowland gorilla 82.5, siamang 86.6, gibbon 87.7, orang 89.3, chimpanzee 91.0. On this basis the chimpanzee and the orang are the most round-headed of the apes and man shares with the mountain gorilla the strongest tendency toward long-headedness. The relative size of the ear is greatest in the chimpanzee among all the higher primates. The orang has the smallest ear, but the gorilla has ears which are relatively but little bigger. Man's relative ear size is only one third of that of the chimpanzee, less than half of that of the gibbon, but nearly twice that of the orang.

LOCOMOTION

The movements of the orang-utan are always described as slow, deliberate, cautious. This great Asiatic ape is generally considered to be a sluggish and awkward animal. Of course, an animal of the considerable weight of the orang which is primarily arboreal cannot be expected to flip lightly from the terminal end of one bough across wide-open spaces to another slender limb, as does the featherweight gibbon. The orang uses its long and powerful arms to embrace tree trunks and to reach up ahead while the weight is being supported with the legs. The lower members are essential in climbing, as contrasted with the gibbon, which progresses mostly with free arm swings. As anyone can attest who has seen moving pictures of wild orangs, this animal also does a certain amount of pure brachiating, but apparently no leaping is involved. When the animal has to cross from one tree to the other, it picks a place where the branches interlace or touch, lies flat, and reaches for the bough to which it wishes to move, testing its strength before committing itself. Even if an orang-utan is being pursued, he does not abandon his cautious and deliberate method of progression. In descending a tree an orang sometimes hangs by its feet, reaches down with its arms, gets a new hold, lets go with its feet, and thus progresses downward by a series of somersaults. Although the legs of the orang are supposed to be degenerate, it is evident that this ape uses its feet and legs more extensively in climbing than do other anthropoids. The long outer toes of the orang foot and its short, degenerate great toe strongly suggest that the foot is adapted for a suspensory function.

On the ground the orang moves very awkwardly on all fours. The very long arms are somewhat bent so that the elbows stick out. The main support, according to Schlegel and Müller, is on the inner edge of the hand and the backs of the first joints of the second and third fingers. The short thumb is placed against the ground as a counterpoise, with its free tip down. This description seems convincing to me. A photograph of a female orang in the Philadelphia Zoological Garden[10] shows her resting on the inner sides of the hands and the first joints of the bent thumb and the second and third fingers, with the knuckles of the hands pointing outward and backward. This photograph corresponds with the description of Schlegel and Müller, with the exception of the thumb position, which is bent instead of straight, resting on the back of the first joint rather than upon the free tip. Now, obviously, this method of hand support would not permit any but a most awkward and painful quadrupedal gait. The photograph also agrees with the description of Schlegel and Müller in showing the toes clenched, so that the weight is borne upon the outer part of the sole and upon the upper sides of the first joints of the flexed toes.

The greater length of the arms raises the forepart of the trunk so that the animal moves in an almost semi-erect position. Observation of moving pictures of the orang-utan on the ground indicates that the animal walks with the legs and the arms not directly in line, fore and aft, but staggered so that one foot is advanced between the hands and the other outside. Yet Schlegel and Müller state that the gait is directly forward and not sidling. Other illustrations show that the orang sometimes swings the legs forward between the arms, using the latter as crutches. A man can probably outstrip an orang on the ground without much difficulty.

There has been some argument about the orang's ability to walk erect. Some observers deny that wild orangs ever do so, unless they

[10]Reproduced in Hooton 1931, Plate 11, p. 116.

are clinging to a branch or other support. There is ample evidence that captive orangs can and do walk erect, especially if they have learned this gait when young. They rest the weight on the outside of the foot and keep the toes flexed and turned inward. The short great toe may be used as an inside prop. The arms may be held over the head to help the balance. Observers agree that the animal easily becomes fatigued and does not persist in this mode of progression for any considerable length of time.

There is also a contention, based upon the absence of ischial callosities in the orang, that this animal does not sit upon its buttocks, but squats upon its heels. I doubt this generalization. Man is an inveterate sitter, but has no ischial callosities, although the blood supply to the buttocks rather suggests that some of our ancestors may have had these convenient natural cushions.

Experimenters have tried to discover the orang-utan's swimming ability by throwing the animal into water. In all cases the result was a frightened and floundering animal which had to be fished out speedily to prevent its drowning.

A few observations on preferential use of the hands in the orang have yielded conflicting results—2 cases of alleged right-handedness and 2 of left-handedness. This finding is quite in accordance with the experiments of Finch on chimpanzee handedness. He found nearly equal incidence of right- and left-handedness, with a majority of animals showing no definite preference.

One notable feature of orang posture is the ability to thrust the leg out from the hip at right angles for use as a brace against a vertical wall or a branch, when the animal is suspended by one or both arms. In other words, the femur is capable of being abducted 90°. Anatomists generally refer this unusual mobility of the hip joint to the absence of the ligamentum teres, which in man and the other apes tethers the head of the femur to the bottom of the acetabulum, or hip-joint socket.

NESTS

At night the orang-utan builds a nest in a tree for a sleeping place. This habit is attested by many authorities and is well illustrated in the film *Rango* which was shown a few years ago in public theaters. The nest is made of interlaced branches, broken-off branches, twigs, and leaves. Just before dark the animal stands upright on a forked branch, using one arm as a support and with the other drawing in distant branches, breaking them, and piling them up all around him

until he is in the center of a circle of twigs 45 cm. or more in height.[11]
He then breaks off smaller twigs and puts them across to form the
floor of the nest. Next comes a process of stripping leaves from the
branches to line the nest. These are pressed into the crevices. Finally,
the orang lies down and draws over himself and interlaces the remaining twigs, which are piled up, so that a domelike roof covers him
completely. Presumably, this nest is supported by the crotch of a
stout limb and its interlaced foundation may be made of partially
broken-off limbs or of wholly detached boughs.

There is some difference of opinion in regard to the roof of the
nest; but whether or not it is actually interwoven, there seems to be
little doubt that the ape covers himself with twigs and leaves. The
animal lies in the nest on its back or on its side, with at least some of
its extremities firmly grasping a convenient and stout bough. Some
observers claim that the nests are built fairly low down in trees—25
to 40 feet aboveground—where they will be out of the wind. Others
state that the nests are placed in the treetops. Probably there is a good
deal of individual variation in this matter. Also the contention of certain authorities is that the branches are piled crosswise, but not interlaced. The nests are said to be 2 or 3 feet in diameter. It is not known
whether the orang-utan builds a new nest every night, but, from the
analogy of the chimpanzee, this is very likely. One writer states that
the orang never uses a nest after the leaves in it have become dry
and withered.

In this nest, piled or woven, low or high, new or old, the orang
sleeps all night, often snoring heavily.

EATING AND DRINKING

Little is known of the diet of the orang-utan. It is generally assumed
that these apes subsist upon fruits, leaves, buds, shoots, and barks
which are indigenous to Borneo and Sumatra. They certainly are
frugivorous and undoubtedly inhabit these islands and, consequently,
they must live on these native products, unless they have cunningly
concealed an altogether unexpected carnivorous regimen. Carpenter,
who has recently made a quick survey of wild-life conditions of the
orang-utan in northern Sumatra, says that little is known of the native
foods upon which the animal feeds. He states that everyone agrees
that orangs are primarily fruit eaters. He himself saw them eating
leaves and bark in addition to fruit. The staple food of the orang is
traditionally the durian or jack fruit. This fruit grows upon a very tall

[11]Yerkes, R. and A., 1929, p. 121, quoting Sokolowsky, etc.

tree which is cultivated for this product. The fruit is very large, with a thick, hard rind, entirely covered with sharp, strong spines. It has a disagreeable, civetlike odor, but is regarded as delicious by the natives of the Malayan area. The part eaten by man is the custardlike pulp in which large seeds are imbedded. The seeds are also roasted and eaten or pounded into flour. The orang is said to waste a great deal of this food, throwing the rejected rinds on the ground. Someone has suggested that the animal bites off a few of the prickles and then makes a small hole into which it inserts its fingers and pulls out the pulp.

In captivity the orang is very adaptable as regards diet, although a natural vegetarian.

The orang-utan, when thirsty, is supposed to protrude the lower lip like a great ladle and catch enough rain for its needs. If the orang is given a cup from which to drink, he will pour its contents into this lower-lip trough, from which it is then sucked into the mouth. Young orangs also suck up water through their funneled lips, and sometimes dip their hands and lick them off. But captive orangs may also drink directly from the edge of a cup as do human beings. In fact, data suggest that this animal is highly adaptable in its eating and drinking habits and probably individually variable, even in a state of nature.

SOCIAL LIFE

Virtually nothing is known of the family and social life of the free-ranging orang-utan. It is reported that the males live alone, except in the mating seasons, and that two or three females, with infants, and accompanied by semidependent young, are often seen together. One observer states that the orang family group consists of a male, a female, and their young, and that the latter leave the family group at the age of 3 years, but this information is not fully authenticated.

There seems to be a general agreement upon the lack of gregariousness of this great ape and upon his migratory habits. In Sumatra orang-utans are found only in the district of Atjeh at the extreme northern tip. Even here the orang population is not dense. They range from sea level up to an altitude of about 1,500 meters, but show a marked preference for the lower altitudes. Reports from the west coast of Sumatra indicate that the orangs come down from the higher regions when certain kinds of fruits, especially durians, are ripe. Although orangs are supposed to travel long distances, natives in Atjeh assert that some families of orangs have lived in the same territory for 20 years or more.[12]

[12]Carpenter 1938, p. 16.

PREGNANCY AND REPRODUCTION

The duration of pregnancy in the orang-utan is 9 months. During this period recent observations have shown that the prospective mother develops an unmistakable and extensive genital swelling.[13] Such swelling is a marked feature of the menstrual cycle of the chimpanzee, but is diminished during pregnancy. In the case of the orang-utan it has been noticed only during pregnancy. The sexual skin in both lowland and mountain gorillas undergoes swelling also during the menstrual cycle. Such swelling, either during the menstrual cycle or during pregnancy, is almost certainly lacking in the gibbon.

As far as is known to the present writer, there is no eyewitness account of an orang-utan birth. In the Philadelphia Zoological Garden 2 Sumatran orangs were mated in 1928, a female, Maggie, with an estimated weight of 130 pounds, and Chief, supposed to weigh about 175 pounds. During the early period of pregnancy Maggie suffered from constipation and her appetite was poor. Toward the end the prospective mother became irritable and peevish. One morning the keeper found her tenderly licking an apparently normal baby, still wet and with the cord and placenta still attached.[14] Maggie cuddled the baby all the day, but made no attempt to put it to the breast. The following morning the baby seemed to be searching for something with its mouth, at one time sucking on the mother's ear. By this second day the mother had become more interested in the cord and the placenta, and at 10 A.M. she took hold of the cord with her teeth, severed it close to the baby's abdomen, and then pushed the placenta over against the bars of the cage. She then immediately took up the baby and held it against her breast. It promptly found the nipple and began to nurse. A few minutes later the mother emerged for the first time since the birth from the shelter to which she had retired at the time of the parturition, climbed to the roof of the shelter, holding the baby, and began a thorough examination of her offspring. The keeper took advantage of her absence from the den to clean it thoroughly and to put in a fresh straw bedding in the end where she customarily slept. When Maggie saw the clean bedding, she at once went in and transferred it to the other end, to which she and the baby retired for their midday nap.

[13]Schultz 1938, pp. 363–66.
[14]Fox, Herbert, "The Birth of Two Anthropoid Apes," *Jr. Mammal.*, vol. 10, 1929, pp. 37–51. Quoted by Yerkes, R. and A., 1929, p. 144.

INFANCY

Scientific observations of the infancy of the orang-utan are not available. Alfred Russell Wallace captured a specimen which was approximately a month old at the time the mother was shot and weighed 3 pounds 9 ounces. It was 14 inches tall. When it fell to the ground it broke a leg and an arm, but the injuries healed so rapidly that they were not discovered until the animal died after 3 months in captivity. A few days after this baby orang was captured it cut its first milk teeth—the two lower incisors. Since no milk was available, the little animal was fed on rice water, with sugar and coconut milk added occasionally. It soon learned to suck very well. It was quiet when handled or nursed, but cried when left alone. The mat in the box fitted up for it was changed and cleaned every day, but the orang was uncomfortable when it dirtied itself and cried until it had been washed. It seemed to enjoy being bathed and having its hair brushed out. The grasp of the baby was most tenacious, and its feet and hands were always reaching for something to seize—its own hair for want of anything better. Wallace made a short ladder to enable the animal to exercise arms and legs by clinging to it. After a week it was fed upon solid food, which it ate with great satisfaction if it was palatable. If the food was not sufficiently sweet, or otherwise displeasing, it would turn the mouthful about with its tongue and then push it out between its lips. If the effort to make it take unliked food was continued, the orang would scream and kick.

After 3 weeks Wallace obtained a very young macaque monkey which he placed in the same box with the orang. They at once became excellent friends. The monkey was far more advanced in every respect. It could dash around and use its hands with precision, whereas the orang lay on its back quite helplessly and could scarcely guide its hands to grasp an object. After about one month it showed some signs of learning to move. When laid on the floor it would push itself along with its legs or roll over. Lying in the box, it would grasp the edge and pull itself up into an almost erect position. After 5 weeks it cut its upper front incisors. During the whole period the animal had not increased its weight and frequently suffered from diarrhea. It died after a life in captivity of about 3 months.

The life span of the orang is not accurately known. Zuckerman gives the maximum life in captivity as 26 years 6 months. Other specimens in captivity have had estimated ages of from 50 to 60 years.

GROWTH

The one complete record of the pregnancy of an orang-utan, reported by Aulmann in Düsseldorf, gives the duration as 275 days or 39 weeks, as contrasted with 38 weeks in man and 34 weeks in the chimpanzee. In the animal born from this pregnancy the milk teeth were erupted at the end of the first year, the first permanent molars erupted in the middle of the fourth year, the canines and last molars in the ninth and tenth years. Growth was complete between the tenth and twelfth years.[15] In the chimpanzee the completion of the second dentition and cessation of growth come at the average of 10 years and 3 months.

The birth weight of 3 orangs averages 1.50 kilos (3.31 pounds). In the case of both chimpanzee and orang, the birth weight relative to weight of adult females is about 4 per cent, as against approximately 5.5 per cent for man and 6.7 per cent for the macaque. Thus these ape babies are born relatively small.

Orangs attain sexual maturity very early, since several mothers have been found with incomplete dentitions and the epiphyses of the long bones (the caps which are united to the shafts at the end of growth) recently fused. On the other hand, some orang mothers with young babies were apparently very old animals. The one orang observed from birth to maturity nursed for 6 years. He is the only animal who has been measured during growth and, unfortunately, the measuring period extended for only one year. The general changes of bodily proportions during growth may be summarized from Schultz, who has utilized all available data, but depends principally upon his own extensive studies of many dead specimens at different growth stages.

The orang trunk, as in other primates, becomes more slender during growth, but in adult males gets stouter again. Relative shoulder breadth decreases. The proportionate width of the pelvic inlet becomes greater during growth and is much larger in the female than in the male. The chest becomes broader and relatively shallower. Limbs grow faster than the trunk in prenatal life and the reverse is true after birth. Relation in length between upper and lower limbs remains almost constant. Leg and thigh relations do not change, but the forearm grows more rapidly than the arm. Hands and feet grow more rapidly than the trunk in fetal life, but thereafter more slowly. Both become more slender with advancing age, and the thumb gets

[15]Schultz 1941, p. 63, quoting Aulmann, G., "Geglückte Nachzucht eines Orang-utan im Düsseldorfer Zoo," *Zool. Gart.*, vol. 5, 1932, pp. 81–90.

relatively shorter. Webbing of the fingers and toes is unknown in the orang. The relative length of the toes increases during growth.

The head of the orang-utan becomes relatively smaller during growth. Cranial capacity at birth is 40 per cent of ultimate size, at 2 years 90 per cent, and at 6 years 97 per cent. At birth the balance of the head on the spine in the orang-utan is about the same as in man. However, after birth the face grows rapidly and the skull becomes less well balanced on the spine. The length-breadth, or cephalic index, does not change significantly during growth, but the corresponding index on the bony skull decreases. In adults it ranges from an excessively long-headed to a very round-headed value. Height of the skull does not change in relation to other cranial diameters. The maximum breadth of the skull is attained at a comparatively early age, but the breadth of the face and that of the orbits increase enormously during growth.

The orbits, or eye sockets, of the orang migrate from beneath the brain forward and upward during growth and increase in size, relatively as well as absolutely. Similar growth changes occur in the gorilla and chimpanzee, but not in man.

VOCALIZATION AND SPEECH

The orang is not a highly vocal animal. It does grunt, chuckle, and, on occasion, scream. William H. Furness has been the only serious student of the orang-utan's capacity for articulate speech.[16] It would be more accurate to describe Mr. Furness as the only successful teacher of human speech to the orang-utan. In 6 months of daily training a young female orang-utan learned to say "Papa." The word was selected because it is a primitive sound and combines the use of the lips and an expired vowel sound, such as chimpanzees and orangs naturally employ. Furness repeated the lip movements and the sound again and again until, finally, the little animal learned to imitate him and associated the name with him. He then started on the word "cup," using a bone spatula to press the orang's tongue back in her throat and then placing his finger over her nose to induce her to breathe through her mouth. After a long course of training she managed this sound and used it with facility thereafter. Unfortunately, her education was soon terminated by death.

The ability of this orang to understand human language was far

[16]Furness, William H., "Observations on the Mentality of Chimpanzees and Orang-utans," *Proc. Am. Phil. Soc.*, vol. 55, 1916, pp. 281–90. Quoted by Yerkes, R. and A., 1929, pp. 164–65.

superior to her capacity for articulation. Furness was wholly convinced that she understood a great many expressions and associated names with the persons or objects which they were supposed to designate. One day he carried this orang into the swimming pool with him. When the water came up to her legs she was terrified, clung to his neck with her arms, kissed him, and kept saying, "Papa! Papa! Papa!" One night when she was lying ill in her hammock, she leaned out and said, "Cup, cup, cup." She was apparently thirsty.

INTELLIGENCE

Persons who have kept captive orangs and have observed their behavior are usually deeply impressed by the "intelligence" of this animal. The experimental psychologist considers these amateur appraisals of animal intelligence to be of little or no scientific value, since the person making the judgment is likely to read into the behavior of the animal emotions, ideas, motives, and objectives which are not there at all. Fond owners of pets anthropomorphize the beasts which they cherish. The scientific student of animal intelligence attempts to control all the factors in an experimental situation and to set for the animal some problem, the solution of which answers a specific question of mental capacity. Unfortunately, even these elaborate experiments often produce ambiguous results.

If you show an animal an image of itself in a mirror, its interest, or lack of it, in the phenomenon is supposed to give the observer some clue as to the extent of its visual perception. However, when we are informed that an orang recognizes its image in a mirror and responds to it, we are not very much "forrader." Just as I wrote this sentence, I decided to try this mirror business on my young cat which was playing about my study. The cat paid no attention whatsoever to the mirror image. However, I have seen other cats which seemed to be temporarily interested in their mirror images, and the same cat may behave differently in such a situation on different occasions. Of course, I am perfectly willing to admit that an intense interest in one's own reflection indicates some sort of perception superior to that of the animal which apparently sees nothing in the mirror but a shiny surface. Nearly every kind of primate, down to a tarsier, is supposed to manifest this degree of perception or intelligence, or whatever it is. Of nearly every primate which has been kept as a pet, it is also alleged that the animal shows interest in pictures of animals and some discrimination between various objects delineated. Naturally, accounts of such behavior in orangs are to be found in anecdotal literature. Garner, an early and little-esteemed student of anthropoid apes, tried to teach an orang to put a round, red peg into a round hole in a red box and a square, green block into a square hole in a green box, or something of that sort. He found that, when the ape fitted the round peg into the round hole or the square peg into the square hole, he persistently followed up this success by trying to put the next peg into the same hole, regardless of shape and color.

Furness tried to teach an orang and a chimpanzee color discrimination and thought that he had succeeded. However, he discovered that the animals were interpreting his glances and attitudes of approval or disapproval rather than basing their choices upon color.

Fooling is less prominent in orang behavior than in that of many monkeys, perhaps, as Yerkes thinks, because orang curiosity is more directed toward exploratory, experimental, and observational activity. Yerkes thinks it probable that curiosity in the orang is much stronger than in the gorilla and gibbon, although probably less developed than in the chimpanzee. One orang, which was being hunted, repeatedly reached out his hand to investigate the places where the bullets which missed him had hit the branches and trunk of the tree. Young orangs readily imitate human beings in such activities as spitting, walking, using a cane, etc., but they do not ordinarily attempt imitation of sounds.

One story of orang sagacity, quoted by Yerkes and Yerkes from an anonymous source, is worthy of repetition.[17] This animal was fed at 5 o'clock. Every day when the clock struck he descended a rope from the ceiling and set it into pendulum motion, so that he swung over to the door leading to the dining room. He rattled this lock until he was admitted and fed. One day the keeper put three knots in the rope, so that it was too short to swing him over to the door. The orang untied one knot and tried it; it was still too short. He untied the second knot; another failure. The third knot was tied high up on the rope. The orang did not attempt to untie it from below, because his weight would merely tighten the knot. He climbed up above, untied it with ease, and then swung to the door.

Hornaday, whose acquaintance with orangs both in the wild and in captivity was probably as extensive as that of any other observer, was of the opinion that the mentality of the orang-utan is quite up to that of the chimpanzee, although the latter is the more alert and showy animal and a better actor. It is for this reason that animal trainers generally select the chimpanzee. The orang is also handicapped in the arboreal specialization of the foot with its very long outer toes and

[17]Yerkes, R. and A., 1929, p. 177.

short great toes. Having known intimately some 40-odd orangs at the New York Zoological Park, Hornaday was prepared to assert that these animals are as cheerful in disposition, as active, and as fertile in droll performance as chimpanzees. He enumerated a large number of feats which were taught to orangs without great difficulty. These include sitting at a table and eating like human beings, utilizing all the various table paraphernalia, lighting and smoking cigarettes, riding bicycles, dressing in human clothes and undressing, driving nails with a hammer, selecting the right Yale key and unlocking boxes and doors.

Several orangs seem to have discovered for themselves the use of the lever. One of the animals used the bar of a trapeze to pry apart the vertical bars of his cage so that he could get his head through the space. This same ape did various tricks with ropes of straw which he twisted for himself. I have seen young orangs in the New York Zoological Park doing this feat. They made a rope of straw, looped it around the horizontal bar of a trapeze, then twisted it and swung from it.

Yerkes credits M. E. Haggerty with the pioneer scientific studies of the orang-utan. This observer worked with two female orangs who were estimated to weigh 100 pounds apiece and were probably more than 4 years old. He devised a couple of experiments which are very similar to those later employed by Yerkes in studying the mountain gorilla, Congo. The first of these involved the use of a stick with a hook on the end of it. The subject was supposed to use the stick to spear a banana placed on a table out of reach outside of the bars. Both orangs managed this problem nicely. The other experiment required the animal to use a stick to poke through a piece of food lodged in the middle of a horizontal pipe. The more intelligent of the two orangs solved this problem after various efforts, including an attempt to push the food through with a straw. The second animal failed to get at the food until she was shown how her more clever mate accomplished the feat. She then did it easily.

Yerkes himself has carried out the most extensive experimental studies which have been performed with the orang-utan, although these are the earliest published primate studies of this veteran observer (issued in 1916).

Multiple-choice problems require the animal to select from a row of boxes, or a series of doors, some specific box or door which gives access to a reward. In various settings the correct choice may always be farthest to the left, the middle one, or alternation of one end box and then the other. Obviously, various problems of increasing complexity may be set with these devices, which have now become standard procedure in working with primates and with other experimental animals.

In this particular series of experiments Yerkes used Julius, a young male orang aged 4 to 5 years, and two macaque monkeys.[18] Julius was a healthy, docile, and friendly animal who weighed 34 pounds, stood 32 inches, and had a chest girth of 23 inches. Two months later he had gained 2½ pounds, one inch in stature, and 2 inches in chest circumference.

The first problem set for Julius was the box at the extreme left. He quickly adapted himself to the experiment, but made no progress for the first week in solving the problem. He persisted in choosing the nearest door and on the last day of the first week made only 3 correct choices in 10 trials. The next morning he made a whole series of correct choices, and, thereafter, even when the settings were radically changed, continued to succeed rapidly and without error. Thus the solution was sudden, or as Yerkes puts it, "ideational." One of the macaques solved this problem in half the number of trials required by Julius, the orang, and the other macaque in one fourth of the number. Yet the orang-utan learned, apparently, not as did the monkeys—by a gradual elimination of errors—but by a sudden dawning upon his mind of the correct method of attacking the problem.

The second problem set for Julius was the second box from the right end. He failed to solve this problem after 1,380 trials. During this long and arduous series he developed the habit of entering the reaction chamber, making a complete turn to the right, and then entering the box nearest him. This habit could not be broken. He showed a tendency to mix his methods without approaching a solution. The third problem was the box at the extreme right, and for this problem Julius developed the habit of selecting the box second from the right, which would have been correct for the preceding problem. He became very discouraged and dropped into the practice of trying to locate the correct box by trial and error. Yerkes thought that he tried to substitute ideational solution for learning by trial and error, but failed.

Next, Yerkes devised the box-stacking experiment, which has since become so familiar to primate students. A banana was suspended about 6 feet above the floor of the cage and well away from the sides. Two boxes were placed on the floor of the cage some distance away from the suspended banana. The only way in which the animal could obtain the reward was by stacking the 2 boxes in a position nearly directly underneath the banana and then climbing up to reach the prize. From the very first Julius made well-directed efforts to get the

[18]Yerkes 1916.

banana, several from the larger of the 2 boxes, very well placed. He also attempted to get Professor Yerkes to stand directly underneath, so that he could climb up his person to reach the fruit. His attention was concentrated, his efforts persistent, and his methods varied. Yet he failed to solve the problem after many trials and gradually became completely discouraged and refused to try. Then Dr. Yerkes decided to find out whether Julius could get the solution through imitation. The professor put the boxes into proper position and climbed up on them to show the ape that the bananas were within reach. It took several days for him to learn the solution, after having been shown. Having once succeeded, he concentrated upon a careful and efficient method of placing and stacking the boxes, and thereafter met the situation with constant success and perfect confidence. Yerkes felt that the entire series of experiments showed that Julius did not work by trial and error, but succeeded only when he grasped the idea.

Given a long pole or stick as a means of getting the banana, with no boxes available, Julius did not use the pole to strike at the fruit, as a human being would naturally use it. He placed the pole vertically on the ground, grasped it with his feet about 15 inches above the floor, and near the top with his hands, and then launched himself through the air at the banana. By this pole-vaulting method he succeeded after 3 trials. Another method he developed was to use the stick as a diagonal brace held against the side of the cage and grasped with one foot, while with one hand and the other foot he clung to the netting of the cage. By the use of this brace he was able to swing himself far enough out from the side of the cage to reach the banana with his free hand.

Yerkes also worked Julius upon a variation of the pipe-and-pole problem used by Haggerty. He used a very long, open-ended box, 4 inches wide and 4 inches deep. The lid was hinged and locked. Two poles were provided with which the animal could push through the banana placed in the middle of the long box. On the first day Julius worked at the lid, but did not touch the poles. On the second day he used the poles from the beginning and solved the problem in 24 minutes. Later on he became very expert and managed in a minute or two.

Getting a piece of fruit placed outside of the cage by means of a stick thrust through the bars and used to pull it in presented little difficulty to this animal. When first given the problem, he picked up a bag and tried to use it, then a bit of wire. As soon as the stick was placed in his cage, he went to work with it, at first unskillfully, using his left hand. However, in 5 minutes he managed to get 2 pieces of banana, and thereafter he used the stick successfully.

Since Julius had been observed to insert a splinter in the keyhole of a padlock and to work persistently with it, he was tried upon a locked-box experiment. A banana was placed in the box, the lid was closed, the padlock snapped, and Julius was given the key. He tried to get the box open in various ways, including the use of the key as a lever to pry open the lid, but he never tried to unlock the padlock with it. Probably, the assistant who saw Julius working at the lock with a splinter misinterpreted the animal's behavior. Certainly, he had not grasped the idea.

Drescher and Trendelenburg used 4 orang-utans, ages estimated from 2 to 4 years, with other primates in experimental tests which included the use of a rake to draw in food, use of a turntable to bring food within reach, use of a string or pole to obtain food, removal of an obstruction in the path to food, opening of the lid of a box which contained food, and the unbolting of the lid.[19] In the rake test an orang was clumsy but purposeful and succeeded. The authors note the inferiority of the orang-utan to monkeys in manual skill, but stress the superior insight and understanding of the anthropoid ape. The orang-utans were also successful in the turntable problem and in the string and pole tests. The observers were impressed by the smoothness of the orang solutions and by the extent to which the direction of the animal's eye movements indicated appreciation of the fundamentals of the problem. Objects placed as obstacles in the way of getting food were promptly, skillfully, and purposefully removed by the orangs. They had no difficulty with the closed-box problem, but in the case of the bolt they seemed to be inadequately motivated. They were more interested, apparently, in the mechanism than in getting the reward. Yerkes feels that these experiments must be accepted with reservation, because the students used zoological-garden apes whose previous background of experience with tools and in problem situations was unknown to them.

Memory in the orang has not been extensively studied. Various observers have reported temporal spans extending over more than a year, for localities, persons, and methods of solving problems.

DISPOSITION

The temperament of the orang-utan is generally described by such adjectives as stolid, depressed, melancholic, apathetic, phlegmatic, sad, grave, brooding, reflective, etc. Yerkes, whose observations on apes

---

[19]Yerkes, R. and A., 1929, p. 192, summarizing Drescher, K., and Trendelenburg, W., "Weiterer Beitrag sur Intelligenzprüfung an Affen (einschliesslich Anthropoiden)," Z. vergleich. Physiol., Berlin, vol. 5, 1927, pp. 613–42.

MOTHER ORANG-UTAN AND INFANT

Photograph Zoological Park .

Courtesy The Zoological Society of Ph.

YOUNG ORANG-UTAN DELINQUENT

are not the mere sentimentalizing of a pet fancier, nor the romantic impressions of a traveler, but rather the careful judgments of a trained investigator, says that the total effect of the orang-utan's appearance upon him is indicated by "such expressions as lack of ambition, of aggressiveness, of determination, and of energy; discouragement, pessimism, decision that effort is not really worth while."[20]

However, such descriptions apparently do not fit many young orangs, who are energetic, playful, and restless. Some mature orang-utans continue to be gentle and tractable, while others become irritable and dangerous to handle. Here, again, I am inclined to disregard the opinions of writers whose experience and competence is unknown to me and to depend upon Yerkes. He states that his personal experience with orang-utans has been limited to 4 captive animals. One of these, the famous Julius, was an immature male—childlike, affectionate, and docile. He contrasted in energy and playfulness with 2 females who were approaching sexual maturity, and even more so with an adult male.

EMOTIONS

One early observer attributes a feeling of shame to a female orang-utan who was alleged to use a foot, usually holding a piece of board or a wisp of straw, to cover her genitalia, in whatever position she might be. Yerkes knows of no parallel instance of behavior in an orang, but says that it has been noted in several chimpanzees. He rightly comments that to infer the existence of modesty or shame from such a circumstance is nothing more than a guess. But in any unusual situation an orang-utan may behave in such a way as to suggest preparedness for retreat or self-protection. Such instances of apparent timidity, reserve, or caution are commoner in young orangs than in adults.

Yerkes quotes with disapprobation various accounts by early writers on the orang which allege that that animal is afraid of turtles, snakes, etc., because none of these accounts includes any adequate description of fear behavior. But Deniker stated that an orang which he had under observation opened his mouth when excited or irritated, displaying his "great, clenched teeth, at the same time showing a minute movement of the middle of the upper lip, raised by the action of the canine muscle."[21] Impatience or resentment are sometimes expressed by the orang-utan by striking his breast, by throwing himself back-

[20] Yerkes, R. and A., 1929, p. 151.
[21] Yerkes, R. and A., 1929, p. 157, quoting Deniker, J., "Sur l'orang et le chimpanzé exposés par M. Bidel à Paris," Bull. Soc. Anth., Paris, vol. 5, 1882, pp. 333–41.

ward violently upon the floor, by beating his head repeatedly against the floor, or even by turning somersaults. This type of behavior, which is also shown by the chimpanzee and the gorilla in their youth, is virtually identical with the childish temper tantrums of man. The accompaniments of screaming, biting, kicking, and throwing the arms and legs about are the same.

Rage and fear in the adult male orang-utan are shown by muscular tenseness, erection of the hair, lips retracted to show the formidable teeth, cheek pads very stiff, laryngeal pouches inflated, eyes glittering, and by screaming or roaring. No one seems to have taken the trouble to observe the orang closely enough to describe the changes of facial expression which are indicative of joy, contentment, amusement, etc. Facial distortions, chuckling, grunting, and gurgling sounds have been identified with smiling and laughter, but Yerkes is very reserved in accepting such interpretations. The lips of the orang-utan and the chimpanzee are extraordinarily mobile and play a far more important role in facial expression than they do in the cases of man, the gorilla, and the gibbon. Yerkes states that, from his own observations of the orang, the lips are protruded only slightly, if at all, and may be held firmly together when the animal is contented or is enjoying something, but are funneled to express impatience, resentment, or appeal, as if to facilitate the sounds which the animal emits in these situations. As resentment develops into anger and rage, the protrusion of the lips may be exaggerated to the accompaniment of screaming, or the mouth may be opened widely and the lips drawn back.

Affection and sympathy are likely to be manifested by embracing and applying the lips to the person or object. Actual kissing in this ape and the other great apes is probably imitative.

There are few accounts of altruistic behavior in the orang-utan, and descriptions of co-operation in the family and species are also absent. Yerkes thinks it possible that the relative unsociability of this animal may account for the scarcity of observations of these types of behavior. He feels that, in general, the affective aspects of behavior in the orang-utan are virtually an untrodden field of investigation.

PATHOLOGY

Schultz has destroyed the illusion that wild animals are almost free from abnormalities of development and from disease. Among the 10 orang-utans which have been dissected, 2 have been found with vascular anomalies, and another with congenital inguinal hernia. Crowding and malocclusions of the dental arches have been observed frequently. In 217 orang skulls examined by Schultz no pathological conditions were found in infants and juveniles. Of 97 adult skulls, 81 had perfectly healthy teeth and no teeth had been lost in life. Alveolar abscesses occurred in 13.4 per cent of cases and caries in 4 specimens, or with a frequency of 4.1 per cent. In the skulls of 45 old orangs with marked wear of the teeth, loss of teeth during life occurred in 5 specimens, or 11.1 per cent, and alveolar abscesses in 60 per cent of cases (27 skulls) affecting a total of 95 teeth. In these old specimens caries was found in 13.3 per cent. Schultz says that the breakdown of the dental apparatus in orangs he has studied is never as thorough as in many old chimpanzees.

Anomalies of the skeleton are common in orang-utans. In 6.6 per cent of 166 orang skulls the cheekbone, or malar, is divided into two parts by a suture. This anomaly is found in 3.2 per cent of Japanese skulls and rarely in other series, but is probably commoner in Mongoloids than in other human stocks. Other skeletal anomalies include divided parietal bones, nearly occluded auditory meatus, premature closure of the sagittal suture, congenitally lacking and vestigial nasal bones, fused central bones of the wrist, various anomalies of the sternum, and many extreme variations of vertebrae and ribs. Healed fractures of bones were found by Schultz in 10 per cent of infants, 14 per cent of juveniles, and 33 per cent of adults. This very high proportion of broken bones is exceeded only by the percentage found in wild gibbons by Schultz (36 per cent). Other pathological conditions found in the bones include numerous cases of arthritic changes, infection of the maxillary sinus, various exostoses, bone abscesses, and abnormal curvatures.

Among 8 Borneo orangs Schultz found macroscopic intestinal parasites in 6 and muscular parasites in 4 (*Dirofilaria pongoi*).

The recuperative powers of wild orang-utans are evidently great, since none of the numerous animals studied by Schultz died of any of the injuries or diseases found in the skeletons and cadavers. All were shot by hunters.

Although many orangs have died in captivity, unfortunately there are almost no available autopsy records which give the cause of death. Internal parasites and disorders of the respiratory and digestive system are probably among the common causes.

ANATOMY

SKULL

A general description of the skull of the orang-utan has already been given in the text, but some more technical details should be added. The short, rounded brain case and the concave, hollowed-out face are the most obvious characters. The supraorbital ridges are molded above the oval orbits and are not confluent. The nasal bones are often fused into a single narrow splint. In a male skull in the Harvard collection this vestigial nasal roof does not even reach to the nasal aperture, the upper portion of which is formed by the maxillae.

The orbital fissures are very small. The lachrymo-ethmoidal articulation is fairly constant. Infraorbital foramina are usually multiple. In the norma lateralis a notable feature is the bent-out zygomatic arch. The temporal fossa is deep and the alisphenoid is channeled. Usually the articulation at pterion is spheno-parietal as in man, but Wood Jones says that the simian specialization, a fronto-temporal contact, is found in about one third of orang skulls. The glenoid fossa is shallow and has a long postglenoid process. There is no mastoid process, but there is, according to Sonntag, an occasional small styloid. The supramastoid crest is not unduly large. The occipital bone, though the attachments of the neck muscles extend up to a transverse crest, usually presents a posterior convexity. In the giant Sumatran orang described by Hill the area is flat and shelving downward and forward, as in the male gorilla. The plane of the foramen magnum is directed backward and the foramen itself is situated far back on the nuchal plane rather than upon the cranial base. The pterygoid plates diverge widely so as to enclose a deep fossa, and the external plate is often large. Sonntag says that the frontal bone has no proper sinus, although the bone is cancellous. However, the maxillary sinuses exist. The sphenoidal sinus is also reduced. The mandible is enormous with a high, broad ascending ramus, a recurved coronoid process, and a shallow sigmoid notch. The symphysis shows the usual anthropoid features, with the genial pit and the simian shelf.

ORGANS OF DIGESTION AND ABSORPTION

Man and the orang-utan are said to differ from all other primates in possessing the apical gland of Nuhn, a part of the basal mucous glands of the tongue which has become separated from the main mass. The orang has an elongated stomach with a well-marked fundus. Sonntag says that it is more like that of the chimpanzee than that of man. The intestinal tract is very long, the ratio of bodily length to that of the canal from the pylorus to the anus being 1 : 6.13, according to Sonntag. The vermiform appendix is long and spiral, as in the gorilla. Wood Jones says that the liver is large but simple, the fissures being reduced.

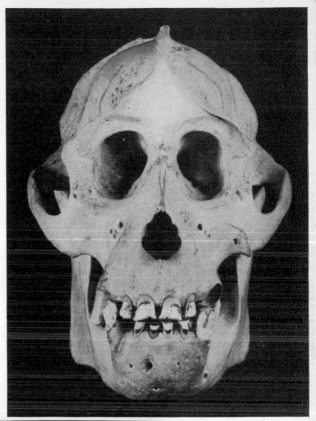

SKULL OF AN ADULT MALE ORANG-UTAN

Photographs F. W. Orchard
Courtesy Peabody Museum

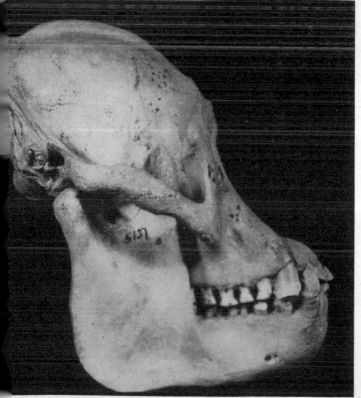

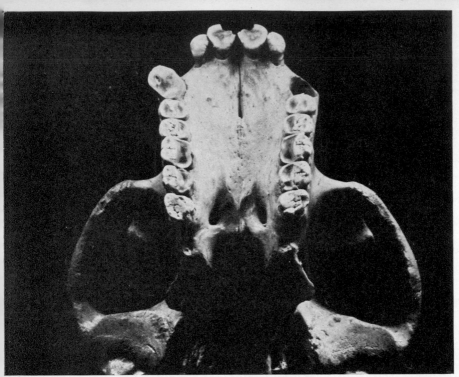

Photographs F. W. Orchard   *Courtesy Peabody Museum*

UPPER AND LOWER DENTAL ARCHES OF ADULT MALE ORANG-UTAN

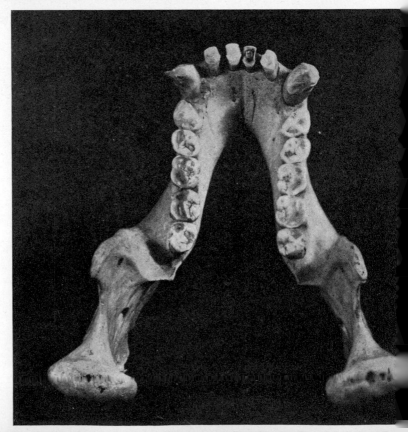

Organs of Respiration and Voice

Traditionally, the orang has no uvula, but Wood Jones says that the statement does not always hold true. The air sacs are very large and complicated; they increase in size with age and are more asymmetrical in the male than in the female. The two main sacs give off many diverticula, ramifying as far as the occiput above, the scapula behind, and the axillae laterally. When inflated, they form a balloon between the mandible and the sternum which extends laterally toward the ears.

The orang is said to stand apart from the other apes and to resemble sloths and marsupials in that the lungs are undivided.

External Genital Organs

The penis of Hill's adult male Sumatran orang is 120 mm. long, 18 mm. deep in the body, and 10 mm. from side to side. A short prepuce covers about half of the glans. There is a slight frenum in the mid-line ventrally. There is no sharp boundary between the caput and the collum of the glans. The meatus is a vertical slit looking downward without differentiated lips. There is a very small os penis in the glans. In the female the outer genital folds are not defined. The clitoris is prominent, grooved, and provided with a prepuce.

Urogenital Organs

The testes are small in comparison with the size of the animal. The spermatic cord is relatively attenuated. The prostate gland is small and has no tissue ventral to the urethra. The ovaries of the orang are stated by Saglik to resemble those of man most closely. The orang kidney has only one papilla.

Nervous System

The brain of the orang-utan has been considered by some investigators to be more like that of man than are the brains of the chimpanzee or gorilla. Sonntag regards the gorilla brain as most humanlike. The keels on the frontal lobes of the orang are said to be more marked than in the brains of the other great apes. In the Bornean orang-utans the anterior part of the insula is exposed, but in the Sumatran orang studied by Hill this island of Reil is completely covered.

CHAPTER IV

The Acrobatic Gibbon

DISTRIBUTION, GENERA, AND SPECIES

THE GIBBON FAMILY, Hylobatidae, is exclusively oriental. Gibbons are found in Assam, Burma, Siam, Indo-China, the Malay Peninsula, Hainan Island, and the British and Dutch East Indies. The animal ranges from sea level to altitudes of approximately 7,000 feet, where there may be frosts, and its limits are set apparently not so much by temperature as by forest zones which contain suitable food trees. The distribution and density of gibbons, as worked out by C. R. Carpenter, suggest that the world population of these animals is to be numbered in tens, if not hundreds, of thousands. The siamang, which belongs to the second genus of the gibbon family (*Symphalangus*), is found only on the island of Sumatra.

The gibbon is a small anthropoid ape which is intermediate, in many respects, between Old World monkeys and the giant primates.[1] The siamang is a larger animal than any gibbon and is considered by Schultz to approach more closely the great apes—especially the orang-utan.[2] As is quite usual, considerable disagreement exists in regard to the subdivisions of the gibbon family. Schultz recognizes two sub-genera: Hylobates proper with seven species, and Brachitanytes which includes but one species. The last is *H. klossi,* which seems to be a kind of dwarf gibbon resembling the siamang.

DESCRIPTION

SIZE

The average body weights of combined sexes of adult gibbons range from 5.2 kilos to 6.7 kilos (about 11.5 pounds to 14.8 pounds). Siamangs average 10.7 kilos (23.6 pounds) and are thus much larger than

[1]Schultz 1940b.
[2]Schultz 1933c.

gibbons. *H. lar,* the species studied by Carpenter in Siam as to its habits in the wild, and by Schultz as to its morphology, may vary in weight in a full-grown adult from as little as 3.9 kilos to 7.3 kilos. Since the females of the series of 80 gibbons studied by Schultz averaged 271 mm. in trunk height, whereas the males had a mean of only 269 mm., it is evident that sex differences in size among gibbons are insignificant. In this respect these small anthropoids contrast markedly with the great apes and even with man. Actually, Dr. Schultz states that, so far, no reliable secondary sexual differences in size or in proportions have been found in gibbons. In other apes the male can usually be distinguished by the far greater size of the canine teeth, by body bulk, which may be nearly twice as great as that of the female, and by a variety of other differences.

Measurements of the standing height of gibbons are not available, but it is usually said that the full-grown animal does not ordinarily exceed a stature of 3 feet. The siamang is somewhat larger.

PIGMENTATION AND COAT

The skin color of the gibbon is ordinarily black. The true gibbons have a thick, woolly coat of hair on most parts of the body. The hairs of the face are thinner and shorter, however, and the palms and soles are naked. In the siamang and the siamanglike *H. klossi* the hairs on the throat and chest are very sparse. Among all the Old World monkeys and apes the true gibbons have by far the densest coat of hair. For example, Schultz says that a square centimeter from the middle of the scalp bears an average of 910 hairs in Old World monkeys, 307 hairs in the great apes, and 2,035 hairs in gibbons. The same area from the middle of the back carries 866 hairs in monkeys, 276 hairs in the great apes, and 1,727 hairs in gibbons. However, the hairs grow much more sparsely upon *H. klossi* and upon the siamang. The former has an average of only 663 hairs per square centimeter on the scalp and 462 on the back, and the latter has closely similar averages. The coat color of the gibbon ranges from black through buff-tan or "champagne" and gray to white. The siamang has black fur with some yellowish white hairs on the lips, chin, and throat. The different coatcolors in gibbons are found in the same species and often in the same family group. The white-handed gibbon (*H. lar*) is said to be distinguishable by the pale color of the backs of the hands and feet and by a complete ring of white hairs around the naked, black face. However, this white ring is absent in some cases.

Generally speaking, the hair on the forearm of the gibbon points toward the wrist, whereas in the siamang it points toward the elbow.

The curious, siamanglike *H. klossi* is badly mixed up in this feature. Sometimes the forearm hair of this gibbon points one way and sometimes the other; even two arms of the same individual may have a different direction of hair tracts.

On the buttocks of the gibbon are naked areas called ischial callosities. These thickened horny layers of the skin overlie the haunch bones upon which the animal sits. Exaggerated developments of this feature are found in many of the Old World monkeys. Ischial callosities also appear sporadically in the great apes. Schultz found them in 36 per cent of 116 chimpanzees. In the gibbon they do not appear until after birth and actually replace primary fetal hair, whereas in the Old World monkeys they are present quite early in fetal life, before any hair is developed on the buttocks.

SKULL AND TEETH

Although the gibbon is a small animal, it has a relatively large brain. As a matter of fact, relative brain size is generally higher in small than in large animals, apparently because there is a more or less irreducible minimum of brain mass required for a complicated organism.[3] Students of the skull obtain a rough measure of brain size by taking the cubic capacity of the brain case. The range of average cranial capacities in different species of gibbons is from 87.1 cc. to 101.2 cc. The larger siamang has an average capacity of 124.6 cc. These capacities are of interest primarily in relation to body weight.

Data compiled by Eugene Dubois and augmented by Schultz give the following brain-weight–body-weight relations among some of the primates: the marmoset (which weighs only .335 kilo or .74 pounds) 3.82 per cent; the siamang 1.16 per cent; the gibbon (average of subgenus Hylobates) 1.67 per cent; rhesus monkey 1.43 per cent; adult white man 2.18 per cent; an orang-utan (weight 73.5 kilos or 162 pounds) .54 per cent. Since the marmoset is the most primitive of all the monkeys, it is clear that these brain-weight–body-weight ratios have more to do with size than with "intelligence."

The brain case of the siamang is much larger than that of the gibbon, but the palate of the former surpasses that of the gibbon to an even greater degree. The skull of the siamang is relatively lower and more pinched or constricted behind the orbits and the brow ridges. Since the entire dental apparatus of the siamang is relatively larger than that of the gibbon, the temporal muscles which work the jaws take up larger areas on the sides of the skull in the former animal.

[3]Schultz says that the brain of the house cat is .94 per cent of body weight, that of the lion only .18 per cent.

WHITE-FACED GIBBON

GIBBON IN SUSPENSORY POSTURE

Actually, in some male siamangs the temporal muscles meet in the center line of the skull and are attached to a low, bony crest, comparable with the much larger crest seen in adult male gorillas and orang-utans. Such a feature does not appear in the gibbon skull. The chin of the siamang is less receding than that of the gibbon.

In the gibbon there is a tendency toward tooth reduction, frequently marked by the decreased size or even suppression of the third molars (wisdom teeth), whereas the siamang displays no such degeneration and sometimes shows the addition of a fourth molar.

The skull of the gibbon impresses the observer who is familiar with the skulls of lower mammals because of the relatively large size of the portion which houses the brain. Viewed from above, the brain case is a well-filled oval. The side view shows a rather flat curve beginning over the root of the nose, rising to its greatest height at about the level of the ear holes, and finishing with a comparatively smooth convexity of the back of the skull. The forehead is low, but by no means devoid of elevation. Ridges for the attachment of muscles on the sides and back of the skull are not inordinately large. Above the very large, oval eye sockets the bony rims are somewhat thickened, but these brow ridges do not form the heavy bar or torus which is found in gorillas, chimpanzees, and many of the larger monkeys. The upper face is short, with broad, flat nasal bones which give little or no elevation to the bridge of the nose. The cheekbones, or malars, are small. Notable are the long, spikelike canine teeth, which interlock at the front corners of the jaws. The upper canines project downward so far that they nearly reach the level of the lower rim of the shallow mandible. The face of the gibbon is protrusive, but not nearly so snouty as that of the gorilla. The palate is relatively long and narrow and has a general U-shape. The jaws and dentition of the gibbon, like those of other anthropoid apes, are adapted for a frugivorous diet. The molar teeth are more primitive than those of other apes in that the upper molars are subtriangular with 3 main points or cusps, and the fourth, at the posterior inner corner, much smaller. The inner side of the upper molars is supported by an undivided root. The folds and wrinkles seen in the teeth of higher anthropoids are lacking. The lower molars have the 5 cusps found in all anthropoid apes and in man. The saberlike canines are a specialization either for fighting, for piercing the rinds of tough fruits, or for both purposes. The incisors are small, primitive, chisellike teeth, leaning forward and well adapted for holding and cutting fruit. The upper middle incisors are not greatly enlarged as in the big apes. The poise of the skull on the spinal column is that of an erect-sitting animal and not of a pronograde.

FACE

The face of the gibbon has a squashed-down appearance. Below a broad, flat brow the widely separated eyes are shallowly set in bony rings of which the relief is scarcely concealed by a covering of flesh and skin. From between these orbital rings there extends downward a pear-shaped bulge which includes the root, bridge, and tip of the nose, the mouth at the level of greatest convexity, and the receding chin at the base. Below the eyes the face seems to be caved in at the sides; the hinder angles of the jaws are not visible. The eye opening is high, with the upper lid especially strongly arched. The bridge of the nose is usually very low and there is virtually no tip—merely a slender partition between the nostrils, which slant backward and upward and are enclosed laterally by no wings. The mouth is wide and slitlike, with very thin membranous lips stretched over the bulge of the jaws. The ear of the adult gibbon, set close to the head, is relatively larger than that of any higher primate except the chimpanzee, but smaller than the ears of most monkeys. The gibbon ear shows patterns of folds which are like those of the orang. The upper and hinder rim, or helix, is well rolled and the inner windings are similar to those found in man. There is never a tubercle or point on the upper hinder angle of the helix, such as is found in many monkeys and sometimes in man. Nor has the gibbon ever the slightest trace of an ear lobe. Gibbon ears grow considerably from birth to maturity. The siamang has a smaller ear than the gibbon.

BODY PROPORTIONS

The trunk of the gibbon is stouter than that of monkeys. The relation of chest girth to trunk height is 103 in Old World monkeys, 150 in gibbons, and 162 to 223 in the great apes and man, according to Schultz. Monkeys have chests which are greater in depth than in width, while gibbons and the other primates show a reversed relationship. Similarly, the gibbon stands with the great apes and man in increased breadth of shoulders and hips. The nipples of gibbons lie somewhat higher than those of siamangs, and the latter have broader and flatter chests. High-lying nipples are characteristic of all of the primates below man.

The limbs of gibbons and siamangs are relatively much longer than those of monkeys. Schultz says that the total lower-limb length in percentage of trunk height is 96 in monkeys, 147 in gibbons, 112 to 131 in the great apes, and 171 in man. Thus the gibbon stands next to man in relative leg length. The elongation of the upper limb in the gibbon is enormous. Relative to trunk length, arm length in monkeys is 107, in man 150, in the great apes 154 to 184, and in the gibbon 238. The gibbon is more specialized in elongation of the upper extremity than man in the lower. Individual gibbons sometimes have relatively longer legs than the human average. The legs of the gibbon are comparatively longer than those of the siamang, the arms of the same proportionate length.

ARMS, HANDS, AND FEET

The hand of the gibbon has not been affected by the enormous lengthening of the arm as much as has the upper arm. Most of all, this elongation is concentrated in the forearm. In different species the length of the forearm ranges from 111.7 to 116.5 per cent of the length of the upper arm. The total length of the upper limb minus the hand ranges in various gibbon species from 126.5 per cent to 132.4 per cent of the total leg length (minus the foot). In the siamang this figure rises to 148.3 (Schultz). Thus the gibbon's enormously long arms allow its finger tips to touch the ground when it stands erect.

The gibbon hand length is about 23 per cent of total upper-limb length, as against 26 to 30 per cent in other apes and about 25 per cent in man. Thus the hand is not disproportionately long, but it is very narrow. Hand breadth is 23.8 per cent of hand length in the gibbon, 28.5 per cent in the siamang, 32.4 per cent in the orang, 34.8 per cent in the chimpanzee, 41.6 per cent in man, 58.6 per cent in the gorilla. The gibbon thumb branches from the palm very close to the wrist, but the larger part of the first metacarpal bone, which in man is imbedded in the palm of the hand, is a part of the "free" thumb. This condition is unique in the gibbon family among all the primates. These animals have relatively much shorter thumbs than man possesses but longer than those of the orang-utan and the chimpanzee. In the gibbon hand the second finger is also as long as or longer than the fourth—a condition entirely absent in monkeys but sometimes found in the anthropoid apes and in man.

The gibbon foot also has a very deep cleft between the great toe and the outer digits. The free portion of the great toe reaches far into the metatarsal region. This wide separation between the great toe and the outer toes gives increased flexibility to the foot and is of great advantage in grasping branches. The great toe of gibbons and siamangs reaches much farther forward than in orangs, but not so far as in chimpanzees. The siamang is called *Symphalangus* because the second and third toes are partially united by a cutaneous web. However, these digital webs are found not infrequently in gibbons and sometimes in chimpanzees.

POSTURE AND LOCOMOTION

The normal posture of the gibbon is upright, but, according to Carpenter, this animal has two positions of arrested locomotion—standing and swinging by the arms.[4] When the gibbon stands on the ground, the legs are somewhat bent, the body curved slightly forward, and the arms may be held in various positions from hanging at the sides to a flexure at the level of the shoulders. When the gibbon swings from a branch, it is supported by its long arms and the legs are partially bent. In such a position the line of the gibbon's vision is upward, since it has to judge distances from below branches, rather than from above the ground as in the case of quadrupeds. Hence a shift from swinging to walking involves an entirely different type of visuo-motor co-ordination.

The most common posture on a branch is sitting with the body bent forward and the knees doubled up nearly to the chin, the feet grasping the bough and the long hands folded over the knees. In sleep the head is buried between the knees and the animal looks like a ball of fur. The long, woolly fur mats down and protects the skin from rain and cold. However, the gibbon may stretch out to sleep in the daytime or even at night, if it is on a large enough branch. Sometimes it lies on its side, with the head resting on an upper arm and the legs flexed. It rarely reclines on its belly.

Carpenter's description of brachiating or arm-swinging of the gibbon is the first adequate analysis of this form of locomotion. He achieved this description by observation and by the analysis of slow-motion moving pictures. The fundamental motion in brachiation is that of a swinging pendulum. When the animal stops brachiating, it oscillates before coming to rest. A gibbon rises from a seated position on a limb, begins dropping to one side of the branch, extending the arm and hand nearest the branch, and then glides smoothly downward and forward, checking the glide at its bottom by grasping the limb with its fingers and establishing the fulcrum for the first half of the swing. The radius of the arc is about the equal of two thirds of the length of the gibbon's arm. As the gibbon swings down, it contracts its arm muscles, raising its body up nearer the branch. Then the free

4Carpenter 1940.

Hansel Mieth Courtesy Life Magazine

GIBBON ON PERCH

Photographs C. R. Carpenter

arm and hand are brought round to grasp the branch in a second contact 3 or 4 feet beyond the first grasp. This movement involves a high degree of rotation of the arm at the shoulder joint, and the second grasp may not be taken for an instant after the first is loosened. At the second contact the grasping arm is flexed, so that the animal is pulled forward by it and by momentum. In the second swing the body of the animal does not go quite so far below the support. In the swing the legs are drawn up toward the body. A gibbon covers about 20 feet in 2 or 2½ swings. It then may be necessary to jump. The gibbon antici-pates this leap by a forceful swing, which may bring it above the level of the branch on which it is traveling. It then hurtles through the air with the trunk bent forward, the limbs slightly flexed, and the arms flexed above its head ready to grasp the next branch. Altitude is gen-erally lost in jumping. If the animal lands on a solid branch after the jump, walking will probably then take the place of brachiation. The gibbon may then stand semi-erect with arms and hands held out to aid in balancing, elbows and wrists flexed. The legs are partially bent and the pelvis rotates as one foot is placed directly before the other. The weight is borne between the great toe and the outer toes. Swing-ing from bough to bough may be done by one or both arms, or when playing, by the feet.

Carpenter has watched many gibbons for protracted periods and estimates that about 90 per cent of their locomotion is brachiating. When walking on the ground, the young gibbon may use both arms and legs, or may hop through the arms, using them as crutches. An adult gibbon, newly captured, also walked on all fours, holding the legs fairly straight, the trunk bent forward, and the arms spread widely apart. It was of interest to note that the fingers were hyper-extended, so that the weight was borne on the palms and on the palmar parts of the second and third fingers. Captive gibbons, reared from infancy, apparently learn to walk in the upright posture much better than those captured in their maturity. Trained animals learn to walk more nearly upright, with less dependence upon the arms for balancing.

Gibbons climb vertical tree trunks easily, even those of large diam-eter. The wide separation of the thumbs and great toes from the other digits makes their hands and feet peculiarly adapted for climbing. The gibbon walks up trees with the rump away from the trunk and face and chest close to it.

Jumping is an important part of gibbon locomotion. Short or average jumps, up to 12 and 15 feet, are taken smoothly, almost as a part of a normal swing. In long jumps the ape glides downward and outward in an arc with the highest point of the arc above the branch from which it took off, owing to the initial upward swing. In such cases the gibbon lands by catching a branch with both hands. It is to be inferred that these animals have a very fast reaction time, well-co-ordinated visuo-motor capacities, and excellent judgment of distance and size. To fixate on an object and keep it in focus while leaping toward it requires a speed of visual perception which may surpass that of any other higher primate.

A gibbon about to make a big jump will swing back and forth several times to get the proper impetus and to set the body for the effort. Carpenter saw a female, under whom a branch had broken as she was about to make a big jump, turn in mid-air, grasp the 6-inch stub of the branch, swing around under, on top, and then, with practically no loss of momentum, make the long outward jump of 30 feet into the next tree. Mothers carrying infants are likely to make detours around the long jumps. In a 35-foot jump made by a group of animals in succession, contact at the end of the jump was made with a slender, flexible branch which projected out from a tree trunk otherwise limbless at this point. Each animal caught the branch and swung down on it to the trunk. As it approached the latter, it released its hold, caught the trunk with perfect timing, climbed up 20 feet, and then continued through the thick part of the forest. Carpenter notes that in jumping long distances the axis of the body approaches a horizontal position, the head and shoulders forward, the flexed legs extended backward so that "the maximum surface is exposed to vectors of air resistance which tend to check the force of gravity."[5] This posture has certain components of gliding, as exemplified by flying squirrels and flying foxes.

The bursts of speed in gibbon brachiation are sporadic and of short duration. A group moves rapidly for 5 or 10 minutes and then travels very slowly or stops. For distances of 800 to 1,000 yards a startled group of gibbons will move through the trees at a speed equaling a fast running pace for a man. Then, if unpursued, they slow down and move in a leisurely fashion. It was possible for Carpenter to keep a group in sight and watch it from ambush for the entire day.

There seemed to be little consistency of order of progression in group movements, contrary to what Carpenter observed in howler monkeys. Young adults, however, seemed generally to set the pace over well-traveled pathways; females with young usually brought up the rear; and there was no dominance of males over females in leadership.

[5]Carpenter 1940, p. 77.

Apparently gibbons cannot swim. Three times Carpenter threw an adult female into a calm pool, in which she thrashed around frantically, while her long, woolly fur became water-soaked. When she began to sink, Carpenter pulled her in by a cord attached to her hips. While feeling sorry for the gibbon, one must admire the thoroughness of Carpenter's investigation and his rich resourcefulness.

MANIPULATION

The gibbon's hand is a kind of anatomical hook by which it clings to branches. Its fingers are so long and its thumb so short that it cannot easily grasp small objects. The thumb is not clearly opposable to the finger tips. A small object is usually grasped between the side of the thumb and the side of the second joint of the index finger. Sometimes the hand is turned over with the palm down and the objects are grasped against the palm with little finger or thumb. The gibbon is not used to grasping objects on a flat surface. It can do much better in picking fruit suspended from a branch. The palm is very narrow in comparison with the width at the base of the fingers, so that the animal, in holding, for example, a lot of grapes, makes a cone of its fingers by flexing the little finger tightly against the palm and by bending the inner fingers successively less to form the sides of the funnel.

Gibbons use their teeth in holding objects and in preparing food. They often break off dead branches and drop them toward the observer. Carpenter thinks—and his conjectures have been experimentally verified—that gibbons in laboratory experimentation are less able to use objects as instruments than are cebus and rhesus monkeys.

FOOD AND FEEDING

Since the gibbon is a light animal and has four prehensile extremities, it can go out to the very end of branches, anchor itself there by one or two members, and use the rest for reaching food, plucking it, and transferring it to the mouth. It uses nearly every possible combination of hands and feet in these activities, within the limitations of holding on by at least one member. Most commonly, it suspends itself by one arm from a bough from which it plucks fruit with the free hand. The teeth are used for preparation of food, such as shelling and seeding.

Gibbons are not markedly competitive in their feeding. Dominant animals rarely take food away from the less aggressive. Even the young ones are usually permitted to eat in peace. A dominant animal sees that it gets its hands and feet full of food and then moves away to enjoy it at leisure, giving the others their chance. This more or less unselfish behavior is similar to that observed in howler monkeys and radically different from that of baboons. Gibbons do not gobble in the same hurried way as do the aforementioned monkeys. They frequently pick food and carry it away for a distance to eat it, contrary to the habits of howlers. However, Carpenter never observed that the gibbon stores food.

One day, Carpenter saw a gibbon swing out to the end of a branch, remove a bird's nest from between two twigs, transfer it with its contents to the feet, and swing back to a more solid branch. It then took the nest into its hands and removed and ate at least two eggs. Gibbons are rather "choosy" about their eating. Foods are examined carefully; pits, seeds, and even small decayed spots may be removed, and the skins dropped. This selection is made with tongue and teeth, although plenty of seeds are often found in the stomach. Sometimes a fruit is partially eaten and the rest dropped, whether from wastefulness, as in howlers, from fastidiousness, or from sheer satiety. On another occasion Carpenter observed a gibbon repeatedly placing its hand against a tree, leaving it there for a few seconds, and then bringing it to its mouth and licking it off. At first he thought the animal was collecting water from a hollow and drinking it, but when he examined the spot on the tree, he found there a large column of ants climbing the trunk at this point. It then appeared that the ape was collecting and eating ants.

From watching the gibbon eat and examining the stomachs of animals which had been "collected" (euphemism for "shot"), it was possible for our observer to make out a satisfactory diet list of this animal. Since his observations were restricted to March and the three succeeding months, the list would be enlarged, no doubt, by studies of the animal during the remainder of the year. About 80 per cent of the food was fruit, and most of the remainder leaves, buds, and flowers. Birds' eggs, young birds, insects, and ants provide the necessary protein.

The most important food is the fig, of various species. Next is a fruit called the bamoo, which is ovoid in shape and has a tough, rusty-greenish shell. It contains 10 to 12 seeds, each covered with a fruity, fibrous meat. The gibbons reject most of the seeds. This fruit ripens at the end of March and through April and is a gibbon staple. It is also eaten by bears, squirrels, and wild fowl. As part of the gibbon diet, Carpenter also mentions wild grapes, blue plums, mangoes, and unidentified foods, as well as a long list of things which go by unintelligible native or cumbrous botanical names. The reader may know what *Sapataceae manilkora* is or are, but the author does not, nor does he care.

<h2 align="center">DRINKING</h2>

Gibbons lick water from leaves, bark, and their own fur. A characteristic wild-gibbon method of drinking is to dip the fist into water and suck the drops from the hair of the back of the hand and knuckles. The hand is moved rapidly and repeatedly from the water to the mouth. It is, on the whole, a wasteful and inefficient method. Captive gibbons also drink by putting their faces directly to the water and sucking. Carpenter suggests that this method is somewhat disadvantageous to a free-ranging gibbon, since lack of snoutiness brings the eyes too close to the water, restricts the visual field, and leaves the animal relatively defenseless. Pools of water, springs, and the water which collects in the hollows of trees add to the supply collected on trees from rains and dews. Of course, the food of the gibbon has, for the most part, a very high water content.

A DAY WITH GIBBONS IN NORTHERN SIAM

Let us accompany Dr. C. R. Carpenter, the most experienced field observer of primates, in a day's study of gibbons near Doi Dao in northern Siam. Presumably, we have been put up overnight in the camp of the Asiatic Primate Expedition, situated in an open-shed guesthouse within the grounds of a clump of temples which have been erected around the mouths of caves near a spring sacred to Buddhists. This camp is about 1,400 feet above sea level. Near by, limestone peaks rise to the height of 7,000 feet. The natives of the region do not shoot or frighten the gibbons, partly because the area around the temple is protected, and partly because the animals are considered quasi-sacred, especially the buff-colored gibbons. The valleys in the region are narrow, and from their floors precipitous cliffs rise above the trees, making it possible to climb up these cliffs and view animals in the treetops of the thin and irregular forest in the valley. Parts of the valleys and foothills are cultivated, so that the jungle of false teak, fruit trees, and bamboos is broken by clearings, through which the animals can be seen to travel. Since it is April, and many of the trees have shed their leaves, foliage does not obscure one's view overmuch. Yet there is enough moisture, and frequent islands of evergreens and fruit-bearing trees provide the gibbons with plenty to eat and drink. We can get through the forest by means of the network of trails made by natives searching for bark, roots, fruit, orchids, and choice teak trees.

We have to get.up early to follow Dr. Carpenter in his daily round of observations,.since he locates a group by their early-morning calls, and he may follow them and watch them until late in the afternoon. If it happens to be a foggy, dark, cool morning with the temperature at about 45° F., we shall not hear the gibbons calling until about 7 o'clock, and the groups will not move for another hour. If, however, the temperature is about 65°, the calls begin more nearly at 5:30 A.M. The group is likely to move in half an hour to an hour.

Having located a group, we take our place on a cliff or in a blind, remaining very quiet, and watching through binoculars, with cameras ready for a chance shot, if opportunity should offer. The first signs of the gibbon group's awakening are the mild stirring around and playing of the youngsters, with occasional desultory picking of food. If there is a nursing infant in the party, it receives its breakfast. Then the adults begin to make their early-morning calls, which arouse other groups in the vicinity so that they answer. These discrete calls continue off and on for the next hour or more. In the meantime, there is some languid feeding and sleepy play. After a while the group sets off on its real business, which is to seek some definite feeding place. Each animal follows the temporary leader. If the distance is 800 to 1,000 yards, they swing swiftly along an arboreal pathway for a few minutes and then stop and loiter, perhaps encountering another group. In such a case they begin. to call to each other in a manner different from the morning calls. These meeting calls are rather long-drawn-out series of sounds which rise in pitch and power until the crescendo breaks off and dies away in a few diminuendo notes. If there is a competition for a food tree, both groups stand and they indulge in a vocal battle, until one or the other gives ground. After a considerable period of hanging about, serious feeding begins at about 8:30 or 9 A.M. The gibbons continue eating deliberately for about 2 hours, plucking food, peeling or shelling it, and removing seeds before eating. As each animal becomes satiated, feeding gradually ceases; the young play about or groom; the mother cares for her infant or rests, and the male also rests or watches for strange gibbons or other disturbing possibilities. The whole group then moves to a shady or protected place and indulges in a siesta period, resting, grooming, etc. After about 3 hours the group moves again toward another food tree, but less directly and more slowly. If it rains, they stop and each gibbon sits hunched up in a ball of fur until the rain is over, after which active grooming precedes the next journey. After the second period of feeding, the group moves back over some pathway, usually familiar, to a tree where it settles down for the night after mild activity. Sleeping begins soon after sundown and lasts for about 11 hours. During the day the gibbon group will travel between 1,800 and 2,000 yards, usually within its own territory, which is about 45 acres in extent.

Gibbons lodge in trees which have rather dense tops, but they do not build nests. They use these trees, which are in the center of their range, regularly, often returning to them nightly for a couple of weeks.

SIZE OF GROUP AND FAMILY

In a single area of northern Siam, Carpenter studied 21 gibbon groups totaling 93 individuals. The groups ranged in size from 2 to 6 animals, the minimal group being a pair, and the maximal families with 4 young. The commonest number was 4—parents and 2 young. In the population of 93 were 22 adult males, 21 adult females, 11 infants still carried by their mothers, and 39 juveniles independent of their mothers and ranging up to young adults. Thus it is clear that the typical gibbon family consists of a father, mother, and their young. In one group were 3 males: one in his prime, a.probably senile individual with badly worn and broken teeth, and a very young adult. Carpenter thinks that the old fellow was reproductively ineffectual, the young one just reaching the stage where he would leave the parental group, and that the mature, vigorous male was the dominant member. In another group with 2 adult females, one was probably just below the age of ovulation. Probably she also was about ready to leave the parental group. An examination of her vaginal smear revealed the presence of no spermatozoa.

Solitary animals were sometimes encountered, but Carpenter thinks that these are ordinarily in the stage of transition to some new group. He doubts that all solitary animals are aged and sexually incapable males. Often such old men are tolerated within the social group. The solitary animals, probably of various ages, seemed to be making contact with, or attempting to join, other groups.

LAND TENURE AMONG THE GIBBONS

Gibbon families do not wander about aimlessly, irrespective of the direction they go and the place where they ultimately "bring up." On the contrary, each group has a fairly well-defined territory and stays within it, using well-known arboreal pathways and resorting to particular food and lodging trees. The natives in northern Siam know very well that a certain gibbon group lives in a specific area. Such "territoriality" was confirmed by Carpenter, who mapped the estates of 11 different groups. Some of the boundaries between groups were not too well defined; and, as a result, some strips, including certain food trees, made up a sort of no man's land where groups were likely to meet and contest for occupancy. The amount of territory covered by a gibbon group depends upon the number of animals in the group, the size and type of forest, the amount of food available, competition from other groups, including human beings, and other obvious considerations. Carpenter estimates the area of land occupied by a single group to be between 30 and 100 acres. It is important to note that gibbon territory is three-dimensional, because it includes the height of the forest. Space occupied by gibbons is cubic, and the square area need not be so large in lofty, thick, tropical rain forest as in low, mixed bamboo, and deciduous woods. Again, Carpenter notes that different primates have their own preferences as to the parts of trees through which they range. Marmosets and capuchin monkeys of South America occupy the entire tree from its topmost branches to the ground. Gibbons, however, stick fairly closely to the middle parts, where sturdy branches interlace with those of adjacent trees and thus furnish convenient trails. Carpenter never saw a gibbon in a clear space on the ground out of contact with trees or bushes, although he occasionally saw animals descend to pick up fruit or to take a drink. He doubts that gibbon family groups migrate for any great distances.

Often when two groups meet in no man's land a vocal battle takes place. Members of both of the families get very excited, and threatening and aggressive as well as retreating movements are frequent.

INTERGROUP RELATIONS

Limitation of territorial range is doubtless dependent upon the food supply. If one group attempts to invade the feeding district of another, the owners rush out and try to drive it away by threatening actions and cries. The gibbon family also apparently becomes accustomed to certain trails, food trees, and shelter trees, and feels at home within its own estate. When there was a strip or region which seemed to be common ground, Carpenter observed that some groups were consistently dominant over others in competition for the various food trees in this no man's land. However, if the one group had intruded rather deeply into the territory of another, it was usually dislodged. The victory seemed to lie with that group which was nearest the focus of its own estate or range.

COMMUNICATION

Friendly gibbons have a characteristic form of greeting when they have been separated for some time. They approach rapidly, slow down as they near each other, and give the gibbon equivalent of a smile (drawing back the lips to show the teeth, and often sticking out the tongue). Their movements in approach are gentle and relaxed, the arms held flexed above the shoulders if they are walking, the legs drawn up and spread apart if they are brachiating. They embrace, with one arm and both feet if swinging, with both arms if walking. Each gives a little squeal, which increases in pitch as they reach the climax of the embrace. This type of greeting is likely to be followed by grooming or other more intimate activities; it is not usually the prelude to quarreling. The relaxation of the movements in such contacts is marked. The backs of the hands are held forward in a position unsuitable for striking. When a tame gibbon approaches a human friend, it may protrude its lips, squint, and make a soft, clucking sound.

The angry and aggressive gibbon repeatedly opens and closes its mouth, as if clicking its teeth together and smacking its lips. The animal is tense, restless, and sly in its approach. Jumping up and down and shaking supports indicate rage. If a gibbon becomes annoyed or frustrated, it throws back its head, raises its flexed arms to the shoulder level, and shakes both them and its head. If the animal gets wet or is bored by a difficult choice problem in experimentation, it may behave in the same way. In such situations it sometimes yawns.

Carpenter used elaborate apparatus for recording sounds made by the gibbons. Distant calls were caught by the use of a large parabolic reflector and a microphone.

Gibbons are vociferous animals. Carpenter has recorded 9 types of vocalizations, each with a probably definite communicative function. The calls which can be heard at a distance have an early peak between 7:30 and 8:30 each morning and diminish until about 11 o'clock. From this time to 2:30 P.M. calls are rarely heard. Also in the afternoon, up to the settling down for the night, calls are infrequent. During windy, stormy days the frequency of calls is greatly reduced. The most characteristic and prominent type of gibbon call is heard in competitive situations when two or more groups come together and compete for food or for established territory. In situations where rhesus monkeys would ordinarily fight, gibbons and siamangs, like howler monkeys, roar back and forth.

Type I calls consist of a series of hoots with rising inflection and pitch, and increasing tempo, with a climax followed by 2 or 3 lower notes. Such calls last from 12 to 22 seconds. They are made by adult males or, more frequently, by individual adult females, when the group is traveling away from the focus of its territory. They seem to be exploratory sounds or sounds defensive of territory and evoke similar responses from animals within the same group and in neighboring groups.

Type II calls are emitted by adult males in the early morning and sometimes when the group is moving. They are usually single, discrete calls, similar to the opening notes of Type I. They evoke responses within and without the group. The function of this type of call seems to be to localize the group within its own territory.

Type III is a loud, high-pitched note of alarm given by animals of both sexes and all ages together when the group is surprised by a hunter or an enemy. The fourth call is a single note with rising inflection used when a member of the group is lost in order to assemble the family. It is given singly by all of the animals, but does not evoke responses outside of the group. Other types of calls include a deep-throated growl emitted by adults when greatly annoyed and on the defensive, chatters and clucks made by the leading adult in order to direct group progression, little chirps or squeals made by the young in their play, and also fretting cries which probably serve for begging, as well as some other calls of unknown function.

Carpenter has been impressed by the fact that different species of gibbons show marked variations in their types of calls and that these persist when they have been caged for long times next to animals of other species which have different calls. This stability of differences seems to suggest that the calls are structural rather than easily modified by learning. Most of the sounds are reinforced by gestures and other overt actions.

In summary, these vocalizations serve to co-ordinate group activity by providing a single dominating stimulus to which all the animals may respond.

FIGHTING

Carpenter saw no real fights among wild gibbons in Siam, but he has no doubt that they occur. Among captive gibbons close confinement probably aggravates their natural frustrations and aggressiveness.

At any rate, they fight frequently and savagely. Carpenter is of the opinion that some of the healed fractures of bones reported by Schultz in collected gibbons are due to canine-tooth bites. Among the 30-odd gibbons collected in northern Siam were found an old adult male with a long slit in the ear, a female with an old infected wound over the temporal muscle, and another with a split lip. In another series of 80 adult gibbons examined by Schultz 11 males had torn ears, but only one female and no juveniles.

Gibbon attacks are the result of explosive fits of rage. The aggressor attacks quickly and viciously, holding his opponent with his hands, plunging in the sharp canine teeth, and then pulling with the neck muscles like a carnivore. The result is often a deep, clean cut which has the appearance of having been made with a knife. The San Diego Zoo made the mistake of putting a whole group of gibbons into one large cage. In less than 24 hours an old female had been badly bitten in her feet and arms. Once the gibbons were loose in this huge cage, it was impossible to catch them and the fighting went on unabated with deadly results. A gibbon and a siamang both received fatal wounds.[6]

A gibbon is a most dangerous assailant if the animal takes it into its head to attack a human being. Mrs. Benchley says that gibbons hang and strike with feet or hands so swiftly that you cannot even see the blows—let alone dodge them. They will grab your hat or hair or sleeve and tear it before you can even think of meeting the attack. These animals will swoop or dive down from a perch, inflict a deep gash with their canines, and be gone before one sees what has happened. However, Dr. Carpenter comments to the effect that it is possible to learn when a gibbon is going to strike by observing its facial expression and attitude. Mrs. Benchley was feeding the female of a pair of apparently tame and docile gray gibbons by handing cherries, one by one, through the wire meshes. Suddenly her mate dropped down from a high bar like a bolt from the blue and Mrs. Benchley felt a sharp jolt and at the same time was struck a vicious blow in the face. Mrs. Benchley then saw blood on the floor of the cage and realized that her middle finger had been laid wide open by the diving male, while the female at the same instant had slapped her face. Thus it would appear that the little apes of Asia are as dangerous and treacherous as some of the little men of that region.

[6]Benchley 1938, pp. 3-7.

MATING AND REPRODUCTION

It is possible that sometimes a young adult gibbon secures a mate from among his siblings. Carpenter observed in one family group two subadults which seemed to go off by themselves for hours and for several hundred yards. He thought this might be an incipient mating, but he was not sure of the sexes. If gibbons mate outside the family group, one or other of the pair must separate itself from its family and either join another group, or, more probably, pair with an unattached animal of the opposite sex, perhaps detaching him or her from parental association. Carpenter thinks that the mating bonds are gradually established over weeks or months, but, once fixed, they are not terminated by the completion of any phase of the sexual cycle. Since neighboring groups do occasionally intermingle, chances are afforded for the beginning of relationships between potential mates belonging to different families. There is no suggestion in observations of gibbons that males are more aggressive than females, either in sexual behavior or in general pugnacity. Consequently, there is no particular reason for thinking that it is the young male who always breaks off from his family and goes a-wooing. In two instances of matings observed between captive gibbons the females took the initiative.

Carpenter in all of his extended observations of gibbons saw only two instances of copulation, and these indistinctly and from afar. First the animals embraced briefly and the male explored the everted labia of the female as she stood on a branch with her body bent forward and her legs sharply flexed. The male partly stood and partly swung to higher branches while performing piston-like movements of the pelvis. Several other cases of gibbon mating have been observed among captive animals. Usually, the female reached back with her left arm (or perhaps her right arm) and held the male to her by encircling his neck.[7]

The genital region of the female gibbon does not present the periodic swellings which characterize the menstrual cycle of the chimpanzee, although "eversion of the vaginal orifice and varying changes of turgidity and color of the labia which vary during the menstrual cycle may be homologous phenomena."[8] Carpenter has studied the menstrual cycle of two gibbons in Puerto Rico. He observed 8 complete

[7]Coolidge 1933, p. 291. In this paper the author reports the observations of Gerrit L. Miller, Jr., upon a family of gibbons in the National Zoological Park, Washington, D.C.

[8]Carpenter 1940, p. 130.

cycles of one animal and nine of the other. The 21 bleeding periods observed averaged 2.38 days and the mean length of 17 entire cycles was 29.76 days, with an average deviation of 4.12 days.[9] Carpenter also took vaginal temperatures on these two gibbons for protracted periods, recording the diurnal variations at 2-hour intervals, beginning at 8 A.M. The first animal averaged 99.37° for 455 readings at 8 A.M. The other gibbon had a mean of 99.52° for 282 readings taken at the same time of the day. Temperatures rose gradually in these animals from 8 A.M. to 4 P.M. The average late-afternoon temperature of the animals was 101.54°, as against the mean of 99.44° in the early morning. No seasonal variations were noted in these animals, nor did they show changes of temperature at the various phases of their menstrual cycles.[10]

Since infants and young gibbons in all stages of development were seen by Carpenter in northern Siam between the months of February and June, it is improbable that gibbons have a definite breeding season. Again, the pregnant uteri of the gibbons collected at the same time showed a considerable range of development of fetuses. Since there is no definite breeding season, copulation throughout the year may reinforce the bond between the male and the female. The sexual drive in gibbons appears to be weak in comparison with that of chimpanzees and macaques. However, observations on a pair of gibbons at the San Diego Zoological Gardens indicate that copulation may take place throughout the menstrual cycle and even during pregnancy —again a contrast to chimpanzee sexual habits.

An adult female given to Dr. Carpenter began menstruating as she approached the approximate age of 10 years. Gibbons are known to have lived in zoological gardens for more than 30 years, and one female shot by Carpenter in Siam carried an infant, although she was physically senile. These data suggest that the reproductive period of the gibbon may last for 20 years, given a normal life span of 30 to 40 years. Observations on captive gibbons also hint that a female ordinarily does not bear more than one infant in 2 years. Thus an adult female gibbon might produce from 6 to 10 infants during her reproductive span.

BIRTH AND INFANCY

Few infants have been born to captive gibbons in Europe and America. Observations upon parturition are confined to one instance. Harold J. Coolidge transmitted to Carpenter an account of a gibbon

[9] Carpenter 1941, pp. 292–93.
[10] Carpenter 1941, pp. 294–95.

birth in Aarhus, Denmark, reported by Hubert B. Hutzelsider. Late one afternoon the latter observed that a presumably pregnant gibbon showed signs of an early delivery. Some hours afterward she was noted to change her position continually and to emit loud cries about every 4 minutes. At midnight she jumped from the sleeping box, gave a shrill cry, and leaped to a branch 2 meters above. Hutzelsider heard something drop and observed a considerable discharge of blood and fluid. He picked up the infant, which was alive, but had a head wound from the fall. The placenta had been passed with the baby and was still attached by the umbilical cord. The mother, who was having her first baby, was indifferent to it and had to be held forcibly so that the baby could nurse. The infant lived only 8 days. The mother seems to have behaved unnaturally.

Mrs. Belle Benchley of the San Diego Zoological Gardens has described the early infancy of a gray gibbon born there, although the actual parturition was observed only by a casual visitor. As soon as she heard of the event, Mrs. Benchley hurried to the cage, where she found the two gibbons, father and mother, sitting together calmly on the floor "with everything in perfect order."[11]

The mother had already severed the cord and cared for herself and the baby. The father was huddled close by, interested, but pursuing a policy of non-interference. The mother was placidly indifferent to the outside world. The baby was lying in a crosswise position across the lower abdomen of the mother and supported by her thighs. The arms and legs of the tiny creature were almost transparent and so thin that they looked like the tentacles of a small octopus. The long fingers and toes reached round the mother to grasp firmly the long, rough hair of her back and sides. The relatively very large head of the baby appeared to be covered, as was its body, with a short, fine, gray hair, and the little face was grayish pink but hairless. The baby's digits were strong enough to keep it firmly in position when the mother walked and brachiated without supporting it. On the second day the infant was observed to nurse without any assistance from the mother, although she did bend forward to facilitate its reaching the breast. It fed vigorously and greedily. For several days after the birth the mother was very tired and languid and either lay flat, with the baby exposed across her abdomen, or sat hunched up with the infant almost entirely concealed by her long fur. She did not object to examination of the baby by her human friends, so long as they did not attempt to remove it. Mrs. Benchley informed Dr. Carpenter that the female ate about two thirds of the placenta and the male finished off the rest. This

[11]Benchley 1938.

occurrence is of great interest. Chimpanzee mothers consistently eat the placenta, and it has been thought that this habit may be a response to some specific endocrine need. However, the appetite seemed, in this instance at least, to extend to the male. In most chimpanzee births observed in captivity the male has been separated from the mother.

For several days after the birth the gibbon mother confined herself to a light diet, principally of oranges and other juicy fruits. About the third day she began to regain her normal vigor, groomed her own coat and that of the baby assiduously, ate bananas and some vegetables, and lost her interest in milk and slops. The baby filled out rapidly and soon lost its skeletal appearance. At the end of the second month Mrs. Benchley thought she observed a tooth in the upper gum. The keeper at this time put his finger in the infant gibbon's mouth and thought he found two teeth in each jaw. At eleven weeks the animal had "a mouthful of teeth."

Ordinarily, the mother did not support the baby with her hands, but when it was nursing and she chose to move, at least on one occasion she held it to her breast by placing her arm across it just below the head. As the baby began to try to move about independently, leaving its mother and clinging to the wires of the cage, she often held it with one arm. Mrs. Benchley thinks that the gibbon baby is much more precocious in its activity than the chimp infant—2 or 3 months ahead. This gibbon mother did not instruct her infant in walking and climbing as do chimpanzee mothers. Neither did she hold the baby away from her when he was urinating or evacuating his bowels, as did Katie, the chimpanzee mother in the San Diego Zoo.

The skin on the baby gibbon's face began to turn black at the end of the first week, and at the age of one month it was "black as ink." By that time the hair on the head was long and ended abruptly, so that it had the appearance of a Dutch bowl-haircut. From the beginning the face was wizened, but the eyes were wide open, bright, and alert from the very hour of birth. At the end of the second month, the infant gibbon's fingers were no longer transparent, but dark and so strong that he twisted them around the hairs of the mother until they evidently hurt her and she had to detach the digits one by one, each coming away with a circlet of hair which had been pulled out.

The mother seemed to trust the baby to exercise himself aloft in the cage in preference to the ground. As he grew a little older, she seemed to realize that he was not altogether to be trusted on his own and was more careful about holding him than in the first few days. Mrs. Benchley first saw the young gibbon hanging to the wire, completely free of his mother, when he was just short of 3 months old. The mother was unworried until he let go with both feet. Then she reached out with a casual arm and gathered him in. The baby was unafraid of the father and pulled at his fur and gnawed him just as freely as if he were the mother. The father was usually gentle and either indifferent or only mildly interested. Sometimes he appeared to be slightly jealous of the infant, but he never tried to hurt it or to remove it from the maternal arms.

Carpenter contributes further interesting detail concerning maternal care of gibbon infants from his observations of wild animals in northern Siam. Most monkeys carry their infants in the earlier stages on their bellies, probably because the grasping reflexes are at first strong. Later the young are usually seen riding on their mothers' backs, assisted, in the case of howler monkeys, by firm grasps with their prehensile tails. However, gibbons brachiate and have no tails. The infant is carried habitually astride the lower part of the mother's abdomen. The latter flexes her legs so that her upper thighs, drawn up almost to the body, form a seat for the baby. The infant also encircles the mother's body tightly with its long arms. Carpenter watched such a mother and child. He estimated the baby's weight from $1\frac{1}{2}$ to 2 pounds. As it clung to its mother, it would occasionally reach out and grasp leaves, fruit, and flowers, which it ate. Sometimes it would release its hold with one arm and swing around to face in the same direction as the mother. On another occasion an adult female was accompanied by an older infant which was semi-independent in locomotion. When the gibbon family left the feeding tree, the animals were obliged to take a 10-foot jump from one branch to another in the next tree. The baby hesitated to make the jump and cried to its mother, who turned back and apparently tried to coax it. After a few moments of obvious excitement, the mother recrossed, took the infant on her belly, and made the leap. Immediately afterwards the young one resumed independent progression.

During the first 6 months of life the baby rarely if ever leaves the warm, furry nest which the mother makes with her lower abdomen and flexed legs. It first moves away from its mother when other young animals of the group approach and attempt to play with it. It begins by reaching out with its long arms and slender legs, and then advances to a stage at which it leaves its mother momentarily but returns hastily to her at the slightest provocation. Gradually, the desire to get food independently prompts the youngster to separate itself from the mother for longer periods, while the growth of its own long hairy coat eliminates the necessity of returning to the maternal breast (or rather belly) for warmth. At the same time its locomotor abilities develop rapidly, so that it gradually becomes able to travel on its own.

The mother usually displays solicitude for the infant. When she gets ready to brachiate, she pulls it to her and arranges it in a suitable position. She handles her baby much more than do platyrrhine monkeys, probably because of its lack of a prehensile tail (or their mutual lack), and because the baby's hands are less capable of manipulating, since it matures more slowly.

Once Carpenter saw a mother gibbon bridge a gap between two branches, so that a timorous infant could cross by brachiating across her body. When another female heard a distant gunshot, she immediately rushed to her infant, which was playing about 3 feet away, pulled it in toward her belly, and prepared for flight. When a family group was being collected a wounded mother forced her infant away from her onto the top branch of a thick tree, and herself moved away into another tree. Such attempts to protect the young by luring hunters away have been observed previously by collectors of gibbons.

GROWTH

One of the curious phenomena of gibbon growth is that the horny callosities over the haunch bones do not appear in fetuses as they do in catarrhine monkeys, but develop only after birth. The ear also grows considerably during the postnatal development of gibbons and siamangs.[12]

As in other primates, the trunk of the gibbon becomes more slender during growth. In one species (*H. concolor*) the chest circumference amounts to 343 per cent of trunk height in the embryo, but only 151 per cent in adults. Comparative figures for this ratio of chest girth to trunk length among the primates are: Old World monkeys 107.1, gibbons 148.8, siamangs 173.6, chimpanzees 171.4, orang-utans 181.1, and gorillas 206.7. Thus the siamang has a thicker torso than the gibbon and exceeds the chimpanzee in relative chest circumference.

YOUNG GIBBON PLAYMATES

Since there are never more than 4 young gibbons in a family, and generally only 2, contacts are more intimate and associations more protracted between the brothers and sisters than in macaque-monkey groups, which usually include 15 to 20 youngsters. Young gibbons are incessantly playing during the daytime. They chase each other round the branches, wrestling, clinching, slapping, and biting. They usually

[12]Schultz 1933c.

go over and over the same circuitous pathway in the trees. A sort of follow-the-leader game is very popular. Early in the morning play begins, before the group has left its lodging tree to seek feeding places. The next active period coincides with the siesta of the adults. A third outburst occurs when the group has sought a tree for the night. From dusk to dawn the young gibbons are quiet and inactive.

LIFE WITH FATHER

Infant gibbons are inspected, groomed, and handled by the adult males. The youngsters frequently attempt to play with the father of the family and are quite aggressive about it. As the young gibbon approaches full growth, the relationship between it and the male appears to change from congeniality to antagonism. Jealousy is often exhibited, because, possibly, of sexual advances toward the mother on the part of maturing male offspring. The fact that a small juvenile was carried most of the day by an adult male in a captive family in Penang indicates that the father exercises considerable parental care.

The defensive function of the father is clear. Any call of alarm by one of the younger members of the group will bring the adult male rapidly to his side, ready to protect him. In captive gibbon colonies the adult males will vigorously bite any person who attempts to catch a young animal, or will go further by placing themselves between the person and the young animal he is attempting to catch, seizing the hand or net stretched out to make the capture.

Ordinary gibbon greetings usually involve mutual examination of the genitalia by touch, smell, and vision. This examination is preliminary to subsequent expressions of friendliness or of antagonism. It is a seemingly neutral form of introduction.

LADIES AND GENTLEMEN

In a few gibbon groups observed by Carpenter there were two fully adult males, but in each case one of them was senile or one of them a very young adult. Two vigorous adults in their prime were not observed in any family party. It thus seems probable that young adults usually leave the family group and that aging males may be succeeded by those in their prime. These superannuated males are either tolerated in the group or may be separated from it. In Carpenter's colony of captive gibbons at Puerto Rico two young adult males, whose canines were two-thirds erupted, displayed toward each other a strong and persistent antagonism of the most vicious character. They were confined in adjacent cages and often succeeded in biting each other through the small openings of the wires. For hours at a time they would sit on opposite sides of the fence, threatening and cursing each other. Once they managed to get to close quarters by forcing a small opening in the wire partition. The results were badly bitten hands and feet and a splintered ulna. Some of the adult females appeared to be equally antagonistic to each other.

Any approach of a young adult male to a family group, and especially to the females, is violently repulsed by the group male. Thus gibbon monogamy and family solidarity seem to be reinforced by their dislike of adult strangers of the same sex and kind.

Sex differences in behavior among gibbons are not marked except in reproductive behavior. Neither male nor female enjoys a monopoly of dominance. The female shares with the male the duties of guarding, leading, and co-ordinating the activities of the family group. Adult females rarely come into competition with each other, since ordinarily there is but one female attached to a single male. There may be, of course, some rivalry between the mother and the maturing daughters for the favors of the group male. Although Carpenter observed some gibbon families in which there were apparently two adult females, he never saw any in which there were two females with dependent babies. Thus it appears that the extra female in every case must have been an almost mature specimen who would have left the family tree shortly.

Captive adult females fight among themselves as viciously as do males. A number of zoos have had fatal happenings owing to the mistaken idea that a large group of gibbons would be happier if caged together.

DOMINANCE

Dominance among gibbons seems to be based upon personality rather than upon sex. Dominance is judged from amount and vigor of individual activity, right of way in food situations and in position with relation to other animals, initiation and persistence in play on the part of young animals, frequency of leadership in progression in the case of old animals. Observation of captive gibbons shows that various individuals show different grades of dominance, more or less connected with their degree of sexual maturation. Carpenter, however, has seen small immature gibbons take food away from adults. His field data on leadership in progression appear to show no consistency of dominance of particular individuals.

GROOMING

Self-grooming and mutual grooming are among gibbons, as in other apes and monkeys, important aspects of individual and social behavior. Any given animal is likely to spend a good deal of time cleaning its fur. When two animals engage in mutual grooming, they alternate between passive and active roles. The animal which is about to be groomed takes a relaxed attitude, usually supine and with its eyes closed, the arms level with the shoulders or above the head. Areas groomed are especially those which the animal itself has difficulty in reaching—ears, neck, shoulders, center of the back and rump. Feet and hands and teeth are all used by the groomer. Both hands may be used to separate the fur, and particles removed are conveyed to the mouth of the groomer. In one case observed by Carpenter the grooming lasted 10 minutes and in this session each animal alternated from the active to the passive role exactly 10 times. Grooming is, of course, a sign of friendliness and sociability.

SENSORY CAPACITIES OF THE GIBBON

Gibbons apparently have excellent vision, judging from their use of visual clues in jumping and from their ability to detect movements of human observers at a distance of 400 to 500 yards. Also from the varieties of sound which they make, it seems probable that their auditory range is large. Such sensations as those produced by grooming and rubbing parts of the body cause marked relaxation, and, in the case of tame gibbons, almost put them to sleep. Carpenter found 80 per cent of gibbon foods sour and bitter to the taste, but several of the fruits eaten are palatable to our species. Gibbons lost or separated from their group have been seen to sniff about as if they were attempting to pick up a trail. However, little is known of their olfactory sense.

INTELLIGENCE

Experimental studies of gibbon intelligence are few and unsatisfactory. Louis Boutan, a French zoologist, obtained in Indo-China a very young female specimen of the white-cheeked gibbon.[13] This

[13]Boutan, Louis, "Le Pseudo-langage. Observations effectuées sur un anthropoïde: le gibbon (*Hylobates Leucogenys* Ogilby)," *Act. Soc. linn.*, Bordeaux, vol. 67, 1913, pp. 5–80; "Les Deux méthodes de l'enfant," *Act. Soc. linn.*, Bordeaux, vol. 68, 1914, pp. 3–146. Quoted by Yerkes, R. and A., 1929, pp. 88–99.

PROFESSOR ADOLPH H. SCHULTZ AND "COLLECTED" GIBBON

little animal was taken to France and studied for 5 consecutive years. Boutan's first interest in the gibbon was concentrated upon its vocalizations and its "pseudo-language." This animal did not imitate human sounds or the sounds of other animals, whether because of inability or because of disinclination. On the other hand, another observer, Mott, stated that a siamang laboratory subject imitated certain sounds made by dogs and guinea pigs. Boutan's gibbon paid no attention to the sounds of human conversation and manifested no interest in music.

As soon as any compelling demand was made upon this animal's attention, she showed signs of nervous fatigue. The image of herself in a mirror at first greatly excited the gibbon. She attempted to seize the other animal behind the mirror, was surprised at her failure, yawned, lay down on the grass, and went to sleep. She quickly desisted from futile endeavors.

Boutan's gibbon was brought up with human beings and studied in comparison with human children. Most of the experiments performed, as reported in Yerkes and Yerkes, involved the solution of box problems in which access to the food was possible by the manipulation of various mechanisms, either visible or concealed. In every case the stimulus was appetite for dainty food rather than hunger, and the animal was left to itself in an experimental room, while the observer watched unseen. The apparatus consisted invariably of a wooden box, two sides of which were covered with wire netting so that food placed inside could be seen. A hinged door in the top gave the animal access to the food. This door was fastened with a variety of mechanisms in the experiments—some visible and some invisible. After a certain amount of fumbling and experimentation the gibbon solved the problems which involved the visible mechanisms, and, eventually, also those with the hidden mechanisms. Shifting the spatial relations of the box only slightly affected her adaptations. When she was brought back to the problems after a vacation of 3 months, she retained what she had learned.

Boutan thought that his gibbon arrived at solutions of her problems abruptly and not gradually. This is the sort of learning method which Köhler calls "solution with insight," and Yerkes, "ideational behavior." It is contrasted with the elimination of useless movements by trial and error. However, this animal, in the opinion of the experimenter, although she foresaw her objective, lacked prevision of the movements necessary to obtain the reward. He thought that the idea of movements was in her case independent of the direction of movements. A heightened attention and a consciousness of the objective enabled the animal to abandon useless movements without the employment of reasoning processes. The flashes of the sort of attention which human beings manifest permitted the gibbon to solve her problem, but rapidly induced extreme nervous fatigue.

Yerkes and Yerkes also report the experiments with a gibbon performed by two German investigators, Drescher and Trendelenburg.[14] They found out that their gibbon, like most monkeys, would draw in fruit with a rake when the fruit was placed in front of the rake, but made no effort to place the rake behind the fruit when the latter was put farther away. In opening boxes the animal had little difficulty, but Yerkes says that their detailed description of the manner in which the gibbon manipulated a bolt indicates distinct inferiority to the great apes in manual dexterity.

W. E. Galt has investigated the capacity of the gibbon to acquire differential responses to visual stimuli.[15] In these experiments the small ape was matched with 2 New World cebus monkeys and with 3 Old World rhesus monkeys. In elaborate and carefully designed apparatus the animals were taught to discriminate between various combinations of paired stimulus-cards marked with different sizes of black and white spots. A correct choice enabled the subject to open one of a pair of doors and obtain a food reward, or to pull in a tray containing the reward. There were 4 series of tests increasing in difficulty. The first series was divided into 3 steps, and each animal was required to become proficient in one step before advancing to the next. All the cebus monkeys and the gibbon succeeded in learning the 3 steps of the first series, but the rhesus monkeys failed in the third step. In the second series, which involved mixing up pairs of stimuli, the gibbon failed and both cebus monkeys succeeded. Both of these monkeys also did the third series, but failed in the fourth.

The gibbon was a young female who weighed 116 ounces and was between 3 and 4 years old. She was tame and affectionate, a good and tireless worker.

The cebus monkeys frequently turned their heads, looking at one card and then the other, before making their choices. This comparison tended to improve the accuracy of choice. Such behavior was much less common in the rhesus monkey, and the gibbon was intermediate in frequency of comparisons. The gibbon was much less successful in these tests than the New World monkeys, but surpassed the Old

---

[14]Yerkes, R. and A., 1929, p. 99, summarizing Drescher, K., und Trendelenburg, W., "Weiterer Beitrag zur Intelligenzprüfung an Affen (einschliesslich Anthropoiden)," *Z. vergleich. Physiol.*, Berlin, vol. 5, 1927, pp. 613–42.

[15]Galt 1939, pp. 387–457.

World monkeys. This result surprised the investigator, because Nissen with similar tests found that chimpanzees did much better than monkeys. Galt attempts to interpret the species differences by the relation of brain-weight–body-weight ratios. The cebus monkeys easily surpass the rhesus monkeys and the gibbons in this relationship. The first-named are, of course, much the smallest animals. I should doubt that the explanation is so simple.

The female gibbon used by Dr. Galt seemed to be quite as well adjusted to the experimental situation, as strongly motivated, and as attentive as the cebus monkeys. Contrary to the findings of Boutan in regard to his gibbon, this animal was not easily fatigued and did not become irritable after a few tests. In fact, she was less disturbed by continual testing than either of the monkey species. During prolonged periods of exertion, she was quiet and attentive throughout, whereas the monkeys often refused to work. At first the gibbon was handicapped in picking up food from the incentive tray because of her very long fingers and rudimentary thumb, but she overcame her natural disability in a few days. Although she had never worked with string tests, as had the monkeys, she adapted very quickly to the pulling-in technique. She occasionally had temper tantrums when she failed to secure the food rewards after successive trials. In these outbursts she would slash around with her arms, biting and crying. They lasted only a few minutes, after which she reverted to her normal, gentle, affectionate behavior. When the experimenter attempted to drive her into her cage by threatening her with a small iron bar, she persisted in her refusal to enter, and, as soon as he turned his back, she seized the iron bar, carried it to the top of the cage and put it in a place where he could not reach it. Galt is quite sure that his results showing the superiority of the cebus monkey over the rhesus monkey in these tests are reliable, but he is not so certain about the position of the gibbon. All the animals used were adolescents.

Harlow, Uehling, and Maslow found the one gibbon they tested difficult to motivate and on the same level as rhesus monkeys in simple delayed-reaction tests.[16] This gibbon was inferior to the best of the macaques in the more complicated delayed-reaction tests. These students found the New World monkeys no better than lemurs in delayed-reaction tests and far inferior to macaques. Gibbons tested on diagonal-string problems hardly reached the lower monkey level. Galt has summarized earlier investigations as follows: "What scant experimental work there is on the gibbon indicates that these animals are certainly not superior, and perhaps may be somewhat inferior, to

[16]Harlow, Uehling, and Maslow 1932, pp. 313–43.

monkeys in solving the type of problem ordinarily required of primates in the laboratory."[17]

DISPOSITION AND EMOTIONAL RESPONSES

Wild gibbons appear to be extremely nervous and excitable. They are easily alarmed into precipitate flight, and, if frustrated in such attempts, sometimes approach aggressively, shake branches, jump up and down on branches, or indulge in typical gestures of annoyance, such as rhythmic shaking of head, hands, and arms. An angered or excited gibbon often opens and closes its mouth with tensed lips, as if smacking them together. Even very young gibbons when captured are wild and attempt to bite the hands of those who handle them. They may for several days refuse food. However, they soon become tame, if they are young enough, and then grow affectionate, responsive, and dependent upon the persons who care for them.

Gibbons captured as adults cannot be satisfactorily tamed. For months they are aggressive and dangerous, and thereafter sullen, irritable, and lethargic. If aroused, they bare their formidable canine teeth and wait for a chance to get in a blow. These observations, according to Carpenter, are based, however, upon so few cases that generalizations may be unreliable. It is certain that young animals, if properly trained and well treated, become playful and affectionate pets and remain tame into adult years. However, their tempers do not usually improve with age; their behavior becomes less predictable, and they are apt to bite someone or destroy something in a fit of rage and have to be sold, killed, or set free. Even in adult specimens which are tame, vigorous destructiveness is often shown in play. The veneer of domestication is thin.

Captive gibbons are playful in their youth and less so in adult years. Individuals caged together soon establish a dominance order, but competitiveness is not vigorous enough to be dangerous until adult years are reached.

FRIENDS AND ENEMIES OF THE GIBBON

Live gibbons are often kept as pets in the Far East. They are usually kept on leashes and staked to some sort of rigging of bamboo poles near the houses of the natives. They are fed upon the diet of native children: rice, fruits, eggs, and, in the case of the very young,

[17]Galt 1939, p. 398.

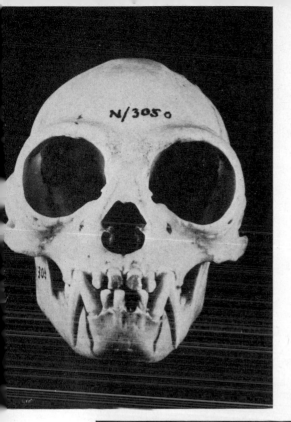

SKULL OF ADULT
FEMALE GIBBON

Photographs F. W. Orchard
Courtesy Peabody Museum

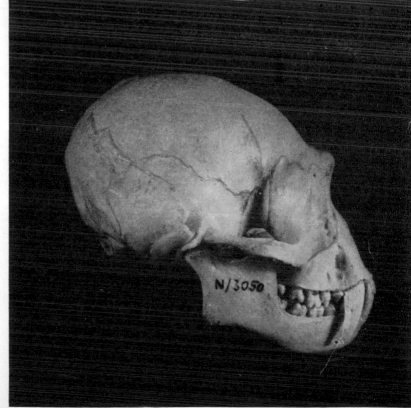

SKULL BASE AND DENTAL ARCHES OF ADULT FEMALE GIBBON

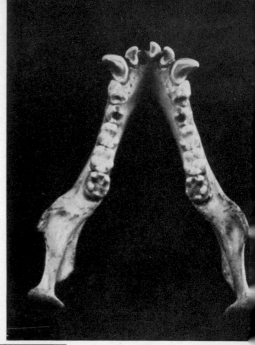

Photographs F. W. Orchard
Courtesy Peabody Museum

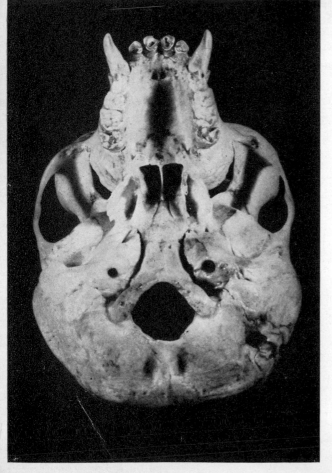

buffalo milk. They are often treated like members of the family. If they get vicious or become inactive as they grow old, the owner disposes of them. Some of the natives of Siam undoubtedly use the gibbon for food occasionally. In Buddhistic countries gibbons are vaguely connected with the idea of reincarnation. Especially because of their mournful calls, they are supposed to be reincarnations of disappointed lovers, who are legion. Some of the tribes, including the Karens and the Meos, are very loath to shoot gibbons, because they believe them to have a beneficial effect upon the crops. There is, as a matter of fact, no food competition between gibbons and men. The gibbons do not rob human gardens, perhaps because they are so strictly arboreal that they do not descend to low-growing vegetables and grain crops.

Carpenter is in doubt as to the extent to which gibbons suffer from the attacks of other animals. Pythons are found in the same region and they are known to attack animals both on the ground and in trees, but whether or not they eat gibbons our reliable observer does not say and probably does not know. He thinks that the big cats which roam the region, especially the leopards, may be enemies of the gibbon. Leopards feed at night and are tree climbers. However, gibbons live in groups and show strong tendencies to attack concertedly when any of their number is assailed. Again, gibbons are very agile in the trees and easily cross wide spaces between the trees over very slender branches. It would be an active cat that could follow them. However, a fallen gibbon, with a cat lurking about, would be out of luck.

PATHOLOGY

Probably many gibbons die of epidemics or of diseases of an infectious character. Schultz[18] reports that the gibbons he examined in northern Siam were heavily infested with filariid worms. These parasites were found in 12 of 19 young apes and in 78 of 80 adults. In the grownups the peritoneal cavity was usually jammed with filarii and in some cases they had also invaded the thoracic cavity. In 2 cases the ovaries were enlarged by cysts caused by penetration of these worms. In 39 of the same series of 100 Siamese gibbons other intestinal parasites of undetermined species were observed. Among 118 gibbon skeletons (all adult), Schultz found 6 cases of unmistakable arthritis of the spinal column. Further, in this series 2 other skeletons showed arthritic changes in the wrists or fingers, 8 had diseased sterno-clavicular joints, and 3 had pathological conditions of

[18] Schultz 1939, pp. 571–82.

the mandibular joint. These conditions may have been due to arthritis or perhaps to some localized infection. Two wild adult gibbons had one shrunken leg (apiece); another had an atrophied right temporal muscle. Still another had an enormous umbilical hernia. At least one gibbon had a badly infected maxillary sinus.

Schultz found that about 20 per cent of the oldest gibbons collected had suffered from alveolar abscesses (gum boils), probably the result of the wearing down of the teeth with consequent exposure of the pulp cavities, followed by death of the tooth and infection around the roots.

Among the 118 skeletons of adult wild gibbons Schultz found 42, or 36 per cent, had healed fractures. Sixteen of these skeletons had 2 to 4 fractures each. There were, altogether, 65 broken bones, most commonly the humerus (upper-arm bone) and the femur (thigh bone). These fractures seem to offer conclusive evidence that gibbons frequently incur serious accidents, such as falling out of trees. Of course, the healed fractures belong only to animals which survived their accidents. Doubtless many others were killed.

Schultz has also found a number of cases of developmental abnormalities among gibbons, including polydactyly (extra fingers), brachydactyly (shortened fingers), spina bifida occulta (incomplete fusion of the spinous processes of sacral vertebrae), incomplete formation of an entire limb or of ribs, impacted and congenitally absent teeth, fusion of the atlas (first vertebra) with the base of the skull, and cryptorchism (undescended testicles). Yet these animals grew up. All of this pathological revelation suggests that wild animals are not as healthy and normal as we are prone to imagine, and, further, that natural selection does not do the efficient job of removing cripples and invalids in a state of nature with which we are inclined to credit it.

ANATOMY

SKELETON

The smooth, ovoid skull of the gibbon has no prominent bony crests, although the temporal ridges rise high up on the vault. The frontal bone generally projects backward in a point to articulate with the parietals in the center. The orbits are capacious. The nasal bones are broad and flattened, and, according to Wood Jones, are generally fused together early in life.[19] The broad nasal aperture has no spine and is bounded laterally by the maxillae and inferiorly by the premaxillae. The suture between the

[19]Jones 1929.

maxilla and the premaxilla is distinct. The infraorbital foramina are multiple, but there are no infraorbital sutures.

The malars are not large and the zygomatic arches are slender and compressed. In the temporal fossa the alisphenoid generally articulates with the parietal, but, according to Wood Jones, the frontal makes contact with the temporal in some 14 per cent of cases. The glenoid fossa is shallow and has a well-marked postglenoid process. There is no mastoid process. The spheno-maxillary fissure is wide. The supramastoid crest is well developed. The palate is broad and not excessively long. Since the third molars are often reduced and slightly rotated, the contour of the upper dental arcade often approaches a horseshoe or elliptical shape. The cranial capacity, according to Schultz, averages 97.5 cc. for the gibbon, except the little *H. klossi,* which has a mean capacity of 87.1 cc. The siamang has an average capacity of 124.6 cc. The mandible has the usual simian features, but in the siamang the chin region is less fleeting than in the gibbon.

Organs of Digestion and Absorption

According to Sonntag, the stomach of the gibbon is more globular than that of man and more elongated than that of the gorilla. In the gibbon fetus Deniker found the small intestine to be 2.6 times the length of the body, but after birth it is from 3.7 to 5.9 times body length (Sonntag). There are no valvulae conniventes. The vermiform appendix is long and opens widely into the end of the caecum. The liver of the gibbon is very similar to that of man.

Organs of Voice and Respiration

The gibbon proper usually has no air sacs, but the siamang has a single large air sac which communicates with both ventricles of the larynx. The left lung has 2 lobes and the right 4, including an azygos lobe.

Genital Organs

In the female the genital folds are not distinguishable, but Pocock records that the genital tubercle is sufficiently large in some species of gibbon to cause confusion in determining sex. The most distinctive feature of the male genital organs is the lack of a pendulous scrotum for the reception of the testes. The latter are covered by folds of the skin of the anterior abdominal wall. The gibbon penis is small and simple; there is no prepuce. The small, ovoid glans has a somewhat ventral, slitlike urethral orifice (Sonntag).

Nervous System

The brain of the gibbon is said to be intermediate between the brains of the Old World monkeys and those of the larger apes. Wood Jones calls it "a glorified langur brain." The fissures are simple but show an advance in complexity over those of monkeys. The operculation of the insula is incomplete, but the arrangements around the anterior part are said by Sonntag to distinguish the gibbon from the monkeys and to ally it to the great apes. In the hind brain the floccular parts of the cerebellum and certain features of the pons ally the gibbon to the monkeys and distinguish it from the other anthropoid apes.

PART II

Totalitarian Monkeys of the Old World

INTRODUCTION

ALL THE Old World monkeys are included in one vast family, the Cercopithecidae. The family name is derived from that of the genus Cercopithecus, which means "tailed ape." However, this family is subdivided into two subfamilies: the Cercopithecinae and the Semnopithecinae. The latter subfamily name comes from Semnopithecus, the generic name of the langurs. "Semnopithecus" means "sacred ape." Actually, we tend to confine the use of the name "ape" to the anthropoid apes. All of the Cercopithecidae are, properly speaking, monkeys.

The whole family is characterized by certain features which differentiate it from the New World monkeys. In the first place, the nostrils are comma-shaped, or sometimes circular, and typically situated close together with a narrow septum between them. The term "catarrhine" applied to the Old World monkeys and to the anthropoid apes means, however, that the nose or nostrils look downward. The nails of these Old World monkeys are less arched and more flattened than those of the New World monkeys. Some authorities claim that the thumbs and great toes are better developed and capable of greater freedom of movement than those of New World monkeys. All the Old World monkeys have sitting pads or ischial callosities, which are naked patches of thickened skin over the haunch bones. Furthermore, these monkeys tend to develop naked and highly colored areas on the face, trunk, and limbs as well as upon the buttock region. The face may be flesh-colored, bluish, purple, or black, as well as various shades of brown.

The ischial callosities are a catarrhine specialization. They are primarily pads of thickened skin analogous to the callous spots developed on the hands and feet. But this is not all; they are secondary sexual features. Among modern students of the primates it is customary to refer to them as the sexual skin, since these areas become swollen and engorged in females when they are "in heat." In the males these frequently brilliant bare patches are supposed to attract the females, according to the old Darwinian theory of sexual selection.

Another specialization of this family is the development of cheek pouches, a feature absent only in the langurs and the guerezas. These pouches enable the monkeys to stuff a great quantity of food into their mouths to be masticated at leisure. Some groups, according to Wood Jones, regurgitate the stomach contents into the cheek pouches and rechew them, after the manner of ruminants.

The subfamily of Cercopithecinae includes a large group of doglike, ground-dwelling monkeys, mostly with elongated snouts. The baboons, mandrills, drills, Barbary apes, macaques, mangabeys, and the black apes of Ceylon, together with the African guenons, belong to this subdivision. Social life and behavior in the wild have been studied in the baboons and the macaques, but in none of the others. The second subfamily, Semnopithecinae, consists of shorter-faced, arboreal monkeys. The principal groups are the langurs, the guerezas, and the proboscis monkeys.

CHAPTER V

Baboon Overlords and Underlings

INTRODUCTION

Baboons are Old World monkeys which live on the ground and have developed physical features and habits which adapt them for terrestrial rather than arboreal existence. Baboons are found in many areas of Africa and, outside of Africa, only in Arabia. The nearest to a baboon in the extreme Orient is the black ape of Celebes. The ancestors of the baboons were certainly tree-dwelling monkeys. The descent to the ground, which parallels that which must have taken place in our own prehuman ancestors, resulted, in the case of the baboon, in a completely different posture and bodily adaptations quite divergent from those of man. The baboon has regrown a tremendous snout and great, tusklike canines and presents a truly bestial appearance. It goes on all fours and superficially resembles a dog; hence the name "dog-faced baboon."

Baboons are large animals with massive bodies and arms and legs of almost equal length. They walk on the palms of their hands and the soles of their feet and have well-developed thumbs and great toes. Their tails are of varying lengths. Baboons usually have cheek pouches and, invariably, large callous areas on their haunch bones. Around these ischial callosities are large patches of a specialized, naked skin, called the sexual skin. These may be vastly enlarged and turgid during certain phases of the sexual cycle. The sexual skin is often brilliantly colored, red or purple. Some species also have brightly colored faces.

THE CHACMA (*Cynocephalus porcarius*)

DESCRIPTION, HABITS

The chacma is a very large South African baboon which is found south of the "great, gray, greasy" Limpopo River. The name is a corruption of that given to it by the Hottentots. This animal has

179

been compared in size and strength with the English mastiff. Its general color is brownish black. The hairs on the crown of the head and the nape of the neck are long and black with a broad yellowish band, the back also black with some yellow. The flanks and limbs are more nearly brown, the scanty whiskers grayish. The hair on the body is long and shaggy. The tail is not tufted. The muzzle is unusually long and the nose extends beyond the lips. The naked part of the face is purplish, but a ring of white surrounds the eyes and the upper eyelids are also white. The ischial callosities are not so large as in most baboons. The chacma, like some other baboons, carries its tail with an upward curve near the base and the terminal half hanging straight down. Elliot says that the upper canines of one of these animals measured 45 mm. in length.[1]

The chacma baboon lives in the mountainous regions of South Africa. It feeds principally upon wild fruits. It is fond of the fruit and leaves of the prickly pear, berries, bulbs, and the sweetish pith of the lower ends of the wild aloe. The chacma turns over loose stones and eats the insects, lizards, and scorpions it finds underneath. It also robs bees' nests for the honey. These chacmas also plunder the orchards and fruit gardens of the farmers, and are alleged to suck ostrich eggs and to kill and disembowel lambs and kids for the sake of the curdled milk in their stomachs. The chacmas are good tree climbers and in some regions are said occasionally to sleep in trees.

Baboons go in troops numbering from 30 to 100 individuals. The old males are supposed to constitute advance and rear guards and flankers, and it is alleged that sentinels are placed on commanding rocks to give warning of danger when the troop is resting. The principal enemy of the chacma baboon is said to be the leopard, which may, however, confine its attention to the females and the young.

On level ground baboons can be overtaken easily by dogs, but in rough country they can hold their own. The farmers hunt the baboons with dogs and the males put up a strong battle, since they hold the dogs with their hands and inflict deep wounds with their long canine teeth.

The Chacma Baboon in the Wild

In 1930 Zuckerman visited South Africa partly for the purpose of making observations upon wild baboons.[2] So much folklore has grown up about the social habits of baboons that the time for "debunking" is long overdue.

[1]Elliot 1913.
[2]Zuckerman 1932b.

BABOON

ADULT MALE HAMADRYAS BABOON

The baboon population is large and pestiferous. One fruit farmer in the Western Provinces told Zuckerman that a troop of 60 to 100 animals regularly pillaged his apple orchards and could not be driven away by shouts or threats. He attempted to poison them by injecting apples with strychnine, but to no avail. In the sheep districts the baboons do damage by breaking down the "jackal-proof" fences and in all areas by breaking off the growing tips of young trees. They also are said to spread the prickly-pear bush by conveying the seeds in their droppings. Bounties are offered for the destruction of the animals, who nevertheless seem not to be decreasing in most areas. They are still to be found on the very outskirts of Capetown after some 300 years of European settlement. The healthy growth of the baboon population is due to the fact that they are not actively hunted by man, that their naturally carnivorous enemies, the leopards, have been exterminated, and that every new cultivation offers them more potential feeding ground.

Nearly every female baboon produces an offspring once a year, and Zuckerman is not aware of any epidemics which reduce the population. In 25 specimens which he examined no serious pathological lesion was found, although all were infected with tapeworms and roundworms. Famine probably reduces numbers, and also drought. It is almost certain that a large number of the animals are destroyed in the fights in which they indulge among themselves. Every adult animal which Zuckerman examined showed the effects of these combats.

As in the case of gibbons, howlers, and rhesus monkeys, the baboon pack apparently keeps to its own rather restricted territory. In one area visited by Zuckerman a pack of 25 baboons was separated from another by a valley 3 miles wide and he could not discover that the two groups were ever united. There is, however, one record of a migration in 1914 involving a pack of about 500 baboons which left one chain of mountains to take up residence in another. Zuckerman has reason for supposing that within their areas baboon packs settle down for the night upon various rocky outcrops wherever they happen to find themselves at nightfall. As many as a hundred animals in a pack may be fairly widely scattered during the daytime, but at night they assemble and huddle in small parties in crevices which usually open on a slope. Many of the sleeping parties encountered by Zuckerman included more females than males. A pack disturbed at night does not travel very far, as a rule, but settles down again as soon as it reaches an undisturbed spot.

Zuckerman observed one pack of about 25 animals for 9 days. There were 3 adult males in this group. The biggest was accompanied by 4 females, one of whom was at the maximum period of swelling of the sexual skin. Two of these females carried young. The other details of the pack composition are not given by the observer, although he does state that about half of the pack were immature. During the 9 days of observation this pack settled down for the night daily at the same rocky place. At dawn they would move down to the bottom of the valley and proceed about 3 miles to a small ravine rich in the prickly pear. Here they would remain for some time and then climb slowly to the crest of the hills near the ravine and spend some hours rooting about there. Sometimes they revisited the prickly-pear ravine later in the day and returned to their sleeping quarters about sundown. Their movements were so regular that Zuckerman could always count upon finding them approaching the pear ravine a little before 8 o'clock in the morning. They usually came over the crest of the ravine in a body, but once the main party was preceded by a young adult male who clattered along the stones like a galloping horse. Before they came in sight the sounds of their squabbling could usually be heard.

The baboons kept out of the shadow and moved with the sun as it crept toward the side on which the prickly pears grew. The youngsters were most lively, chasing each other about the rocks and bushes and squealing. Old males were most sedate. Occasionally Zuckerman was able to recognize the sounds of a young animal being chastised. There was a good deal of conventional sexual behavior, females presenting to their males as they passed them and being momentarily covered, young males presenting to older males, to females, and to each other. A female who carried a baby on her back walked behind her male. She was tagged by an immature male, who occasionally pulled her tail or touched her loins, as if he were contemplating mounting her. Now and then some of the baboons settled down in the sun and groomed each other, grunting with content.

Zuckerman observed few signs of the fabled baboon leadership, although there were individual evidences of dominance. When the baboons were disturbed they began to bark, and they always fled in the same direction, toward some hills that were about 2 miles above the summit of the ravine which contained the prickly pears. They scattered widely, over an area of almost 2 square miles, and moved quickly, some of them reaching the haven in less than 10 minutes. In this escape the leader was once a female with full swelling, closely followed by an adult male. At another time this male moved off, followed by his females in a compact group. None of the directional cries, rear guards, and flanking parties reported in literature about the baboon was confirmed by Zuckerman's observations. On two occasions a couple of immature males hung back when the rest of the party was disturbed and fled (because Zuckerman was trying to shoot some of the females for anatomical purposes). These youngsters remained swinging on a fence, barking now and then, and peering in the direction of the fleeing troop. After 10 minutes an almost full-grown male returned and barked for a long time, finally disappearing with the two younger animals.

For hours Zuckerman watched the baboons through powerful glasses. They spent a great deal of time sitting about and picking each other's fur, the partnerships changing frequently. Every now and then animals would present to other animals and be mounted. Usually, the baboons sat on the crest of the hill, but often some would rush down the slope, making a clattering noise among the stones which the observer could hear at the distance of a mile. A great deal of indiscriminate chasing took place. The baboons often dug, apparently for edible roots, scooping with their hands. Many of these holes were arranged in lines, so that it was possible to tell in what direction the troop had headed, since the front of the hole is vertical and the back sloping. Foraging for food, they scattered widely, but Zuckerman never saw any sentinels.

The troop evidently consisted of a number of family parties with some isolated younger members. Not infrequently it broke up in this way.

All experienced observers, says Zuckerman, agree that, although any baboon in a pack who sees a human being approaching is likely to bark, often a man may stumble upon a pack of baboons when he crosses a ridge. Such an accidental meeting could hardly occur if sentinels had been posted. Zuckerman is skeptical of the reports that baboons deliberately attack human beings. He often came up to them and they never showed fight. Domesticated animals and other wild animals move about among the baboons without fear. Zuckerman has seen chacma baboons playing about in a flock of sheep grazing on the mountain side—a sight which is hardly compatible with the story about their tearing open young lambs to eat the curdled milk in their stomachs. There have been two or three reports of baboons attacking and killing native children, but these require corroboration. Zuckerman also discredits the accounts of baboons throwing stones as a means of attacking, since he says that throwing loose objects is not a common practice among captive primates. He has never seen a wild baboon pick up a stone in his hand and throw it.

FEEDING AND DOMINANCE OF THE CAPTIVE CHACMA BABOON

When the captive chacma adult baboon is feeding alone, it hoards as much food as it can gather in between its legs and its belly, holding food in both hands and taking alternate bites.[3] Thus it disposes of whole vegetables, eating very rapidly and wiping the food on the back of the lower forearm and wrist between bites. The first few bites seem to be swallowed without chewing, and then the cheek pouches are stuffed to distention until, it is alleged, food falls out of the open mouth. There is no discrimination between foods at this time. After the first pangs of hunger have been satisfied, the baboon settles down to enjoy itself, chewing steadily but rejecting the more unattractive parts of the food such as the outside leaves and stumps of cabbages. After all of the best food has been consumed, the animal proceeds to chew and swallow that food which has been stuffed into the cheek pouches. The rejected food on the floor will be consumed before the next feeding. If anyone molests the baboon in the early stages of his feeding, he gathers all of the food in his hands and against his chest and retreats, walking on his hind legs. The baboon will scream and attack anyone who attempts to take food from him.

Male and female chacma baboons may be the very greatest friends and groom each other with apparent affection, but as soon as food comes into the situation, friendship is entirely forgotten in the effort to obtain the larger share.

Getting food depends upon dominance. In one pair the female was the more aggressive animal and when food was put into the cage attacked the male and drove him into the corner, where he sat crestfallen. She would repeatedly turn, raise her eyebrows, and give him "dirty looks" if he made the slightest movement, and any attempt to feed him aroused her to fury. Eventually, this male became so run down and unhappy that the pair had to be separated, since he could not get even a scrap of food until the female was completely satiated. When alone, he was aggressive and even vicious.

In the other case the female was so afraid of her overlord that she summoned up courage to groom him only after repeated presentations. When food was introduced into the cage she would retire into the corner, screaming; the male would collect all of it in front of him, sit down, and eat with great gusto. In the height of her sexual swelling she would approach her partner cautiously while he was eating and arouse his sexual interest. When he smacked his lips and began fingering her sexual skin, she would seize some food and retreat

[3]Gillman 1939, pp. 178–81.

across the cage. Thereupon he would forget the food and attack her, but often she would manage to swallow or retain a little. Thus she got food by "sex appeal."

If two females are together, the dominant animal gets all of the food, unless the subordinate manages to sneak some when the attention of the other is distracted. The frustrated animal flies into a rage and is likely to "take it out" on any smaller animal which she can find, or upon the keeper.

Baboon females seem to be strongly endowed with what used to be called "maternal instinct." Gillman reports that for one reason or another many young in the Johannesburg colony have to be taken from their mothers. All other females are usually anxious to adopt the orphan, will take it in their arms, remove it to their quarters, embrace it, and guard it jealously as if it were their own. However, as soon as food appears, the maternalism disappears and the infant gets none. Even if the foster mother has more than she can manage, she will snatch anything given to the babe and will even take the food out of its mouth with her fingers. Infants have to be removed to prevent their starving.

When young baboons feed together, dominance is quickly established and the No. 1 animal soon gets all of the food; the others become resigned to their fate and hardly make an attempt to get any. In one case a wild young female was put into the cage with a tame young male, who at first dominated her. After she became accustomed to the environment she lost her fear and put up a fight for food, often worsting the male and getting it.

THE HAMADRYAS BABOON

(Papio hamadryas, Cynocephalus hamadryas)

DESCRIPTION

The hamadryas baboon is found particularly in Abyssinia, but also in Arabia. The males are said to be about the size of a large pointer dog. The male is easily recognized not only by his ashy gray color, but more particularly by the large mane which covers the neck and shoulders. The muzzle of the hamadryas baboon is very long and the nostrils are terminal—or set at the end of the muzzle. The eyes are deepset underneath overhanging brows. The face and ears are naked, but the latter are covered by whiskers and mane. The nude buttocks have large, bright-red callosities; the tail is tufted at the end and carried arched for the basal third, the rest hanging down. The hair on the limbs and under part of the body is sparse. The hamadryas has, in general, a flesh-colored face, with the region along the sides of the nose, the ears, and hands somewhat brownish. There is much regional variation in the coat color. One specimen described by Elliot had a good deal of yellowish and light-brown hair on various parts of the body, but usually the mane is ashy gray, washed with greenish color, since the hairs are ringed with black and green-gray. The forearms and legs are generally grayish black and the underside of the body grayish white.

In both sexes of the hamadryas air pouches in the neck reach nearly down to the armpits. These sacs open into the windpipe above the larynx. The females and the young are devoid of the mane.

Hamadryas in London

VITAL STATISTICS OF A ZOO COLONY. In 1925 about 100 hamadryas baboons were turned loose in a large, oval, rock enclosure in the London Zoo.[4] Most of these were adult males. Two years later 30 adult females and 5 immature males were added to the colony. By the time this new batch arrived the population had been reduced to 56. Most of the deaths were apparently due to pathological conditions, but some animals succumbed to wounds received in fights. In 2 months after the introduction of the 30 females half of them had been killed in fights. All the old males attempted to secure these females, with the result that the latter were torn to pieces. More deaths from disease and fighting reduced the colony to 51 males and 15 females at the beginning of 1928, and to 39 males and 9 females in January 1930. After more fatalities, the 5 surviving females were withdrawn, leaving the colony populated by only 34 adult males.

Eight males died from injuries received in fights and 53 from disease. Post-mortems showed most of the common pathological diseases, including valvular heart lesions, other cardiac conditions, pneumonia, pulmonary abscess, pleurisy and empyema, enteritis, colitis, peritonitis, nephritis, septicemia. No tubercular lesions were found.

Of the 33 females who died, 30 were killed in fights in which they were the prizes sought by the males. The injuries were of all sorts: fractures, wounds which penetrated chest or abdomen, extensive lacerations of the genito-anal region, miscarriages precipitated by fighting, etc. Some deaths seem to have been the result of exhaustion from prolonged sexual fights. The folly of turning loose a large group of adult males with an insufficient supply of females in an enclosure only

[4]This entire section on the hamadryas baboon is based on Zuckerman 1932b.

100 feet long and 60 feet wide is apparent. The smallest knowledge of the social habits and group composition of wild baboons would have made the disastrous result predictable. Certainly, the extermination of most of the colony in sexual fights cannot be attributed to any savagery peculiar to baboons. It will be remembered that some 9 white men and about 6 Tahitian men, together with approximately 12 Tahitian women, landed on Pitcairn Island after the mutiny of the Bounty, and in 10 years all of the men had been killed except one. The principal difference between Pitcairn Island and Baboon Hill is that the abnormal social conditions resulted more lethally for the males in the human colony and for the females in the subhuman group. If 30 women were turned loose in a prison containing some 150 adult male convicts and all left to work out their own salvation, I doubt that the outcome would be radically different from one or other of the historical incidents already cited.

During the life of the baboon colony on Monkey Hill in the London Zoo, at least 15 baboons were born, all but one of which died, mostly within 6 months of birth. All 5 of these young ones whose bodies were recovered died of injuries. These animals often had been strangled. The young baboon clings to its mother's fur and is supported by her arms. In a sexual fight the female becomes the center of the melee, to the detriment of the baby, who may accidentally be squeezed to death.

Little is known of the infancy and growth of the baboon. At the age of about 2 weeks the young begin to try to walk, and solid food becomes a recognized element of the diet in the second month. At about 6 months the animal's movements are extensive and well coordinated. Puberty is reached, probably, between the ages of 4 and 6 years. The life span of the baboon is not known, but Zuckerman quotes Flower as stating that a male chacma baboon lived 45 years in captivity and that two hamadryas baboons appeared to be flourishing after 24 years of captivity. The same observer thinks that the males of the hamadryas species attain their full size and strength in 8 or 9 years and continue in their prime up to the ages of 13 or 14 years.

FAMILY ORGANIZATION. The baboon family group consists of a male overlord and his females—one or more—with their young. The group may also include one or more unmated "bachelors." The latter are not an essential element, but may remain attached to the family group for as long as a year, according to the observations of Zuckerman. Interest in the females probably determines their attachment, although other factors may be involved. They are found oftenest in the groups in which the male overlord owns more than one female, possibly because such mated males are more complacent than the monogamous males. The family groups keep to themselves except in communal feeding and in general quarrels. The degree of isolation varies with the family. In movements of the family group the overlord generally leads, but any animal may occasionally take up the leading position.

When Zuckerman began to observe the London colony in 1930, the population consisted of 41 males (4 immature) and 9 females. The latter were owned by 8 males. There was only one bigamous family. The relationships were very stable. There was little promiscuity. Five of the 9 females soon lost their lives in fights which resulted from attempted abductions by unmated males.

SEX RELATIONS. The chief wife of the harem is always the female who shows, at any time, the maximum swelling of the sexual skin. She is most attractive to the overlord and keeps closest to him. She grooms him oftenest and he even allows her to take a limited supply of food, although he would attack her if she attempted to secure food when her sexual skin was quiescent. Copulation usually takes place only between the overlord and his females, and may be preceded by manual and oral examination of the genitalia, although such examinations often occur independently both of copulation and of grooming. The female usually presents as the preliminary to copulation. This presentation varies from a slight turn or waggle of the hindquarters to the full copulatory position in which the animal presenting extends its hind limbs fully with the body bent downward from the hips, the head turned away from the animal to which the presentation is made. A female is rarely observed to refuse a male, but copulation ordinarily does not take place during pregnancy, lactation, or the quiescent phases of the sexual skin. In the time of maximum receptivity females persistently present, sometimes in a crouched attitude, with the chest against the ground, and solicitation is augmented by turning the head and looking at the male. Or the female may rub up against the body of the male and squeal. He may respond by mounting, or, if he is satiated, by assaulting her with hands and teeth, pulling at her hair and biting her in the scruff of the neck. One male who was persistently accosted by his female responded by moving away and mounting another male. Another female, who was assiduously presenting and had been mounted 5 times in as many minutes by her overlord, then half-mounted a bachelor attached to the harem.

Females are rarely unfaithful to their overlords and apparently never during the period of maximum sexual-skin swelling. At such periods the female is in close association with the overlord and there are few opportunities for philandering. On the other hand, when her sexual skin is quiescent, a female may wander some distance from the overlord, perhaps out of his sight. Zuckerman observed only three cases of infidelity, always when the back of the overlord was turned. Two of the unfaithful females belonged to the bigamous family group and the other was a particularly assertive individual who belonged to a very powerful male. This animal quickly presented to a bachelor in the group when her overlord turned his back, and was mounted for a moment. Just then the overlord turned his head slightly, whereupon the treacherous female rushed to him, squealing and presenting and threatening her seducer with grimaces and gestures. The overlord then attacked the bachelor, who fled incontinently. This same female was left alone on another occasion for 40 seconds while her overlord chased a bachelor round Monkey Hill. During this interval she was mounted and penetrated by two other males to whom she had presented. Both of these quickly made off and, when the overlord returned, this baboon Messalina made up to him in the same way as in the preceding case.

The two bigamous females who committed adultery always did it with the bachelors attached to their family group, at convenient times and in great haste. When the overlord was leading the group, closely followed by the female in heat, the other female would hang back and indulge in a little illicit business with the accompanying bachelor. Or perhaps the overlord would become interested, although not participating, in a general fight in progress, and the sexually quiescent female would take advantage of his preoccupation with the ever-ready bachelor. The overlord never seemed to notice these lapses from virtue on the part of his wives. Often females indulged in sexual relations with immature males in full sight of the overlord, who was apparently indifferent to these peccadilloes with the boys. Such activities of females with immature males varied from mere mutual genital examination to mounting and penetration. They might be interrupted by the overlord's moving off and the female's desisting at once from her diversion and following him.

Homosexual relations are common, if one accepts as homosexual the perfunctory mutual genital examination and grooming which takes place between the overlord and a bachelor, or between these and any male of whatever age in the group. Actually, these attentions seem more in the nature of a friendly social greeting. Even mounting of one male by another, or of a young male by a female, seems ordinarily to fall into this category. Adult females do not come into contact with each other, unless there is more than one female in the family group. When there is a plurality of wives, one female may assume the male role and mount the other.

Females on Monkey Hill were not observed actually to masturbate, but it is a common practice of males, both mated and unmated. This activity seems not to arouse the interest of the other animals. Masturbation has been observed among wild animals, but it may be a habit encouraged and exaggerated by captivity.

PROSTITUTION. A monkey presents sexually in order to indicate submission, to gain favors of food, or to ward off attack. Turning and offering the hindquarters is a symbolic act of subordination. Food or any object acquired by an inferior animal may be retained by such an approach. If a young animal draws upon itself the threats of an elder, it may rush away squealing, or, alternatively, present. Then the animals pay no further attention to each other, or the younger approaches the dominant and is groomed, embraced, or even mounted. If an animal runs screaming for protection to another, the latter will often mount it and threaten the aggressor. Also presentation may be used as a lure to attract an enemy. Thus an immature male pretends to be about to mount an immature female, and, when she presents and turns her back, he bites her in the hindquarters. Such an action is often repeated in play. Zuckerman says that, as a preliminary to some fight or scuffle on Monkey Hill, one baboon would approach another, smack its lips, and present, and, having evoked a favorable response, would turn and threaten some other animal which did not seem previously to have been involved in the situation. Thus symbolic "prostitution" seems to be a means of gaining allies. This method of diplomacy in a less crude manifestation is not unknown in human societies.

DOMINANCE. The male is dominant over members of his family group. If a limited quantity of fruit is thrown to him when sitting with his females, he will eat it all. Six bananas thrown to a pair—a male and a nursing mother—were all snatched by the male. Those which he could not stuff in his cheek pouches he kept in a heap in front of him and the female did not attempt to get any. But she might have obtained some if her sexual skin had been swollen. This dominance extends to objects other than food. If a small baboon picks up a glove or a basket or some other object dropped by a visitor, he immediately drops it and runs off squealing if an older and dominant male appears.

Females are treated as objects the possession of which is secured and maintained by dominance. The weaker males remain unmated. However, continued possession of females may not imply that an overlord is dominant in every case of food competition. He may scuffle with bachelors for the possession of food and be worsted, without losing face or stirring up a serious conflict. However, if the contest is one between overlord and other males for a female, the struggle is bitter. If the overlord is worsted, he loses his dominance in the family with the females and immediately becomes submissive to the victor.

Assistance one monkey gives to another which is being tormented depends upon place in the relative scale of dominance. If a bachelor in a family threatens an immature animal, the latter is likely to squeal in terror and attract the attention of a more dominant adult male, who at once threatens the persecutor.

Females are always completely dominated by their males and are very passive and almost completely non-resistant. Zuckerman thinks this condition is in strong contrast with that obtaining in many lower mammals, in which the female controls the time of mating. In the case of baboons, the time and frequency of coitus is largely determined by the male, depending of course upon the stimulation produced by the physiological condition of the female.

Zuckerman regards social relationships based upon dominance as a series of responses conditioned through fear and pain. An animal's activities within the group are restricted by his fear of encroaching upon the desires and privileges of a more dominant animal. An equilibrium is established by recognition of the scale of dominance. When this is upset, an entire readjustment of group life follows. Most baboons appear to live in fear that their actions may arouse the resentment of more dominant animals. Even the dominant monkey, when taking food passed into the cage, will start in terror at an unusual noise made by one of its subordinates. An inferior animal will move toward proffered food, stop, turn, look toward its dominant companion, and retreat, making noises that are associated with fear and submission.

Female Efforts to Dominate by Sexual Means. In a family group an ambitious and managing female may try to lead the party off in a certain direction and fail to be followed by the overlord and the rest of the group. Her subsequent procedure in trying to get her own way is to go back to the overlord and present persistently, probably squealing all the time. He may respond by attacking her, or he may follow along after her as she advances in the direction she wants to go, at the same time waggling her "behind" to indicate sexual submission. Then the whole family follows. A female customarily presents to her overlord when she has been unfaithful to him surreptitiously, even if she has merely had trifling sexual contact with an immature animal.

Scale of Female Dominance within the Harem. At the end of the disastrous experiment with the large baboon colony in the London Zoological Gardens the surviving five females were removed with one accompanying male and were put in new quarters. The male was the overlord of an immature female who had been born on the hill some 2 years before. This small female, who was well adjusted to the overlord, dominated the four adult females for about 3 weeks. She was conspicuous because of her lack of fear of him and the confidence with which she came forward when food was offered, without paying any attention to him. For the first week after this harem was formed the four adult females were in a quiescent sexual phase and the young female continued in her role of privileged favorite. Then all four began their swelling process. The overlord then mated with the female most assertive both in approach to him and in homosexual behavior. Still the little female was able to get food when it was put into the cage. He paid no attention to her, although he viciously attacked one of the sexually desirable females and killed the baby she was nursing. He evidenced his new favorite's sexual attraction for him not only by mating with her, but by following her around and biting her in the scruff of the neck. It was this female whose sexual swelling persisted longest. These love bites did not appear to draw the attention or interest of the other females. But the young female who had been the "sugar baby" now no longer was able to accept food with impunity, because the overlord would threaten her. She would drop it, squealing in fear. From that time forward the favored female was the one who had, at any given period, the greatest sexual swelling, and it was she alone who could accept food without fear.

The four adult females who were put into the harem with the overlord had had little or no association with each other in the previous 2 years. They immediately began to strike up friendships among themselves and to manifest clear differences in temperament and dominance. The first female was especially aggressive and masculine. She was the one who most frequently mounted her fellow females. She paid more attention to the overlord in all of her sexual phases and made him participate in her threatening of the other females by persistently presenting to him and squealing. The second female was the most independent of the lot and in the best physical condition. She was nursing a 6-months-old baby. She manifested her independence by attempting to secure food, although very cautiously, and usually not without presenting to the overlord. The third female was passive and subdued, and rarely attempted to take food offered her. She became the favorite only when she was in the maximum swelling phase. It should be mentioned that, after the first coincidental swelling of all four females, it was rare that more than one was in the phase of maximum sexual receptivity at the same time, because of differences in their sexual cycles. The fourth female seemed to be consistently downtrodden, oppressed, and in a state of subdued terror, although the overlord had never been observed to attack her. The female with the baby, which was a general favorite with all of the animals in the cage, was attempting to secure some food which had been thrown into the cage, when the male attacked her. She persisted and he bit her in the neck and suddenly transferred his attack to the baby, who was riding on her loins. The youngster was thrown to the ground and badly bitten. The mother picked it up and retired to a corner, nursing it. A similar attack upon the mother and baby occurred a quarter of an hour later and in the evening the infant was found dead. After the death of the infant the independence of the mother became even more marked.

Bachelors. The principal tie binding a baboon bachelor to a family group is probably his interest in the females. After the death or removal of a female the bachelor does not have anything further to do with the overlord. He may join another family party or may remain unmated. Bachelors not infrequently strike up friendships with each other and with young males. Zuckerman records one such relationship which lasted for 3 years and was terminated only by the death of the younger animal. This young baboon rarely mixed with its age mates and, when attacked, was always rescued by its protector, with whom it engaged in frequent homosexual activities. As soon as the females were removed from Baboon Hill, the overlords merged with the bachelors.

Fights. Fighting among the bachelors was an everyday occurrence on Monkey Hill. It was difficult to determine how these fights started. Sometimes they began when a baboon tried to secure food which was snatched from him by a more dominant fellow. Other fights were occasioned by the protection of a young animal which had been threatened by an adult and was rescued by another. Usually, they seemed to start from displays of aggression and dominance. The belligerent animal begins to grind its teeth and yawn, to grimace and stare at its enemy, and to thrust at the rocks with its hands. The other animal responds in kind and soon a fight is started in which most of the bystanders join. They usually rush to the support of the animal which seems for the moment the less dominant. Sometimes the fight spreads to the family groups. The baboon who has started the trouble seems not in the least daunted by the increase in the number of his enemies and carries on alone against the whole gang. As a matter of fact, he usually repels the enemy. Every time he darts forward they retreat, and the wounds inflicted occur in these sudden dashes. At any time two animals of the group opposing the principal No. 1 enemy may take to fighting among themselves. Then the attention of the group is attracted to the new fight and the original aggressor may change sides and fight with the rest of the group against the No. 2 enemy. In a lengthy fight sides are changed many times.

Ordinarily, the overlord of a harem does not actively participate in the usual bachelor scuffles, although he may become involved. Sometimes, such a dominant animal may suddenly arouse the antagonism of his fellows, perhaps at feeding time. On such occasions his female or females immediately assume copulatory positions and crowd round the overlord, who may mount one of them and threaten the aggressors. Or he may attack actively and the attacked bachelor may mount a female and threaten. Usually, the overlord routs his enemies and there is no serious outcome of such scuffles. No one at the London Zoo has actually seen an overlord observing real adultery on the part of his females; so there is no telling what might result from the dominant male's catching one of his harem in *flagrante delicto*.

Normally, the bachelors seem to be relatively indifferent to the mated females, but rarely the entire atmosphere of the whole colony changes and every unmated male attempts to secure a female even at the peril of his life. There ensues a protracted and deadly "sexual fight." On Monkey Hill these fights resulted in the death of no less than 30 females, and in every such fight the female round whom the battle raged was killed. Sexual fights seem to be presaged by a decline in the dominance of the overlord whose females are sought by the bachelor. Such overlords who are slipping seem to avoid contact with their fellows, and the latter display toward them an increasingly aggressive attitude.

One sexual fight in a monogamous family was preceded by unusual behavior of the attached bachelor. He kept very close to the single female, and when she lagged back he dropped back with her. At the same time he watched the overlord more closely than usual. Five days before the actual fight broke out, the bachelor threatened the overlord, but was routed without a struggle. When the battle ultimately began, the bachelor seized the female, consistently covered her, and fought off the overlord. All the other bachelors combined against the overlord, the bachelor, and the female. At first, the overlord was more interested in dispersing the outside assailants than in the fact that the attacked bachelor had taken his female. On the second day the overlord took back the female, but lost her to the bachelor again inside of 24 hours. At the same time other bachelors were contesting for this female. During such a fight the female remains completely passive, but is always covered by one or another contestant, with.all of the rest grabbing at her, biting any part of her body exposed, and generally giving her a very bad time. In the intervals between active contests she grooms, or is groomed by, her seducer. Ordinarily, an attack lasts only a few minutes and then the assailants retire, but later re-engage. The male who has captured the female usually manages to retain possession of her through more than one attack. Whatever male it may be, the female is equally submissive and non-resistant. Eventually, in one of these prolonged sexual fights the female is sure to be killed. She is unable to get food; she is mounted by every male who succeeds in capturing her; and the fight goes on finally over her dead body, which is carried around from place to place and treated as a sexual object. What would become of the corpse is not known, since the keepers at the zoo always removed it as soon as they could.

If an overlord loses permanently the possession of his female, he becomes one of the bachelors. In some cases he may become completely dominated by another bachelor. No animals other than the coveted females were killed in these sexual fights, and a few bachelors remained indifferent to the contests. Also, some of the mated males whose families were not imperiled steered clear of the fracas. The bachelors are so concentrated upon the main female prize that they do not notice other aggressive females who join in the fight, and they rarely transfer their attentions to any other female.

The last fight on Monkey Hill involved an overlord with two females, both of whom at the time were in the stage of maximum sexual-skin swelling. The first attacker was a powerful unmated male, who took away one of the females. The peculiar thing about this fight was that the overlord, having once been deprived of one of his females, ignored her and took no further part in the fight. He contented himself with attacking his remaining female, while the mob of bachelors fought over the first wife for several days, including a period of more than 24 hours after she was dead. The body changed hands several times, was carried about, groomed, and used for purposes of copulation before the keepers could get it away.

MENSTRUAL CYCLE AND PREGNANCY. In the gelada baboon, according to Pocock, the genitalia and the adjoining sexual skin show no cyclical variation. However, in these animals a brightly colored bare spot on the chest and neck is found in both males and females. This patch is shaped like two triangles with their points together, and, in case of females, in whom they are confluent, the shape resembles an hourglass. Along the lateral and inferior borders are numerous flattened, ovate elevations or caruncles. These become enlarged during menstruation. In the London Gardens the keepers call this changing chest patch of the gelada baboon "the bleeding heart."[5]

Baboons and mandrills show more pronounced external changes during the sexual cycle than most other monkeys or apes. The cycle of the chacma baboon, the Anubis baboon, and the yellow baboon is said to vary between 30 and 40 days. In the hamadryas baboons of the London Zoological Gardens the average duration of the cycle was 31.4 days and the range 22 to 46. The sexual-skin swelling lasts about 17 days in various baboons. Details of this swelling as to size and location are unnecessary here. It is enough to say that it is very large and very bright-red. Such swellings, which are confined to females, do not occur before puberty, but they precede the onset of menstruation. The duration of pregnancy is difficult to determine because baboons copulate during pregnancy. Six pregnancies of the hamadryas baboon in the London Zoological Gardens, on the basis of estimates, averaged 171 days, which is exactly the average for the pig-tailed macaque as estimated by Zuckerman. The hamadryas baboon nurses her baby for about 5 months, during which time the sexual skin is inactive. In fact, Zuckerman says that the rhesus monkey is the only subhuman primate in which the sexual skin remains active after parturition.

Baboon females toward the end of pregnancy become subdued and inactive. Such a female spends most of the day sitting quietly beside her overlord. In monogamous families the male has his activity restricted by the female's condition and the entire group life is slowed down.

MATERNAL CARE OF THE YOUNG. Only one baby born in the London hamadryas colony survived and the opportunities for studying parental care were very limited. Apparently, the newly born baby does not leave its mother's arms for a fortnight and may not set foot on the ground before the sixth week. Mothers watch their offspring carefully and at the first sign of danger or fighting gather the young to their bosoms. In the earliest stages the youngster clings to the hair on the mother's belly. Later it rides on her back. Mothers usually do not play with their young and fathers never, although a male has been seen to tease a baby, and one baboon father was once observed to gather up his infant, embrace it, and walk a few paces with it, after which it ran back to its mother. Baboon mothers have not been seen

⁵Zuckerman 1932b, p. 91.

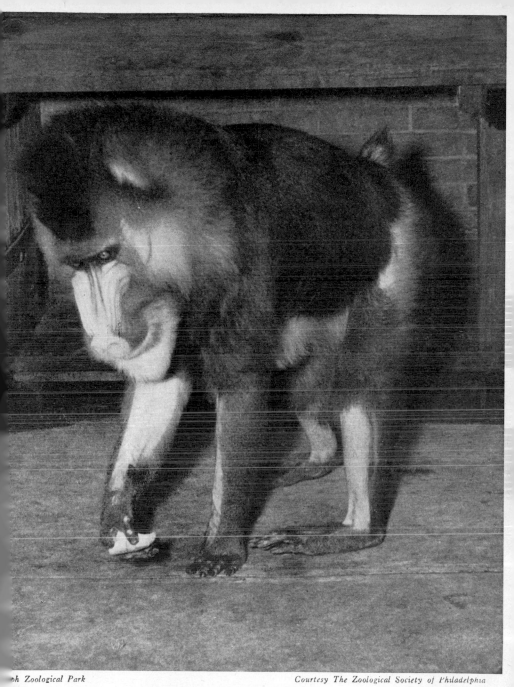

ADULT MALE MANDRILL

to try to teach their offspring to walk, although they will reach out and pull the baby back if it moves away too far. At the age of 4 months the movements of the young baboon are fairly well co-ordinated, and when the family moves it may follow by itself, jump on the mother's back, or cling to the hair of her belly. When it gets to be about 6 months old, the young baboon wanders around with other youngsters and spends a good deal of time moving about in the colony. As a young animal passes adults of either sex, they characteristically smack their lips and reach out and touch it with their hands. Often females pick up a young animal, embrace and groom it, and then play with it. Apparently, females play with infants which are not theirs, but not with their own. The play of the females with the young is described as a dance "built up of incompletely formed somersaults." The bachelors associate elaborately and intimately with the young animals, but do not play with them.

YOUNG BABOONS. Young baboons are very playful and active. They do a good deal of fighting, tumbling, and chasing. They also like to tease and torment each other. Zuckerman records an instance of two immature baboons teasing a crippled adult male until they were set upon and driven off by a larger immature animal. Whatever objects are thrown into the enclosure are taken up and played with by the young baboons. Bags are carried in the hands, baskets put on the head. They love to tinker. In Munich, Zuckerman has seen baboons playing with toads which they had dug up out of the wet earth. In play one baboon may ride another jockey-fashion or by clinging to his belly. Often these youngsters attach themselves to bachelors, with whom they carry on grooming and sexual activities. An older animal folds one of these young friends in his arms, as the mother nurses her baby. Even an overlord may thus embrace a young animal.

The immature and very young animals soon learn to use the sexual approach as a means of warding off attacks and gaining favors. When they are afraid, they make sexual presentations. They also masturbate and mount each other. Similarly, they mount and are mounted by adults of both sexes and engage in genital examinations. A playful trick of the young animals is to terminate sexual activity by biting the partner and then running away. As the young males grow up, their greenish brown coats turn to gray; they grow a mantle, and join the band of bachelors as equals.

COLOR VISION

Grether tested one Guinea baboon (*Papio papio*) for color vision and found that in difference limens (thresholds) and complementary color mixtures this animal compared favorably with man.[6] Optimal complementary mixture for the baboon resembled human optimal mixture more than did that of any of the other monkeys. The baboon required only 32 per cent of additional red in the mixture to match white, as compared with human beings tested. This finding seems to refute any idea that color vision in the baboon is inferior to that of the more arboreal monkeys.

INTELLIGENCE

In spite of the elongated snout and generally bestial appearance of baboons, these primates are not inferior in intelligence to most other monkeys. On the contrary, Maslow and Harlow found them definitely superior to the rest of the Old World monkeys which they tested.[7] They experimented with 12 baboons and 13 other catarrhine monkeys. Successful delayed responses after an interval of 120 seconds are typical of baboons, whereas other Old World monkeys can usually manage, at best, only 30- to 60-second delays. The role of bodily orientation in delayed action is of some interest. It apparently plays no important part in the more able animals. Baboons typically roam about during the period of delay. Maslow has seen a yellow baboon retire to the inner compartment of his cage during the delay, come out when called, and make the correct response after 180 seconds' delay. Harlow reported one of these animals as copulating with his mate during the delay. But lemurs, platyrrhine monkeys, and even gibbons are disturbed by unfavorable placing of reaction cups or other circumstances of orientation.

THE GELADA BABOON (*Theriopithecus gelada*)

The gelada baboon is an inhabitant of Abyssinia and is not unlike the hamadryas baboon. The nostrils are set on either side of the nose rather than terminally. The body is massive and large; the head is crested and the shoulders carry a long mane in the males. The tail is long and tufted, and well-developed whiskers are characteristic. The face is black, the nude chest red, the ischial callosities black. Mantles, back, flanks, whiskers, and arms are sooty brown, most other regions black or iron gray.

The geladas live in the mountains of southern Abyssinia at heights of 7,000 to 8,000' feet above sea level. These animals are found in large troops among the rocks and shrubs. They keep to the ground and subsist upon seeds, roots, and tubers, occasionally descending to pillage farms. The lateral placing of the nostrils distinguishes them from the true baboons.

[6] Grether 1939.
[7] Maslow and Harlow 1932, pp. 97–107.

THE MANDRILL (*Papio sphinx, Cynocephalus mormon*)

The mandrill is found in West Africa from Senegambia to the Congo. The mandrill and the drill are two species which are distinguished from ordinary baboons by the reduction of the tail to a mere stump and by longitudinal bony swellings on either side of the nose, which are covered with brightly colored hair and impart an unusually hideous appearance to the face. Further, the head is disproportionately large, the muzzle tremendous, the canines huge, and the lower jaw deep and massive. The eyes are deep-set under tremendous brow ridges, the forehead flat, and the brain case generally small. The ears are pointed. The forequarters are very heavy compared with the hinder region and limbs. The legs and arms are short and powerful.

The top of the mandrill's nose is red, the tip scarlet, and the rostral ridges which flank the nose are bright blue. The ischial callosities are violet, while the sexual skin around the genital and anal region is scarlet. The nose, instead of projecting in front of the upper lips, as in the hamadryas baboon, is somewhat truncated. The tubercular or rostral swellings of the bones on both sides of the nose are sausage-shaped and almost the size of a man's fist. They are ribbed transversely in light blue, with deep purple in the intervening grooves. The eyes are described as "hazel"; the general color of the fur blackish olive, darker on the crown of the head, the middle line of the back, the nape of the neck, and the flanks; lighter on the cheeks.

The top of the head has a pointed crest of dark hair directed backward, while the chin has a peaked beard of an orange-yellow color. The naked ears are pointed and bluish black in color. The brilliant scarlet of the middle and end of the muzzle develops only after the second dentition has erupted, and the swellings on either side of the snout are large only in males. In the young and in the females the swellings are blue only, and in very young animals the entire face is black. The length of the upper canines is given by Elliot as 44.2 mm.

THE DRILL (*Papio leucophaeus, Cynocephalus leucophaeus*)

The drill is another West African baboon which is distinguished from the mandrill by the absence of bright colors on the face, the naked parts of which are entirely black. The tail, which is short, is covered with hair over the whole of its surface, whereas the mandrill has a stumpy tail which is naked on its under side and carried erect and bent over the back in pug-dog fashion. The drill is the more slenderly built animal of the two, and the sausage-shaped swellings which flank the nose are smaller. The general color of the fur is brown, tending to whitish tints on the forehead and crown of the head, darker on shoulders and limbs. The ischial callosities are red.

CHAPTER VI

Domineering Macaques

INTRODUCTION

THE MACAQUE (genus *Macaca*) is the most common monkey of southeastern Asia and the Indo-Malayan Archipelago. In general, macaques have stout, compact bodies and relatively short limbs with well-developed thumbs and great toes. The snout is projecting, but the nostrils open downward short of the terminal end of the muzzle. The eyes are close together and surmounted by heavy brow ridges; the ears are naked. Cheek pouches and ischial callosities are present —the latter usually large. The tail varies greatly in length. The brain case is small, the canines formidable. The first and second molars in the lower jaw have 4 cusps, but the third molar, which is largest, has 5 cusps and a posterior talon.

SPECIES AND DISTRIBUTION

Elliot recognizes more than 50 species of macaques. These monkeys are found throughout India and south to the island of Ceylon, in Burma, Siam, Indo-China and the Malay Peninsula, in Singapore, Java, Sumatra, Borneo, the Philippines, Hainan, China, Formosa, the Sulu Archipelago, and Japan. The island forms differ considerably from each other, as would be expected from their isolation. The mainland species are fewer. In India, for example, by far the commonest form is the rhesus monkey, which dominates the northern part of the peninsula. Two other species occupy southern India.

Elliot, in his elaborate *Review of the Primates,* which is an authoritative but unsatisfactory book, divides up the species of the macaques primarily on the basis of tail length. This caudal member varies from a mere stump, 1½ to 3 inches in length, to one which is longer than the combined head and trunk.

200

Zoological Park   Courtesy The Zoological Society of Philadelphia

LION-TAILED MACAQUE

MALE RHESUS MACAQUE

THE RHESUS MONKEY (*Macaca mulatta*)
AND OTHER MACAQUES

The Bengal or rhesus monkey, the bandar of the Hindus, is found all over northern India. It has no beard or ruff and is generally brown in color with a tinge of.gray. It has straight, moderately long hair. The buttocks are naked for some distance around the ischial callosities. The tail is about one-half the length of the head and body, and tapers to the tip without any terminal tuft. In the adults the ears and face are flesh-colored, while the callosities are bright red. Elliot gives the total length of a specimen as 930 mm., of which.330 mm. is tail. The rhesus monkey is thus a good-sized animal.

The rhesus ranges from the Himalayas to the Godavari River in southern India. In.Kashmir it is found up to elevations of 5,000 feet, and at Simla. (where it is said to have been introduced) up to 8,500 feet. At this place the monkeys live on.a.certain.hill.and.are regularly fed.by a fakir, who has taken up his abode on.the same mountain.

Social Group

Dr. C. R. Carpenter has observed groups of macaques ranging in size from a single pair and young of *Macaca nemestrinus* (the pig-tailed macaque of Sumatra, the Malay Peninsula, etc.) to 150 individuals in a troop in the Waterfall Gardens of Penang, Malaya. In Thailand, Carpenter found that a typical undisturbed group of *Macaca assamensis* included 2 adult males, 6 adult females (2 carrying infants), and 2 juveniles. Another group had 4 adult males, 10 adult females (4 with infants), and 8 juveniles. The groups of semi-domesticated rhesus monkeys introduced on Santiago Island, Puerto Rico, ranged in size from about 13 to 150 animals. A group observed by Carpenter; which he considered typical, contained 6 adult males, 32 adult females (25 of which had infants), and 10 juveniles, making a total of 73 animals.

Females predominate in number over males in all groups observed except the little-known *Macaca nemestrinus*. Within organized groups the male is dominant over all other individuals, but not to the extent observed by Zuckerman in the hamadryas baboon. Males sometimes live alone and frequently more than one male is found in association without any female.[1]

[1]Carpenter 1941b, MS. p. 10.

SEX LIFE IN FREE-RANGING MACAQUES

The field work of Carpenter's study of macaques was done on a small island of about 37 acres, less than one mile off the southeast coast of Puerto Rico. The surface of the island is covered with coconut palms, scrub trees, rocks, and newly planted shade and fruit trees. Here were released, late in 1938, 409 rhesus monkeys which Dr. Carpenter had collected in India. On the first of March, 1940, the colony consisted of about 350 monkeys in various stages of development. There were 24 adult males, 16 subadult males, and approximately 150 adult females, the rest young in various stages. In addition to the rhesus monkeys, there was a small family—male, female, and infant— of the pig-tail macaque (*Macaca nemestrinus*). The animals had organized themselves into 6 heterosexual groups ranging in size from 3 (the pig-tails) to 147. The smallest heterosexual rhesus group consisted of 13 individuals and the average about 70. In addition there were 12 subadult males living in unisexual groups.

Since these monkeys had been semi-domesticated by hand feeding, they could be approached without disturbing their normal behavior. Large numbers were tattooed on their thighs so that individuals could be identified. Carpenter observed all day, from 6:30 A.M. to 4 P.M., for 2 whole months, with time out for meals and only 2 days missed.[2] He also observed the sexual cycle of this monkey for 3 additional months, "not quite so systematically."

The term oestrus is applied to that portion of the sexual cycle of the female when she seeks coitus with the male. In the rhesus monkey this condition is sometimes marked by swelling of the sexual skin and the bright red color of this region and also of the animal's face. It is further indicated by the active approach of the female to the male and by certain rhythmic lip movements, given with elevated eyebrows, a projected muzzle, and distinctive facial expression. Again, the female "presents" to the male by orienting her hindquarters toward him in a posture inviting copulation. There are also certain arm reflexes indicative of intense sexual excitement. These consist of a rapid flexion and extension of the arm and hand and are usually observed when the female is strongly aroused during a series of copulations. During this oestrous period the aggressive female is characteristically attacked by the male when she is attempting to form a temporary mating, or when she is shifting from one male to another, or returning to the non-oestrous female group. Grooming is markedly increased during

[2]Carpenter 1942.

oestrus and there is a very close association of the female with her male. consort, lasting perhaps over a period of days.

The sexual swelling is noted in only about one half of the receptive females and is especially extensive in adolescent females, although persisting in some: which have borne three or four young. It is usually accompanied by a raspberry redness, which bleaches out after consort relationship with the· final male is broken. About one tenth of the oestrous females develop an intense redness of the face, which persists after the swelling of the sexual skin. subsides and its color pales. The female in the early stages of receptivity becomes irritable and restless. She abandons her sisters and makes advances toward the males. If one of these follows her, she detours away from the rest of the group, an act which may cause the latter to travel much farther than normally when her consort happens to be the dominant male. This hyperactivity of the oestrous female, together with the attacks made upon her by males, causes considerable ructions in the entire group. When the female approaches the end of her period of receptivity, she becomes sluggish, unresponsive, and sleepy, especially if her oestrous season has been marked by numerous and prolonged copulations. This fatigued condition frustrates the male and incites him to new attacks upon her unless he is too exhausted. The aggressive oestrous female gets into trouble at first with the males she approaches and is viciously attacked, but she persists and ultimately gets her man.

Presenting, or offering the hindquarters, is not only the regular invitation of the female to the ready male, but is a greeting of playful juveniles among themselves, of females to females, males to males, and every monkey to every other. These presentations are a response to generalized excitement when a group fight occurs, when an animal wants to express submission to another, and in various situations.

In copulation the male mounts the female, placing his hands on her hips or her back and grasping her thighs with his feet. Thus she has to support all of his weight. In this position he makes a few piston thrusts and then dismounts, and after an interval (which may be less than one minute or as much as 20 minutes) repeats the procedure. True copulation occurs in series of mountings varying from 3 to over 100—the latter in males approaching sexual satiety. Obviously, most of these mountings do not lead to ejaculation. When this is imminent, the number of thrusts of the male increases and he shows tenseness or rigor, usually bares his teeth, and squeals. The female twists and turns, grabs the male, and tries to look at him. Carpenter with a stop watch recorded one series of copulations between a single male and female which lasted 40 minutes and involved 37 mountings, with thrusts varying from one (male yawning) to a final mounting with 22 thrusts. Slaps, squeals, grooming, arm jerks, and coy behavior on the part of the female, slight attacks by the male, and other interesting manifestations accompanied the series.

From the onset of oestrus the sexual motivation of the female rises in intensity to a climax and then gradually subsides. The duration of this period ranges from 4 to 15 days and averages 9.2 days. During this period of receptivity the female satiates one consort and then usually moves on to another. The average female has 2.93 male consorts during this period. The number of copulation series for a female during the period is estimated to range from 25 to 60.

Mating was observed for the Santiago colony of rhesus monkeys during the months of February, March, and April. During May and June no primary sexual activity was observed and there were modes of birth during August, September, and October. Thus a breeding season for this colony was established, but, because of climatic and environmental change, it does not necessarily correspond to the breeding season of these animals in their native Indian habitat. Dr. Carpenter attributes the precise time of the breeding season mainly to selection of specimens—females with babies—and to segregation during their shipment to Puerto Rico.

During 45 oestrous periods 22 females were observed to be attacked by males. Sixteen females were wounded, sometimes seriously. Fourteen of these oestrous females made attacks upon other females or upon subordinate males. Such attacks occur at other times, but probably much less frequently. The male is at all times completely dominant over the female, but shows an increased tolerance for her during oestrus. He may allow her to eat from the same food tray and he associates with her very closely. At this period the oestrous female, with the reinforcement of her mate, becomes the dominant female of the group.

Self-grooming and social grooming increase markedly during oestrus, possibly because of the effect of sex hormones in causing skin irritation, and certainly as a result of the wounds acquired during the period. A female may gain the tolerance of the male by special grooming.

The shift of the oestrous female from one consort to another depends upon a number of factors: the sexual drive and dominance of the male, the presence or absence of other oestrous females, and especially strong attachments between two animals. The period be-

FEMALE RHESUS MACAQUE

DR. C. R.
CARPENTER
AND MACAQUE
ASSOCIATES

tween oestrus in 5 female rhesus monkeys averaged 19.4 days. The length of the menstrual cycle is about 28 days.

Carpenter observed 8 different females indulging in homosexual behavior, varying from single and sporadic mountings to persistent association and repeated mountings. The female who plays the masculine role attacks the subordinate or receptive female in the same way in which males normally attack receptive females prior to mating. These active females then carry out irregular successions of mountings. They seem more strongly motivated than the receptive females. This homosexual behavior may be interspersed with normal heterosexual activity.

In June 1940 the Santiago colony of rhesus monkeys included two groups, exclusively male, one with 7 animals and the other with 12, varying in age from early juvenile to early adult development. Typically, the young male rhesus leaves his parent group in early adolescence and lives with other young males until he is adult. He then hangs around some heterosexual group until he is tolerated and finally accepted as a subordinate. He secures access to food and to oestrous females and eventually may become the autocrat. In the young male group the number of mountings is greater than that observed in infant and early juvenile development. These mountings may involve anal penetration, but they are not done in series. Active play, excitement, or the close approach of an observer may stimulate such behavior. The more dominant individuals play the male part. Attacks may be foiled by the subordinate's presenting and stimulating the attacker to mount him. There is also some tendency for the young males to pair off together. This behavior may be homosexual, but again it may be merely a stereotyped and patterned response to a non-specific stimulation.

In the organized heterosexual groups, mountings of male by male also occur, most frequently involving the more subordinate males, but sometimes the dominant animals. Young males who are trying to join the group often secure tolerance by submitting to being mounted. Among the more dominant males mounting seems to be something in the nature of a friendly greeting.

Sucking and pulling their own nipples was observed in a few females and masturbation in males. In 3 cases Carpenter observed completed masturbation in adult males who were associating with females. These are to be contrasted with the more frequent stimulation of penis by hand or mouth noticed in immature males. The latter seems to be a substitute for sucking the maternal breast in infants which have lost their mothers.

In 4 of 40 cases observed by Carpenter oestrous females went outside of their own ordinarily closed groups to copulate with males in strange groups. One of them even consorted with the male of the very small *Macaca nemestrinus* or pig-tailed macaque group. These animals belong to a different species. Such promiscuous behavior is probably due to the inability of the female to have her sexual hunger satisfied within her own group. Ordinarily, a female not in oestrus who attempted to join a strange group would be attacked by both the males of that group and the females, and would probably be killed. Thus oestrus seems to stimulate non-conformist behavior and what an anthropologist would call exogamy.

The dominance order and ranking of each of the adult males in the half-dozen groups of the macaque colony were carefully tabulated by Carpenter. He counted for each male the observed number of consort relations and the number of different females possessed. Thus in Group 1, which included about 85 animals, of which 8 were adult males, the dominant male in the 2 months of observation had 55 consort relations involving 17 different females. The No. 2 male had 33 relations with 10 different females, and so on down to the No. 8 male, who had one relation with a single female. Similarly, great differences in sexual achievement between dominant and subordinate males were observed in the other groups.

A female during a single oestrous period is possessed by from one to 9 males. The mode falls at 2 or 3, and the number of cases over 5 is small. Usually, the oestrous female is possessed at first by a subordinate male and later by the prime dominant male. When he has finished with her, she usually returns to the other subordinates. Usually, more than one female in a group was in oestrus at the same time, and in such cases the female might not consort at all with the No. 1 dominant male, or she might be possessed by several of the dominant males, one after another. However, when a single female was in oestrus, she was always taken by a dominant male. Degree of dominance of one male over another, rather than mere dominance rank, seemed to be the determining factor in securing possession of a female.

More females go through the entire oestrous period with one male than with more than one. The extreme number of shifts of consorts observed was 14.

FETAL GROWTH AND DEVELOPMENT

More is known of the fetal growth and development of the rhesus monkey than of any other primate save man, thanks, in considerable part, to the researches of Dr. Adolph H. Schultz.[3] This investigator studied a series of 26 fetuses of the rhesus monkey, most of them of known age. The average length of prenatal life in this monkey is 166 days, as contrasted with 266 days in man. The fetal period in man is 1.6 times as long as that of the macaque. Postnatal growth to the completion of the second dentition averages 6 years 10 months in the rhesus monkey and 19 years 11 months in man. Thus, man's postnatal growth period is 2.9 times as long as that of this Old World monkey. Of the entire life span 6.2 per cent is embryonic in the rhesus monkey and only 3.5 per cent in man. Birth is relatively later in the monkey. At birth this monkey averages only 435 grams in weight and has a sitting height of 189 mm., whereas the newly born human infant averages 3,250 grams and has a sitting height of 360 mm. The weight of the monkey at birth is only 13.4 per cent of the weight of the human infant, and at maturity this ratio decreases to 11.8 per cent. The macaque is relatively heavier at birth. The monkey at birth is also much more advanced than man in the matter of ossification (the changing of membrane or cartilage into bone). Birth then really occurs at a much later stage of development in the macaque. At the beginning of the fetal period man and macaque of the same conception age have roughly the same sitting height, but at the end of the fifth lunar month the monkey goes ahead and is bigger than man. The latter catches up only in the last 4 weeks before birth.

Most of the changes in bodily proportions which take place in the rhesus monkey parallel those observed in man, but the changes are usually much greater in the monkey. Some of the parallel changes include a relative decrease in breadth and girth of the trunk, a more rapid increase of the lower than the upper limbs, narrowing of the hand and relative shortening of the thumb, slower size increase of the brain part of the head than of the trunk. The relative size of the head is greater in young macaque fetuses than in human fetuses. The newborn macaque already possesses half of its ultimate brain size, but the human infant only one fourth.

The first hairs visible to the naked eye appear in both the macaque and man in the eyebrows, but in the tenth week in case of the monkey and the sixteenth to nineteenth week in man. These hairs are colorless. A macaque fetus 100 days old has black, long eyebrows meeting in the middle line; fine, short, unpigmented eyelashes; black mustache, a few other hairs on the cheek and the scalp, and some long dark hairs on the tip of the tail. The trunk and limbs are still hairless. Between the ages of 100 and 120 days there is a decided increase in both number

[3] Schultz 1937, pp. 71–98.

and density of scalp hairs, but during the remainder of fetal life the number remains constant and the density diminishes. During post-natal growth the density decreases still further, although the number of hairs becomes somewhat larger. The fetus of 145 days has a hairy covering as dense and as heavily pigmented as the newly born, but the hair growth on the head is ahead of that on the trunk and limbs, and the hair on the upper limbs and on the thoracic portion of the back is more advanced than that on the lower limbs and on the abdominal part of the trunk. This is a general embryonic sequence found in other mammals.

Change in the skin color of the fetal rhesus monkey from pale pink in very early specimens to very light gray-brown does not become noticeable until about the 125th day—some time after definite pigment has appeared in the hairy coat. The darkening of the nails of the fingers and toes appears a little earlier—about the 120th day. The pigment in the skin is visible in the rhesus monkey only a very little earlier than in the chimpanzee fetus, but much earlier than in the colored races of man.

The ischial callosities of the macaque can be seen in the fetus of 75 days as heart-shaped areas of thick, smooth, white skin between the anus and the scrotum. In all Old World monkeys these are much more precocious in their appearance than in gibbons and siamangs. In these small anthropoids the callosities do not appear until shortly before, or even after, birth, and replace a coat of primary hair. In all older macaque fetuses the testes have descended into the scrotum.

In young macaque fetuses there is to be seen a threadlike filament, hairless and thickened at the end, which terminates the tail. This caudal filament usually disappears before the age of 100 days, but sometimes persists to a later stage. In man this caudal filament has a very brief existence in embryonic life, but it may also last to later stages of fetal existence. In a male white fetus with a sitting height of 140 mm. Schultz detected an extremely small and hairless appendage at the tip of the coccyx, consisting of a tiny knob attached to the body by a short, cutaneous thread.

It is interesting to note that in the course of embryonic growth the eyes and the nostrils of the macaque move closer together. In a 75-day-old fetus figured by Schultz the septum between the nostrils is as wide as in New World monkeys and the nostrils are directed almost laterally. The parallel bones which form the roof of the nose become fused together before birth, a sign of the retrogression of this feature. In the anthropoid apes these bones fuse in childhood, and in man rarely at all, except in individual Negroids. In the youngest macaque fetuses the hinder and upper parts of the ears are folded forward and it is not until after the fifty-seventh day that the ears lie flat against the head.

MATERNAL BEHAVIOR

Yerkes observed the behavior of a macaque mother which had given birth to a dead baby. She and her male consort (not the baby's father) both groomed it, and she carried it with her wherever she went, until by decomposition and handling it was reduced in the course of 5 weeks to a mere strip of skin.[4] Yerkes in 1915 interpreted the behavior of this macaque as a manifestation of maternal instinct, but Zuckerman, who has seen a number of primates retain dead bodies of their fellows and carry them around, is inclined to regard this behavior as fundamentally the monkey's reaction to a furry object.[5]

POSTNATAL GROWTH

Zuckerman and Fisher have studied the growth of the brain relative to body weight in 66 female and 42 male rhesus monkeys, with additional data on body weight in a considerably larger number of these monkeys.[6] Schultz has studied the eruption of the teeth, both as to time and order, so that some general classification of age of macaques can be made on this basis, even when their actual chronological age is not known.[7] The young macaque cuts its first permanent molar teeth probably at the age of 20 to 21 months. The females are slightly precocious as compared with the males. The next to the last teeth cut are the canines at the age of 51 to 52 months. The third molars, or wisdom teeth, are seemingly late and irregular in their eruption. Omitting them, it would appear that the permanent teeth are erupted at about the age of 4 years 3 months. The wisdom teeth may not appear until the animal is 9 months old or more. Rhesus monkeys between the ages of 6 and 24 months which have not yet cut any permanent teeth average 2.44 kilos for males and 2.40 kilos for females (roughly 5.38 pounds for each sex). Animals which have erupted all their teeth or all except the last molars, aged about 4 years and upward, average 5.51 kilos for males (12.15 pounds), and 4.79 kilos for females (10.56 pounds). The brain of this monkey increases in weight about 10 per cent between the eruption of the first molars and of the permanent incisors and second molars. Thereafter no significant

[4] Yerkes 1915, pp. 403–05.
[5] Zuckerman 1932b, p. 299–302.
[6] Zuckerman and Fisher 1937, pp. 529–38.
[7] Schultz 1935, pp. 489–581.

brain growth occurs. The mean weight of the brain of the adult male rhesus monkey is 89.45 grams and of the female 82.03 grams. Comparative data on other primates indicate that the brain of the chimpanzee probably grows about 10 per cent between the eruption of the first and second molars. Thus the brain of this anthropoid apparently grows longer than does that of the macaque.

SEXUAL DEVELOPMENT OF PIG-TAILED MACAQUE

Zuckerman has described the general and sexual development of a pig-tailed monkey born in the London Gardens.[8] The father was removed from the cage at the time of the birth. As the movements of the baby macaque became co-ordinated, it began to move over and explore its mother's fur. She often reacted by pulling away its hands and feet. After 3½ weeks, the monkey began to leave its mother's arms and to crawl along the floor of the cage and the perches. Its range of activities increased and it began to show an interest in monkeys in the neighboring cages. When hanging on the wire of the cage or standing on perches, it began to make rhythmic shaking movements of the body, which Zuckerman interprets as copulatory movements. At first these were ill-defined play activities, but at the age of 6 months they began to be accompanied by erections. Probably the play movements and the sexual movements arise from a common foundation. Next, this small animal began to display an interest in its mother's pudendal region and to explore it. Its attention was also attracted to the genital regions of other monkeys. When 6 months of age, it mounted its mother in response to her repeated presentations, and a month later this action was accompanied by erection and pelvic thrusts. At this time it was often observed to present to the mother and neighboring animals. This young animal was still taking the breast, was occasionally carried in the ventral position, and always slept in its mother's arms. Its age of 8 months corresponded in a human child to that of 2 years. Now it is probable that, if the father had been present in the cage, these incestuous activities of the young monkey would have been prevented, for the socio-sexual activities of this youngster with his mother often occasioned the displeasure of the father in the neighboring cage and prompted him to make violent lunges against the intervening wire partition. The mother was still interested in the father and frequently presented to him. The young male monkey was removed from the cage at the age of 16 months. Twenty-three months after the birth of this pig-tailed monkey the mother produced another infant, a female. As before, the father was

[8]Zuckerman 1932b, pp. 271–73.

removed from the cage on the day of the birth. The sexual development of this female followed the same course as that of her brother. At the age of about 7 months she responded to the mother's presentation by mounting.

DOMINANCE

Carpenter regards one individual as dominant over another "when it has priority in feeding, sexual and locomotor behavior and when it is superior in aggressiveness and in group control."[9] He considers that such dominance is of great importance in monkey and ape societies in establishing group integration. Animals within the same species and in the same organized group vary individually in dominance, even when of like sex. Carpenter spent one month observing a single group of 85 rhesus monkeys in which there were 7 males. By counting the number of times in which one individual took precedence over another, or manifested aggressive behavior, he was able to establish a dominance ranking which was completely definitive. The supremely dominant male, on the basis of actual frequencies, was 5 times as dominant as the second ranking male, about 6 times as dominant as the third, and more than 50 times as dominant as the last of the 7 in rank order.

Carpenter has also been able to demonstrate the relationship between the maintenance of a group's territorial range and the dominance of the males in the interacting groups. After determining the dominance ranking of the 7 males in Group 1 on Santiago Island, he captured and held in confinement, first, the most dominant male, then the next, and, finally, the third in dominance rank. He then observed the rest of the group for 5 consecutive days, following the removal of each dominant male. The important result of the removal of the most autocratic male was to reduce markedly the territorial range of the group. Previously, this group not only had its own exclusive territorial range, but at times roamed freely throughout the territories of the 5 other groups on the island. With the autocrat gone, the group was now restricted to its own coconut grove, especially at feeding time. Evidently, the wider movements of the group depended upon the dominance of its leader over males in command of other groups.

Yet Carpenter thinks that the extremes of dominance which seem to characterize baboon groups are not found in macaque society. The male despot of the rhesus group will make all the other animals wait until he has satisfied his hunger from a food tray. But during an intergroup fight or in leading the group from one place to another he will

[9]Carpenter 1941b, p. 18.

co-ordinate his behavior closely with that of the other males of his group.

A. H. Maslow's studies of dominance in Old World and New World monkeys provide most searching and illuminating analyses of this enormously important social and individual trait. In one set of experiments Maslow and Flanzbaum used 20 monkeys in various pairings, of which 17 were macaques of 3 different species.[10] Omitting interspecific pairings and two pairings of macaques in which dominance seemed incomplete or uncertain, the observers were able to summarize dominance in 10 pairs. The dominant animal pre-empts all or most of a limited food supply (97 per cent); assumes the masculine position in copulatory behavior, regardless of sex (98 per cent); does practically all of the bullying observed in a pair (98 per cent); initiates most of the fights (85 per cent), and is victor in nearly all of them; initiates roughly twice as much play (65 per cent), and shows an equal superiority in activity and exploration (65 per cent) to his subordinate partner; possibly shows a greater tendency to groom rather than to be groomed (62 per cent); is rarely passive under sexual aggression (1 per cent), and never cringes and almost never flees from the subordinate animal.

Maslow and Flanzbaum were not able to use sexual presentation as a criterion of dominance, as emphasized by Zuckerman in his study of hamadryas baboons, because the dominant animal presents almost as often as the subordinate animal and the latter often fails to show this behavior. There are also a number of situations in which presentation is by no means an attempt to adjust to a system of social dominance. This act may be a mere manifestation of playfulness, of curiosity, or it may be an attempt to lure an enemy within striking distance. There is also some doubt as to the significance of being groomer or groomee as relating to dominance. Some animals prefer the one role and some the other. Again, a subordinate animal can be coerced into submitting to grooming, but not into acting as groomer. Among chimpanzees Yerkes regarded grooming as a sort of social service, often performed more or less "altruistically." No such motivation can be attributed to Old World monkeys in their grooming activities. Dominant animals often force their subordinate partners to be groomed willy-nilly. A dominant animal which wishes to be groomed will frequently make a vicious attack upon a subordinate which has refused to groom. Dominance between pairs is established very speedily and often immediately. The status is recognized by attitudes and gestures long before it can be scored on the basis of

[10]Maslow and Flanzbaum 1936, pp. 278–309.

FORMAL AND INTIMATE VIEWS OF MACAQUE FAMILY

JUVENILE MACAQUES

overt activity. The observers compare the situation with the remark of a "trench-worn sergeant" during the last war, who said, "You go over the top, pick your heinie, look him in the eye, and one of you is a dead man before you start fighting."[11] In their macaques and other monkeys Maslow and his associate did not find that either size alone or fighting ability determined dominance. Rather it seemed to be a composite of social attitudes of aggressiveness and confidence, which had to be backed up by physical prowess when challenged. When two animals meet, they size each other up, and it is usually at this time that dominance is established. Dominance is generally achieved independently of food competition, although it is often sharpened by hunger. In 11 of the 12 pairs studied by Maslow and Flanzbaum the dominance, once established, persisted through the experiment. An animal dominant to another may be subordinate to a third, and dominance is by no means a masculine monopoly.

In a further study of dominance Maslow used 6 rhesus monkeys and paired each one with every other to establish the hierarchy of dominance.[12] This hierarchy was definite, so that from top to next to the bottom every animal was dominant over those ranking below him. It was clear that great superiority in size and weight was often a determining factor, although a small disadvantage in body bulk might be overcome by unusual determination and aggressiveness on the part of the smaller animal. When a third monkey, which is dominant to both of a pair, is introduced into the social situation, there are interesting new elements of behavior discernible. Punishment is then handed down from the middle monkey, who has received it at the hands of the overlord, to the most subordinate animal. The middle animal becomes more pugnacious and bullying than it was when paired alone with the subordinate. This middle monkey tries to ally itself with the overlord in picking upon the weakest animal, and tends to initiate the fighting and tormenting. Also, when an animal is attacked, other animals tend to join the attacker rather than rally to the defense. Thus, monkeys which have been dominant in pairings may be set upon by alliances of their subordinates and beaten severely. The monkey which Maslow determined to be last in dominance ranking in pairings proved to be the most vicious and aggressive of all when it was put into groups of four animals. Yet this same animal, a female, when subsequently paired with a male whom she had nearly killed in one of these group conflicts, was just as subordinate and submissive to him as she had been in a previous pairing.

[11]Maslow and Flanzbaum 1936, p. 304.
[12]Maslow 1936, pp. 161–98.

Maslow in another paper has discussed the difference in quality and manifestation of dominance between chimpanzees, rhesus monkeys, and cebus monkeys.[13] In general, the dominance of the chimpanzee is mostly of a friendly kind; that of a macaque is usually brutal; whereas in the cebus monkey dominance is both tenuous and relatively "non-contactual."

The dominant chimpanzee is a friend and protector of the subordinate, to whom the latter shows no fear. They are dependent upon each other for company and consolation and are often deeply attached to each other. They share food and play, and aggression of the dominant takes the form of rough play or teasing rather than of brutal attack. Chimpanzees in pairs are rarely scarred, but macaque pairs show by their old wounds the nature of the life-and-death struggle which determines dominance. In times of danger the subordinate chimpanzee will fly to the arms of his dominant partner for protection and comfort, and either one will resent injury or danger to the other. Again, the subordinate chimpanzee is more likely to show anger than the dominant ape, as a result of being teased. The subordinate will often fly into a screaming rage and attack, while the dominant animal will run away, "laughing." This sort of teasing behavior and exasperated response never occurs in macaque pairs. The subordinate never attacks and the overlord rarely flees. In a group of three chimpanzees the weakest is protected by the middle animal and seems to suffer mostly from the preference of the middle animal for the company of the dominant ape of the three. The worm may turn, but only petulantly, and the revolt occasions merely amusement on the part of the dominant animal.

Macaque, and, in general, Old World monkey, dominance is brutal, savage, and ruthless. The subordinate is afraid of the dominant animal, often to the extent of being utterly terror-stricken and cowed. No friendship is displayed. A weak or sick animal is likely to be set upon and killed by the stronger, and a subordinate is in great danger of starving if the food supply is limited. The subordinate always has to orient his behavior with reference to the dominant monkey; he or she watches the overlord fearfully, slinks about the cage, and is generally miserable. The dominant animal behaves as if it were alone.

The platyrrhine monkeys, such as the cebus and spider monkeys and the howler, are very low in dominance, and sometimes it takes a protracted period of observation to determine which of a pair is the ruler. In any pair the subordinate is likely to get 5 or more pieces out of 20 bits of food set out in the cage, and there is little squabbling

[13]Maslow 1940, pp. 313–24.

over the food, very rare aggression, and none of the persistent sadism observed in rhesus monkeys. Vocalization rather than fighting is the principal expression of dominance, and an animal attacked is more likely to scream until it is released than to fight back. Actually, these New World monkeys pay little attention to each other, either in pairs or in large groups. They rarely show friendship or dependence, and their roles in sexual behavior are not fixed. A subordinate animal may even mount the dominant.

VISION

Walter F. Grether's recent studies of vision in the infrahuman primates furnish new data on this subject and adequately summarize the contributions of previous investigators. In one series of experiments Grether used 6 rhesus monkeys and one pig-tailed macaque, in addition to a couple of other Old World monkeys and some New World animals.[14] None of the monkeys except the New World cebus monkeys had limens (thresholds of color discrimination) significantly inferior to those of human beings. In other words, they were quite as able to distinguish between red, yellow, and blue-green as were the men tested. But the cebus monkeys were definitely inferior in discrimination in the yellow and red regions of the spectrum. Compared to the average for 3 men, all the monkeys tested required more red in a complementary mixture in order to match white. The additional amount of red required was 32 per cent for a Guinea baboon, 79 per cent for 3 rhesus monkeys, and 270 per cent for 2 cebus monkeys.

Grether has also found that the visual acuity of the rhesus monkey, and also of the chimpanzee, is slightly inferior to that of the human beings tested as regards visual angle, but the difference vanishes when retinal-image widths are considered.[15] Cebus monkeys are slightly inferior, and pigeons and gamecocks markedly so. The density of the cone population at the fovea of the retina and the actual diameter of the cones are other major factors in determining visual acuity. Dr. Polyak supplied Grether comparative data on the number and diameters of cones in the inner and outer fovea for the rhesus monkey and man. In an area 350 microns in diameter these are 8,000 to 10,000 for the macaque and 12,000 to 15,000 for man. The diameters of the rhesus cones are from $1\frac{1}{2}$ to 2 times the cross-sectional diameter of human cones (foveal center: rhesus 2.3 to 3 microns, man 1.5 microns; slope of outer fovea: rhesus 3.5 to 4 microns, man 2.3 to 2.5 microns). Under these circumstances the equality of visual acuity is rather surprising.

[14]Grether 1939, pp. 1–38.
[15]Grether 1941a, pp. 23–33.

Intelligence

Since macaques are the commonest of all laboratory monkeys, they have been used most extensively by psychologists in experiments having to do with intelligence and learning ability. There is no unanimity of finding upon the position of the macaque in the primate rankings of intelligence. The debate seems to center about the comparative ability of the macaque, the commonest Old World monkey, and the cebus, which occupies a similarly undistinguished position in the New World assemblage. Maslow, Harlow, and their associates, in a considerable number of carefully conducted experiments, have come to the conclusion that the macaque and other Old World monkeys are distinctly superior to the cebus and the generality of New World monkeys in discrimination and delayed-response tests. They are inclined to place American monkeys not far above the lemurs. Baboons, on the other hand, are better than macaques and quite close to anthropoid standards of achievement.[16] Harlow found that certain Old World monkeys could solve two delayed-response problems concurrently, but none of the New World primates. However, another investigator, Koch, compared the learning ability of rhesus and cebus monkeys and found no difference, but the cebus monkeys learned the processes in about half the number of trials required for the macaques. In discrimination tests involving visual stimuli Galt found cebus monkeys far superior to rhesus monkeys and probably also to gibbons. A gibbon tested by Harlow, Maslow, and Uehling was not so good as the best of the macaques.

In problems supposed to test abstraction some apparent success has been achieved with macaques. One animal was found to respond to triangularity or to form per se. Another learned to respond to the odd of 3 stimuli. Gellerman found that rhesus monkeys could learn a double alternation of 4 responses in a temporal maze. A couple of young macaques were also taught the idea of the number 3. Another, in multiple-discrimination tests, learned to respond to the second from the left. Yerkes in early experiments upon ability in multiple-choice experiments with two macaques, the one a rhesus and the other an *irus,* was surprised by the slow progress of these monkeys toward the solution of the problems. They succeeded less well than did pigs. They also failed completely in box-stacking problems. As a matter of fact, Galt reports that De Haan is the only investigator who has found in monkeys an ability to solve box-stacking problems, and these were cebus monkeys. The macaques also failed in the box-and-pole problem

[16]Maslow and Harlow 1932.

Photograph Hansel Mieth

Courtesy Life Magazine

MACAQUES: ABSENCE OF FOOD-SHARING

GUENON MONKEYS: THE GRIVET

which involves the using of a pole to poke out food placed in the middle of a tube or long, narrow, and shallow open-ended box. They were also unsuccessful in problems requiring the drawing in of food with a stick or rake. Two Belgian investigators (Verlaine and Gallis) are said to have tested a young macaque on this type of problem and to have found him quite up to the anthropoid level. He is stated to have used objects as tools, to have fashioned tools, and to have negotiated obstacles and got round detours in drawing-in experiments. No other investigators have found macaques so proficient. One of Yerkes' macaques, an *irus* called Skirrl, seemed to have considerable imitative mechanical ability, since he was not only intensely interested in a hammer and nails, but learned by himself to drive nails with a hammer quite efficiently. He even drove them through the bottom of his sheet-iron water pan. This same macaque, when given a saw to play with, held it between his teeth, gripping the handle with his feet so that the saw-teeth were directed upward, and sawed through boards by rubbing them over the cutting edge. He refused to imitate the human method of sawing and persistently stuck to his own.[17] In this same series of experiments Yerkes made some casual tests upon handedness. The monkey, Skirrl, always drove nails with the left hand, but persistently took food with the right. Three other macaques seemed to show a preference for the left hand, while another was apparently ambidextrous, and still another right-handed. Yerkes did not consider his data sufficient to be of any great value.

EXPERIMENTS ON BEHAVIOR. Some of the most impressive demonstrations of the problem-solving capacities of lower primates have been made by Dr. Heinrich Klüver.[18] His experiments afford most interesting glimpses of the "intelligence" of the macaque. Three of these monkeys were taught to respond to the heavier of two boxes, which could be pulled in with strings to obtain food rewards, in the event that the correct box was chosen. The trials were begun with two boxes of the same size and appearance, one weighing 450 grams and the other 150 grams. In general, these monkeys made little or no progress for the first 7 or 8 days. Then they began to compare the weights of the two boxes by pulling upon the strings. Quickly, as these comparisons were instituted, the curve of errors began to drop, so that, in the case of one typical monkey, 30 trials were made on the sixteenth day without an error. These were animals previously unused in laboratory experiments. All passed from initial unceasing activity and restlessness to stages in which their activities were primarily determined by the

[17]Yerkes 1916, p. 108 ff.
[18]Klüver 1933.

stimulus objects. They would work quietly and persistently for an hour or more. Klüver then tested the stability of these differential responses to weight relationships by varying the relative and absolute weights of the boxes, by changing the material and appearance of the boxes and of the gliding surface, by altering the pulling-in devices, varying the distance of the boxes from the cage, increasing the number of the boxes, and even caging wild rats on the front of the boxes. None of these modifications upset the responses of the animals, although more errors were made when the difference between the weights of the boxes was radically reduced. Similar experiments· were conducted with success upon a cebus monkey, two spider monkeys, and an ordinary lemur. Of these animals, the macaques were the most rapid in their pulling movements. As a rule, they pulled the two strings in rapid succession, and sometimes compared when holding the two strings simultaneously. They often made as many as 8 comparisons in one trial.

A second series of Klüver's experiments related to auditory stimuli. In each of the two boxes was fixed a buzzer, which sounded when the cord was pulled taut and continued as the box was pulled in. The right buzzer gave a much louder and different sound from the wrong one. In the course of 28 or 29 days the macaques mastered this response also. Comparisons began almost at once, but made relatively slight difference in the number of errors. The buzzer sounds were then replaced by different sound pairs of a totally different quality, including doorbells, vibrator horns, etc. But these monkeys were able to "transpose" noises and find widely different pairs equivalent. After an interval of 200 days these differential auditory responses were well retained. Klüver was especially impressed by the smoothness of the comparisons made by the monkeys and the lack of pause between the pulling-in efforts and the choice.

The next set of Klüver's experiments involved visual relationships. In the first of these the macaques were taught to respond to the larger or smaller of two black rectangles pasted on the front of the stimulus boxes. The larger had, in the first instance, twice the area of the smaller. One of the macaques reduced his errors to 1 in 30 on the eighth day. In these experiments the monkeys made their comparisons by eye movements from one box to the other. Often they stood up on their hind legs and, with hands on the bars, looked from one rectangle to the other. Then followed numerous critical experiments in which the sizes and relationships of the rectangles were changed; triangles, circles, and crosses of different sizes were substituted for the rectangles; different distances of boxes, altered pulling-in devices, and other variations were tried. Evidently, size discrimination was fairly fine. There was some degree of discrimination when two rectangles differing in height—a 232.56 sq. cm. rectangle and one of 218.88 sq. cm. —were presented at a distance of 125 cm. In a pair in which one rectangle had 1.16 times the area of the other discrimination was made without difficulty.

Similar results were secured when the tests involved color and brightness of the stimuli and of the ground on which they were presented and changes in the figure-ground relationship. A very interesting series of tests related to visual acuity. In a perfectly dark cage a piece of opalescent glass was lighted from below and on this glass was laid the black thread attached to the food box. The illumination was then diminished until it came to a point where the monkeys had to locate the thread by mere fumbling. Klüver found that these macaques had no difficulty in seeing and picking up a .204 mm. thread at a distance of 28 cm. until the brightness was reduced to .007 foot-candles. He found, further, that a macaque was able to locate a .204 mm. thread in complete darkness by the sense of touch.

A great variety of further experiments involved strings put within easy reach of the monkey and arranged in various configurations by changing the direction, length, and distance between them, crossing them, etc. Only one of the strings was attached to food and the animal, to be successful, had only to pull the correct string. There were 128 experiments of this class. No matter what were the optical properties of the field, the monkey tended to move first toward a point directly opposite the goal and nearest it. Usually, he pulled in this shortest string, irrespective of its attachment. However, even during the short period of training, optical continuity became more important. Failure to obtain food by pulling in a string not connected with the prize seemed to emphasize the significance of the gap.

In connection with the various tests, Klüver kept some record of preferential use of the hands. One macaque used the right hand 1.76 times oftener than the left hand, another almost twice as often—both cases in picking up the string in pulling-in experiments. A third macaque used the right hand 170 times in 171 trials in picking food out of a box; another used the right hand only 28 times in 185 trials; a fourth used the right hand 73 times in 126 trials. In two monkeys tested in picking raisins from a turntable the preferential hand was changed according to the direction of rotation—clockwise or counter-clockwise. No generalization as to species handedness seems to be possible on the basis of these tests.

The macaques were given a comparatively large number of tests requiring the use of tools, or of objects as tools, but they failed to utilize them. Nor would these monkeys pay any attention to moving pictures which were shown to them.

"SYMPATHY"

Yerkes in 1916 may possibly have interpreted some aspects of animal behavior differently from the appraisal of the same phenomenon which he would make today after a quarter of a century more of experience in working with primates. The incident in question had to do with a young female macaque who amused herself by trying to stir up the other macaques to attack each other by pretending that she herself was the object of assault. She would then remove herself from the scene of the trouble when she had succeeded in arousing some older monkey to protect her against a pretended assailant. Presumably, in the course of this monkey business, she had been bitten in the finger by one of the animals in the next cage, for she was seen nursing the finger and trimming away the loose skin around the wound. She then. lured an animal in the next cage up to the meshes by making provocative movements and thrusting·her fingers between the meshes. When a macaque in the next cage, Gertie, attempted to seize her, she drew back her hands and quick as a flash sunk her teeth into the middle finger of Gertie's left hand, pulling and twisting and putting her entire weight into the bite, which went to the bone. Gertie retired, crying, to the other end of her cage, wringing her hands, sucking the injured finger, and, in general, making a great row. Thereupon Gertie's mate, Jimmy, who had been. watching in interest and perplexity, made several violent efforts to get at the biter, Tiny. Yerkes regarded this action as a rare exhibition of monkey altruism.[19]

OTHER MONKEYS

THE "BARBARY APE" (Genus *Simia*)

The so-called "Barbary ape," which is really a monkey, is found in the mountains of Morocco and Algeria and has been introduced on the Rock of Gibraltar. It is a good deal like a macaque and has been so classified by many zoologists. Elliot contends that it is not a macaque because it has no tail, the shape of the head is peculiar, and the face is oblong. He is not very specific about these differentiating features. This animal is usually called the magot by French writers. Although widely separated in space from its Asiatic congeners, the Barbary ape is undoubtedly the survivor of a European, generally western, type of macaque.

[19]Yerkes 1916, pp. 121–23.

This monkey is as large as a good-sized dog. The upper part of its body and the outer sides of its limbs are yellowish brown in color, with some deeper yellow on the head and the cheeks. The under parts are said to be a dull, yellowish white. The ears and face are flesh-colored, the hands and feet darkish or grayish brown. The ischial callosities are also pink or flesh-colored. The rudiment of the tail is a mere slip of flesh without any vertebrae in it. In fact, it may be said with some accuracy that this is the one practically tailless monkey. It was from this animal that the ancients derived their knowledge of human anatomy. It was described by Galen.

In Algeria these monkeys used to live in the forests of the Atlas Mountains, near the seashore. In the closing decades of the eighteenth century they were said to be so common near Stora, Algeria, that the surrounding trees were covered with them. They were said to live upon pine cones, chestnuts, figs, melons, pistachio nuts, and the vegetables which they could steal from native gardens. The well-known tale of sentinels, posted on trees or rocks to give warning of the approach of danger, is current in regard to these monkeys also.

The Rock of Gibraltar is the only place in Europe where wild monkeys are found and these are exclusively Barbary apes. No one is certain as to the origin of these Gibraltar monkeys—whether they are the remnant of indigenous animals or an imported colony. Monkeys ranged continental Europe as late as the Pliocene period, but became extinct before, or during, glacial times. It is certain, however, that the Gibraltar colony has been reinforced from time to time by other monkeys brought over from Algeria or Morocco. Before the middle of the nineteenth century there were said to be several troops of these monkeys on the Rock, but they became so much of a nuisance by descending to the gardens and robbing them that most of them were poisoned, trapped, or shot. In November 1856 an order was issued forbidding the destruction of the monkeys on the Rock and giving directions to the sergeant in charge of the signaling corps to make periodic censuses of the colony. At this time there were only 4 or 5 monkeys. The number was reduced to 3 in 1863, at which time the governor of the Rock turned loose 2 young pairs freshly imported from Barbary. These newcomers gradually made friends with the older inhabitants and the band increased slowly, perhaps, as it was alleged, because of the predominance of females. In 1872 two of them were shot by a newly arrived officer, who probably was not aware that the monkeys were preserved. He replaced them with 2 or 3 imported from Africa, but the local monkeys killed the immigrants. In 1874 a fire broke out on the Rock one afternoon and the wind carried it up the cliffs. The monkeys were greatly alarmed and after the fire an adult was missed. In 1875 the colony consisted of 6 adult females and 2 large males with several young. One of the males was mangy and had a bowed back. Apparently he was old and decrepit. The other was a powerful animal, judged to be nearly 3 feet long in the body and nearly 5 feet when standing on his hind legs. He was the leader of the band and kept it in order by chasing and biting refractory members. He took the lead when the troop moved from one part of the Rock to another. This large male was found dead in that same year. At the end of 1877 the colony consisted only of 4 large adult females, 4 females and one male of middle size, and 5 small animals. The band was then somewhat disorganized because of the death of the adult male, and there had been no births since 1875. In 1880 a young male, born in 1874, was master of the band, which was doing well. They numbered at that time about 25, and there had been 4 births in the spring of the year and several more expected in the summer. I saw the Gibraltar colony in 1915. It was then flourishing, and, presumably, still is.

Pocock, reported by Zuckerman, says that the sexual skin of the Barbary ape becomes turgid and slaty or purplish in color during every menstrual cycle. In the female the area between the anus and the externally invisible tail rises into a high, dome-shaped expansion.[20]

The "Black Ape" of Celebes (Genus *Cynopithecus niger*)

The "black ape" of Celebes is a little-known monkey which in some respects seems intermediate between macaques and baboons. So far as known this genus is restricted to certain parts of the island of Celebes and two small neighboring islands. The fur and all parts of the body which are naked are jet-black in color, with the exception of the ischial callosities which are flesh-colored. The hair on the body is long and woolly, that on the limbs shorter. The head has a hairy crest. The tail is reduced to a mere tubercle, not more than one inch long. The snout is markedly protruding, but blunt, the nostrils opening obliquely some distance behind the end of the snout. It is this latter feature which distinguishes the black ape of Celebes from true baboons, whose nostrils are at the tip of their muzzle. But the black ape has the longitudinal facial swellings found in baboons and very capacious cheek pouches. The overhang of the brow ridges is only moderate and there is some forehead elevation.

The ischial callosities of this animal are said to be small and divided during immaturity, much larger and nearly united in adult years. The black ape resembles macaques in being arboreal and fruit-eating.

The menstrual cycle of the black ape of Celebes varies roughly between 30 and 40 days. At the height of the swelling, toward the middle of the cycle, the undersurface of the stumpy tail is expanded and, with the circum-anal tissues, forms a bright red, spherical swelling continuous with the elongated, vulval swelling.

The Guenons (Genus *Lasiopyga* or *Cercopithecus*)

The guenons are African monkeys which constitute the largest genus of the primates. More than 80 species or races are recognized. They are found all over Africa with the exception of the Sahara and the Mediter-

[20]Zuckerman 1932b, pp. 90–91.

ranean coast region. In general, these monkeys have slender bodies and long tails and limbs. The head is round and the face is not very projecting, the nostrils close together. Whiskers and beard are generally present. Cheek pouches are large, but callosities are of moderate size. The hands are long, with small thumbs and fingers webbed at the base. The skull is flattened but has only small brow ridges. The orbits are very close together. The back lower molars have 4 cusps, with transverse ridges uniting the 2 anterior and the 2 posterior. The facial angle is about 58°, which denotes a relatively straight profile.

The guenons are among the most brilliantly colored and striking monkeys. They are exclusively arboreal and very active and agile. They progress from bough to bough and from tree to tree by leaping. Ordinarily, they do not make much noise, but they are said to be very inquisitive and ready to stop and examine any unusual object which they encounter. Their principal food is fruit, but they probably eat also leaves, birds' eggs, etc.

Bates, describing these monkeys in the southern Cameroons, states that they are not easily approached, because they are shy and very keen of sight and hearing. This observer says that guenons go about in companies of a dozen or less, with an old male leading. The leader may often be heard giving a gruff bark which is supposed to keep the company together. Solitary and, possibly, exiled males are sometimes seen.

The colors of the coat vary so markedly in different regions of the body and there are so many species distinguished by different characteristics of color and pelage that a fairly long printed paragraph is necessary for adequate description of each kind of guenon monkey. Anyone who is interested in these minutiae should consult D. G. Elliot's *Review of the Primates.*

According to Zuckerman in almost all the species of the genera *Cercopithecus* and *Erythrocebus* the only external sign of the menstrual cycle (of approximately 30 days) appears to be menstruation itself.[21] There seems to be no variation in form or color of the perineal region. The only known exception is the talapoin monkey (*Cercopithecus talapoin*), smallest of the Old World monkeys. In the one captive animal observed, the clitoris and the skin surrounding it expand into a lobe about an inch in diameter, and the skin surrounding the labia majora swells into a series of folds. Color does not vary and the changes are slow.

The Mangabeys (Genus *Cercocebus*)

The mangabeys are a small group of monkeys found in the tropical forest area of Africa, from Guinea and the Congo basin to Uganda and the river Tana in East Africa. They include some 11 species, according to Elliot. Mangabeys have slender bodies, oval heads, muzzles of moderate length, large cheek pouches and ischial callosities, and long tails. The fingers are webbed at the bottom and the great toe is united to the next

[21] Zuckerman 1932b, p. 87.

toe by a short web. The second and third toes are webbed for nearly their entire length and the fourth is united to the third and fifth up as far as the middle joint.

Mangabeys are lighter and more slender than macaques, with somewhat shorter muzzles, less overhanging brow ridges, and larger ischial callosities. The teeth, like those of macaques, present a fifth cusp on the last lower molars. Laryngeal pouches or air sacs are wanting and the stomach is simple.

The eyelids are white, but these African monkeys lack the brilliant coloring of the guenons. Most of the species are arboreal, but one is said to descend to the ground to seek food. Mangabeys are noted for "making faces," grimacing at the observers, and liberally displaying their teeth.

One group of mangabeys has a hairy crest and the other lacks it. The non-crested species are more brilliantly colored. Grays, browns, and blacks are the prevalent coat colors of most of these monkeys.

Coloration and swelling of the sexual skin are very marked in the mangabeys and have been observed in the sooty mangabey, the white-crowned mangabey, the white-collared mangabey, and the gray-cheeked mangabey. The menstrual cycle lasts from 30 to 40 days and the swelling begins during or soon after the menstrual bleeding. The swelling may be 4 inches in length, 2 in width, and 2 in depth. It disappears rapidly about the middle of the cycle.[22]

THE COLOBUS MONKEYS OR GUEREZAS (Genus *Colobus*)

The colobus monkeys, or guerezas, are a large African genus consisting, according to Elliot, of some 31 different species. They are widely distributed and generally present in the tropical forest area of Africa. The term colobus, coming from the Greek, means "docked" or "curtailed" and refers to the thumb, which in these monkeys is either absent or vestigial. Sir Harry Johnston collected three specimens of the red colobus monkey in the district of Toro, on the east side of Mount Ruwenzori, at an altitude of 4,000 feet. He states that the adult has only the minutest trace of a thumbnail in the place where the thumb should be, but the young ones have thumbs about as large as a monkey thumb would be expected to be in relation to the fingers. As the monkey grows the thumb dwindles.

An almost equally remarkable feature of the colobus monkeys is the elongated and sacculated stomach, a feature which they share with their Asiatic relatives, the langurs. Here, again, the specialization of the stomach is referred with probability to a diet which consists largely of leaves.

These guerezas have large brain cases and straight faces with comparatively small muzzle projection. The lower posterior molar has 5 cusps and the canines, as usual, are long. The cheek pouches are very small, the nostrils widely separated.

[22]Zuckerman 1932b, pp. 87–88.

COLOBUS MONKEYS

Note wide separation of nostrils and docked thumb on right hand

Guerezas are large monkeys with long tails. In some the hair of the sides of the body is so long that it hangs down like a fringe and the tail is tufted to such an extent that it resembles an enormous brush. Elliot says that the guerezas can be divided into red and black groups. The black guerezas have the long white fringe of hair which decorates their sides. The red species are rarer. Lydekker says that the hair of the guerezas can be distinguished from that of other African monkeys because it is always of uniform hue and not ringed.

The ordinary guereza of Abyssinia is said to live in small companies, inhabiting the highest trees it can find near running water. It is silent, but prodigiously active, and makes tremendous leaps from tree to tree.

THE PATAS MONKEYS (Genus *Erythrocebus*)

The patas monkeys are a genus of the family which includes the guenons. They are found about equally divided between East and West Africa. The patas monkeys are large animals with long slender limbs and long tails. The coat color is prevailingly reddish. The skin is whitish or pale blue, the face short but snouty. The canines are very long and curved. The top of the skull is flat. Some of these patas monkeys dwell in open country and plains. Yet the Senegal patas is described as descending from the tops of the trees to lower branches and hurling dry branches and other missiles at passing boats.

THE LANGURS (Genus *Pygathrix*)

The langurs are an oriental genus of slender monkeys with long limbs and long tails, short muzzles, and round heads. They have laryngeal sacs but no cheek pouches. A notable feature of this genus is a sacculated or pouched stomach. The thumb is very short, with a flat nail. A ridge of stiff hairs projects forward over the eyes. The orbits are large and close together, the brow ridges moderately prominent. The upper molars have 4 cusps and the posterior lower molars 5 cusps.

The langurs resemble the African guenons, but are distinguishable from them in external features by their shorter muzzles, shorter thumbs, and absence of whiskers. In their pouched stomachs they diverge from every other type of primate except the African colobus monkeys. This feature of the stomach is supposed to be a specialization of a ruminative character and may be connected with their leaf-eating habits. In addition to leaves, the langurs eat fruits and are said not to be averse to certain kinds of grain.

Langurs are mainly arboreal, although they move with ease and rapidity on the ground. Some species live at low altitudes and others inhabit high mountains and seemingly do not mind the snow. Ordinarily they are not brilliantly colored.

Langurs go about in troops. They are said to be peaceable, but fights do occur among the males. Langurs are found throughout India, in Ceylon, Tibet, Indo-China, the Malay Archipelago, but not in the Philippines. Elliot lists some 56 species and subspecies.

THE SNUB-NOSED LANGUR (Genus *Rhinopithecus*). In northwestern China, Tonkin, and Eastern Tibet are found four species of large monkeys of the langur type which are notable for their retroussé noses. The end of the nose is turned sharply upward, the tail is long, and the coat color is striking—orange, grayish black, blown with various white patches. All of these monkeys are large.. One specimen measured by Elliot has an all-over length of 1,270 mm., of which 700 mm. is tail. These langurs have heavier bodies and shorter limbs than the Indian species. They inhabit mountain regions where snow lies the greater part of the year. They are stated to go about in numerous troops. They are arboreal, feeding on fruits and on the leaves and shoots of the bamboo.

THE PROBOSCIS MONKEY (Genus *Nasalis* or *Nasalis larvatus*)

The proboscis monkey is an inhabitant of Borneo and quite the most remarkable in appearance of the oriental monkeys. It has a nose which projects a couple of inches beyond the mouth and is capable of dilatation. This nose is hooked, and the nostrils open downward and are separated only by a very narrow septum. The full development of the proboscis is attained only in adult males, and not in all of them. In the female it is much smaller and in the young of both sexes is said to be snubbed, like that of the snub-nosed monkey of Tibet. The base of this nose is cut off almost horizontally, so that, with its curving tip, it resembles a faucet. The nose in adult males is furrowed in the center, so that it appears double.. Nasal cartilages which form the soft portion of the nose consist in primates of a septum cartilage, a roof cartilage, smaller and larger wing cartilages on each side, and sometimes small intercalated or sesamoid cartilages. In the proboscis monkey the roof cartilage is an exceedingly small triangular plate on the upper edge of the septal cartilage, but the wing cartilages are not only very long, but also very broad in the middle. The prominent nose is entirely supported by the wing cartilages. The movability of the nose is due to the fact that the septum cartilage is too small adequately to support the tip.

The facial skeleton of the proboscis monkey differs from that of langurs in that the nasal bones which roof the nasal cavity extend below the level of the orbits of the eyes. In this respect the proboscis monkey resembles the macaques. The eyes are widely separated, the forehead low, and the jaws moderately protrusive. The canines are large. Over the low brow chestnut-colored hair is directed backward from a nearly straight line. The hair on the temples continues down as whiskers and beard. The naked face is of a reddish brown color. Proboscis monkeys are large. The length of the head and body of the male is about 30 inches, with 27 inches more of tail. The head and other upper parts of the body are chestnut-colored and the under parts ocher yellow. There is a white patch on the rump and the tail is whitish with a black tip.

The habits of the proboscis monkey are little known. It is supposed to be strictly arboreal and to go about in small troops. Hornaday saw them invariably in the trees over submerged ground. He says that they make a long-drawn-out and deeply resonant sound like a base viol, which might be written "Honk," or occasionally "Kee-honk." Mr. C. William Beebe saw one of these monkeys swimming in midstream, moving his arms downward and back in dog fashion, but with the body turned first on one side and then on the other. When he turned his head back to look at the steamer (on the Rejang River) his arms swept far apart, but he returned almost immediately to the dog paddle. Beebe thought that these monkeys had learned swimming because they occupy the delta region with half-submerged nipa palms and must frequently swim across the tidal reaches. The natives say that they often swim. The captain of the steamer on which Beebe was traveling fired at the swimming monkey, but Beebe nudged his arm and the shot missed. Then the monkey dived and remained below surface for 28 seconds, after which he came up a few feet ahead and swam on as strongly as ever.[23]

GROWTH AND DEVELOPMENT. Professor Adolph H. Schultz of Johns Hopkins University has recently published one of his excellent papers, giving for the first time adequate information upon the growth and development of the proboscis monkey.[24] This study is based upon 51 bodies and the skeletons derived therefrom. Ages range from fetal specimens to adult years. At birth the proboscis monkey weighs 0.45 kilos, or virtually one pound. The adult female averages 9.87 kilos (21.76 pounds) and the adult male 20.34 kilos (44.85 pounds). Thus there is a great sex difference in body bulk in these large monkeys. The birth weight of the female proboscis monkey is 4.6 per cent of its full adult weight, as against 6.7 per cent in the macaque, and 5.5 per cent in man. Proboscis monkeys, in contrast to macaques and orang-utans, do not become pregnant until their second dentitions are fully erupted, at the age of about 7 years. These monkeys have, in all probability, no set breeding season.

During growth the trunk of the proboscis monkey becomes more slender, but in old males there is a secondary increase in breadth. The shoulder breadth becomes relatively less and the chest breadth relatively greater with increasing age, but these monkeys have narrow chests when compared with higher primates. The relative length of the tail decreases in the later periods of growth. The lower limbs grow faster than the upper limbs; the hands and feet become relatively more slender during growth and the thumb proportionately shorter. The relative size of the head decreases markedly during growth. The cranial capacity of the adult female proboscis monkey averages 85 cc. and that of the adult male 102 cc.

[23]Elliot 1913, III, pp. 113–14.
[24]Schultz 1942a, pp. 279–314.

The face grows more slowly than the trunk, but more rapidly than the brain case. The skull of the proboscis monkey becomes more dolichocephalic in the course of maturity, as do those of the orang-utan and chimpanzee. The adult female proboscis averages 72.4 in cranial length-breadth index and the adult male 69.7. The face also gets relatively longer and narrower as adult years are attained. Eyes come closer together during the early period of growth, but the distance between them increases again in old males. Ear size is at its relative maximum in infants.

In the fetus, pigmentation of a gray-brown color first appears on the scalp, the digits, around the perineum, and on the already prominent nose, which latter is a deep slate blue. First hair on double-ovum twin fetuses consisted of dark long eyebrows and light and dark hairs on the upper lip and chin. The ischial callosities in these fetuses were already apparent. In these specimens, which had sitting heights of 119 and 124 mm., the ears were still of moderate size, the rims not yet rolled, and a marked Darwinian tubercle as well as a distinct lobule was present. In a somewhat larger fetus hair on the scalp was longer, and in a still bigger specimen the hair on the scalp was parted and had become reddish brown, while the outer sides of the limbs and back had a few short, reddish hairs. In older fetuses the hairy coat was complete. The nose in the fetus and in young infants is deep blue, but in later years it becomes brick red. The adult female has an infantile nose but in the males the nose becomes enormous, especially in old age.

The sequence of eruption of the milk teeth is nearly the same as in the macaque and quite similar to that of man, but differs significantly from the order found in the great apes. There is a high degree of stability in the number of segments in each part of the spinal column in this monkey. As in other primates, the cervical and thoracic regions become shorter during growth and the lumbar region longer. The epiphyses of the bones fuse after the eruption of the second dentition and in much the same order as in other primates. At birth the skeleton of the proboscis monkey is not so mature as that of the macaque. The sutures of the skull vault close after the completion of the second dentition, but the coronal suture may remain open until old age. The internasal suture in this monkey does not close until after maturity has been reached, whereas in macaques it disappears before birth. The bregmatic fontanelle in the newborn proboscis monkey is still wide open. This is a surprising finding since this "soft spot" on the crown of the head is already diminutive or non-existent in newly born macaques, chimpanzees, and orang-utans. Dental abnormalities and diseases are far less prevalent in proboscis monkeys than in anthropoid apes. No caries could be found in any of the skulls, although two adult crania showed alveolar abscesses. Healed fractures of bones occurred in 28 per cent of adult skeletons, as contrasted with 33 per cent of adult orang-utans and 36 per cent of adult gibbons. Two skeletons showed arthritic conditions of the bones.

ANATOMY OF THE OLD WORLD MONKEYS

Comprehensive descriptions of the general anatomy of the Old World monkeys have been given by Wood Jones[25] and by Sonntag.[26] The present brief summary is based principally upon these two authorities.

SKULL

Wood Jones distinguishes the catarrhine, or Old World monkeys, from the platyrrhine, or New World monkeys, by the following internal characters: In the catarrhines the jugal never articulates with the parietal; the fronto-nasal and fronto-maxillary sutures are practically on the same level; the premaxilla extends upward on each side of the nasal opening and may articulate with the frontal; the auditory bulla is absent; the tympanic annulus ceases to be a simple ring and from its outer margin is developed an elongated external auditory meatus; the palate is relatively long and the basi-cranial axis relatively short when compared with those of New World monkeys; there are 2 instead of 3 premolars, the uppers possessing 3 roots and the lowers 2. Sonntag adds that the frontal bone in the Old World monkeys articulates with the squamous portion of the temporal, thus cutting off the spheno-parietal contact. Wood Jones regards this feature as a catarrhine specialization, but says that it varies in the constancy of its development in different groups, and is not usually found in langurs. Again, in the interior of the orbit a fronto-maxillary suture is found instead of a lachrymo-ethmoidal suture. However, this specialization also fails to occur most frequently in langurs.

Both Sonntag and Wood Jones mention the fact that the muscular impressions leave strong markings and ridges on the skulls of the Old World monkeys, as contrasted with the New World group.

In Old World monkeys the interorbital space tends to be very narrow, so that the nasal bones make contact with the frontal over a very small area. The narrow, long nasal bones are fused together in the middle line in early life, often before birth.

The projection of the snout varies tremendously in the Old World monkeys. Projection is at a maximum in baboons, mandrills, and drills, but the other terrestrial monkeys of the subfamily Cercopithecinae, such as macaques, "Barbary apes," the "black ape" of Celebes, and the mangabeys, are usually more snouty than the Semnopithecinae, which are primarily arboreal.

TEETH

The semnopithecine monkeys, according to Gregory, represent an herbivorous specialization of the primitive catarrhine stock. The caecum is

[25]Jones 1929, Chaps. XXVIII and XXIX, pp. 216–36.
[26]Sonntag 1924, Chap. III, pp. 47–61.

enormously developed for the digestion of vegetable food and the two-crested molars are adapted for the cutting of leaves and tender shoots. The long, shearing canines, which have been specialized from the smaller canines of more ancient primates, are useful in piercing the tough rinds of fruits, as well as in fighting. In some groups, such as the colobus monkeys, the shape of the palate differs markedly in males and females, because of the enlargement of the canines in the former sex. These tusklike canines cause the upper dental arches to diverge anteriorly, whereas in the females they converge. Gregory states that the proboscis monkey is remarkable for an oblique downward growth of the upper jaws and a secondary antero-posterior elongation of the molars.[27]

The cercopithecine branch of the Old World monkeys and the semnopithecine division, although varying in length of face, are alike in certain dental characters. The first and second upper and lower molars are always divided into unequal anterior and posterior halves, which often bear high transverse crests. Gregory thinks that this specialization was acquired at a very early date. Such molars are called "bilophodont." Analogous developments are found among tapirs, kangaroos, and other animals. This early pairing of the cusps in groups of two, together with the relative unimportance of the fifth cusp on the lower molars, are characters, which, according to Gregory, rule all cercopithecoid monkeys out of the line of descent leading to the anthropoid apes and man.

DIGESTIVE ORGANS

Cheek pouches are present in all the Old World monkeys except the langurs and the guerezas. In these last two genera the stomach is long and sacculated, whereas in all the other monkeys it is simple. It has been suggested that the first compartment of the stomach replaces the pouches. The pouched stomach is reminiscent of the condition seen in ruminants. In all these monkeys the caecum is conical and lacks a vermiform appendix. The large intestine is sacculated by longitudinal muscle bands. The liver is extremely variable in size, position, and its manner of subdivison into lobes.

RESPIRATORY ORGANS

In the family of Old World monkeys the epiglottis is at such a high level that it is easily visible through the open mouth. Many species have air sacs communicating with the larynx. Tracheal rings are incomplete behind. The left lung has 2 or 3 lobes and the right 4, including an azygos lobe.

UROGENITAL ORGANS

The kidneys have a single papilla. The penis has a well-marked bone. The testes lie in the inguinal canal. The uterus of the females is simple

[27]Gregory 1922, p. 290.

with thick, short Fallopian tubes. There is no hymen. The external genital folds are not recognizable. The clitoris is large and penislike and possesses a well-developed preputium. It is not traversed by the urethra. Swelling of the sexual skin and the external genital organs is characteristic of the females during certain phases of the sexual cycle.

Nervous System

The brain in the Cercopithecidae is large and, according to Duckworth, conspicuous for certain details of specialization.[28] Foremost among these is the large size of the corpus callosum, an indication not only of the increased size of the neopallium, but also of augmentation of the association areas of the cortex. The cerebellum has also increased in bulk. The olfactory apparatus is small, but the visual area of the neopallium is well developed. There is complete apparatus for stereoscopic vision. The convolutions of the brain vary in complexity, but Wood Jones notes that a conspicuous feature in the entire family is the development of the simian sulcus.[29]

[28]Duckworth 1915, p. 138.
[29]Jones 1929, p. 236.

PART III

New World Democrats and Proletarians

INTRODUCTION TO THE NEW WORLD MONKEYS

THE AMERICAN MONKEYS are confirmed isolationists, since they have been separated from the other higher primates throughout their entire evolutionary existence as monkeys. They may indeed have evolved separately from primitive tarsioid or lemuroid ancestors which pioneered in the New World. In many anatomical features these New World monkeys are farther away from the anthropoid apes and from man than are their monkey cousins in the Old World. Thus the American primates, like lemurs and the tarsier, have three premolar teeth instead of two. In spite of this extra tooth on both sides of the upper and lower jaws, American monkeys are usually less "snouty" than Old World monkeys and anthropoid apes. The easiest way to distinguish an American monkey from an Asiatic or African simian is by looking at the nose. Nearly all American monkeys have a very wide partition between the nostrils and the latter are directed sideways rather than forward and downward. All the Old World monkeys and apes have very narrow nasal septa. They are called catarrhines, because their nostrils are supposed to be directed downward, although it would be more accurate to describe them as comma-shaped openings, placed diagonally. Again, the term platyrrhines is applied to the New World monkeys as a group. This word means "flat-nosed" and is no more accurate than the other. It is too bad that zoologists who give scientific names to animals insist upon using Greek and Latin descriptions when they obviously have "small Latin and less Greek."

If a monkey has a grasping or prehensile tail, it is invariably one of our New World primates. However, not all American monkeys possess such capable tails, although all of them have tails.

American monkeys consist of two families: the Hapalidae or mar-

233

mosets and the Cebidae. The marmosets are either the most primitive of all monkeys or the most degenerate—probably the former. The Cebidae are far more diversified and advanced. It is in this family exclusively that the prehensile tails occur. Possibly American monkeys are less greedy than their transoceanic relatives, because none of the former has a cheek pouch into which food can be stuffed and stored. Our New World simians also lack ischial callosities—garishly colored naked rumps—and, in the case of females, periodic and repulsive swellings of the ano-genital region. Their hinder parts are unobtrusive.

There is a sharp conflict of opinion between psychologists as to the comparative intelligence· of New World and Old World monkeys. Hemispherical solidarity inclines me to favor the American primates, but the reader must decide for himself. There can be no doubt of the contrast between these·widely separated monkey groups in their social characteristics. If you have any fascist leanings you will prefer macaques and baboons to howlers and spider monkeys, but if you are democratic or communistic you will share my partiality for American monkey institutions.

CHAPTER VII

The Communistic Howler

DESCRIPTION AND DISTRIBUTION

THE HOWLING MONKEY (genus *Alouatta*) is the largest monkey in the New World and the noisiest. The males of one species range in weight from about 16 to 20 pounds, while the females run a couple of pounds lighter. The average body length of 15 males was 114.6 cm. and of 16 females 111.1 cm.[1] The body is heavy and thick-set, the long tail prehensile and naked at the tip. The face is naked, but the chin is bearded. The brain case of the howler is depressed and the back of it is truncated. The face is large and projecting, with an enormous expansion of the hinder part of the lower jaw. The hyoid bone in the throat is inflated into a great bony capsule, which is lined by a continuation of the thyroid sac. The entire larynx is extraordinarily developed and there is an especially strong muscular arrangement which seems to act as a bellows in forcing blasts of air through the resounding bony cavity of the hyoid. Thus this animal has a specialized apparatus for making a prodigious noise, which it utilizes to the full, making the jungles of tropical America hideous with sound. The coat color varies from almost pure black to dark mummy-brown and walnut.

The howlers, which include a number of species and subspecies, are found from the state of Vera Cruz, Mexico, southward through the forests of Central America and South America. Dr. C. R. Carpenter spent a total of about 8 months observing the howlers, mostly upon the reservation of Barro Colorado Island, a densely forested island of about 3,840 acres in Gatun Lake, Canal Zone. This island is the seat of the Institute for Research in Tropical America. Carpenter also studied howlers in Costa Rica and on Coilia Island. All the facts in the account of the howling monkeys which follows have been taken from Dr. Carpenter's great monograph.[2]

[1] Carpenter 1934.
[2] Carpenter 1934.

HOW HOWLERS BEHAVE TOWARD HUMAN BEINGS

The commonest reaction of a group of howling monkeys to the presence of a man is to howl at him. As Carpenter says, "The males almost always come to the border of the clan nearest the observer and roar." However, after Carpenter got really well acquainted with a certain clan, called by him Group 1, they ceased greeting him with "defensive roars." The more infrequent the human contact, the more loudly and aggressively the animals roar when approached, except groups which have been hunted and shot at, which "pipe down" and conceal themselves or beat a retreat to the tops of trees. Two "significant" types of behavior manifested when an observer is near some group of howlers are the breaking off and dropping of dead limbs upon or toward the intruder, and, as Carpenter puts it, "fecal matter may be released with reference to the observer."[3] Here are some of the trials of the observer: "I would usually be sitting quietly observing the animals as they were in the trees above me. Either seen or unseen, an individual would slowly approach to a place directly above me or as near-by as possible, and then would release excrement, either urine or fecal matter or both." Carpenter has "seen" half of the group of animals, who were on a line of march over a blind, pause when directly above the target, perform, and hurriedly continue on their way. He does not regard this as a fright reaction, but a "primitive instrumental act." The present writer regards this as a dirty trick or perhaps a piece of monkey symbolism. Howlers also frequently yawn when an observer approaches, apparently from excitement rather than from boredom.

HOW HOWLERS USE THEIR HANDS, FEET, AND TAILS

The howler's thumb is not opposable, although, in grasping an object, the fingers move concentrically toward the thumb and oppose it at a sharp angle. There is a functional division between the first and second fingers, so that when an animal moves down a limb, the thumb and index finger are on one side of the branch and the outer digits on the other. The weight is balanced along a line approximately in the center of the palm. The hand is poorly adapted for delicate movements of prehension. Carpenter is inclined to guess that howlers are

[3] Carpenter 1934, p. 27. I should call this "saying it with flowers."

A HOWLING MONKEY

HOWLING MONKEYS ALOFT

ambidextrous, but wants more evidence on the subject. The great toe is fully opposable to the other toes and the animal grasps limbs and vines with ease and sureness.

The howler uses its tail to anchor itself to branches of trees when at rest or asleep. An infant about one month old will hitch itself to its mother by its tail when she is at rest or moving. The tail is also used for driving away flies and insects and for currying or grooming. The tip of it is used by adults to manipulate their genitalia. The tail is employed for grasping in locomotion and the animal could hardly do without it. The prehensile or business part of the howler's tail has a naked lower surface and is about 20 cm. long—roughly a quarter of the whole tail length. The flexibility of the tail decreases from the naked part to its juncture with the body. The functional arc of the tail is about 90° up from the spinal axis and 120° down. Laterally it is about 90° to each side.

THE VARIETIES OF HOWLER POSTURE

In a typical resting posture the howler sits on a limb with the rump and thighs in contact with it and with the tail coiled round the branch; the forefeet may be free or in contact. Starting from this position, the animal may lie down with its head resting on its arms, hind feet dangling, and tail extended and coiled round the limb; or all four feet may straddle the limb. Sometimes, when resting, the howler lies on its back, holding onto near-by branches with hands and feet or with the tail only. In feeding, the howlers are usually out on the ends of limbs, supporting themselves with hind legs and tails and using the hands to pull in leaves, fruit, and stems, which are then eaten directly. Sometimes an animal may feed for as long as 12 or 15 minutes suspended by its tail alone.

HOW THE HOWLER MOVES AND WHERE

The animal walks on all fours with the back slightly arched and the tail ready for business, feet and hands grasping the boughs. This kind of monkey does not make long jumps, but looks for bridges. However, leaps of 10 to 12 feet are made when necessary, but always with extreme caution. The young jump oftener and farther. Occasionally, when crossing from one limb to another, howlers swing by their arms. They can walk along a branch upside down as well as topside up.

Howlers stick to the trees. Carpenter saw a group on the ground but once in his long period of observation. Probably they have to descend to the ground occasionally to cross open spaces. They can swim when they have to; Carpenter marooned an adult female on a small islet and she subsequently turned up on the large island—a 50-foot swim away. The natives say that howlers swim with an over-hand stroke *"mismo un hombre."* Howlers often utilize the swaying of trees to help their progress. They wait until the branch is blown near enough for them to reach it and then go with it. A youngster will wait until an adult has pulled two branches together and then cross over this bridge. These animals also use swinging vines or limbs as conveyors, setting them in motion and increasing the oscillations until the pendulum swings are large enough to enable them to bridge the spaces which they want to cross. Compared with some other American monkeys, the howlers move slowly and for short distances. They almost always go in groups at a pace which Carpenter judges to be about equal to that of a man walking fairly fast. Movements occur in spurts, for distances of 25 to 30 yards at a time. Group progression averages about 100 yards an hour and rarely does a clan move more than 500 yards in a day.

HOW HOWLERS FEED

The newborn howler finds its mother's nipples, with her help, before it is dry and sucks frequently thereafter. The milk diet begins to be supplemented with solid food between 2 and 3 weeks of age. Adult howlers spend about one quarter of their time feeding, when food is abundant. The most active feeding takes place for a couple of hours in mid-morning. There is usually a siesta between 11 and 2 o'clock. From 2 P.M. to 6 P.M. another period of active group feeding may take place, and between 6 P.M. and 7 P.M. the group moves to a tree and settles down for the night. Howlers usually feed directly from the branches and do not handle their food or carry it away to be eaten. They drop and waste about one third as many fruits and leaves as they eat. An animal may sham feeding in order to get close to the observer or to approach another animal for one purpose or another.

Carpenter collected specimens of the leaves and fruits eaten by howlers and had them identified. The list is long and the trees are strange. It is enough to say that howlers eat a wide variety of buds, blossoms, fruits, leaves, berries, and nuts. The food is bulky and fibrous. Carpenter has removed as much as 3 pounds of mash from the stomachs of adult howlers, and the young do equally well in proportion to their size. The water content of their food is about 95 per cent. Howlers also lick water directly from leaves or branches or wet their fingers in water and lick them off.

CLAN TERRITORIES AND REAL ESTATE AMONG THE HOWLERS

Carpenter spent an entire month following one clan of 26 howlers and plotting their movements on a map. As a result, he was able to map the territory of this clan, which covered about 300 acres and was free from encroachment by other howlers except at two or three places which were trouble spots. The clan moved on the average about 200 yards a day, and when they reached their territorial limits they turned back. Within each territory are certain food trees and lodging trees which are regularly used. There were 22 other clans, each of which may have had its own territory. A clan which grows may enlarge its territorial range and, when new clans are formed, they may take over territories apart from those ranged by the parent clans. Each clan territory includes, in addition to food trees and rooming houses, definite arboreal routes and pathways. When the clan gets out to the edge of its territory, it becomes slowed up by unfamiliarity with the roads, and a good deal of milling about and frustration results, so that it eventually turns back to the known pathways and haunts.

ORDER OF MARCH

Howlers move in irregular formation, but at all critical crossings over from one tree to another most animals use the same route, one by one. Carpenter made a great many checks upon order of progression and found that adult males were usually the leaders, but no single individual male. Occasionally females lead. Mothers with young tend to bring up the rear, but immature animals occupy no particular place. Howlers prefer primary forests with their high trees to secondary forests or scrub, because they need high, interlacing trees. They get as far from the ground as possible. When two routes of different altitudes are possible, the howler "takes the high road." The various clans avoid each other and, when they do meet, indulge in what Carpenter calls "vocal battles," but which a less-refined writer might describe as the sport of "bawling out each other."

SOCIAL PITHECOLOGY OF THE HOWLERS

The first thing the scientific pithecologist (word coined for the occasion) does when he begins his methodical studies is to spot or locate a group and take the census of that group, rechecking many times. Thus Carpenter determined that in April 1932 the total howler population of Barro Colorado Island was 398 ± 50.[4] A year later he made the count 489 ± 25. In this later census there were 65 infants still carried by their mothers and probably less than one year old. Carpenter thinks that the rate of increase on Barro Colorado is about 15 per cent per year. Of course, this is a protected area. There is still plenty of unoccupied forest on the island. It might support a population of 2,000 howlers. The census does not include solitary males. These hermits perhaps constitute 3 per cent of the population. The 398 individuals of the first census lived in 23 separate groups and the 489 of the next year in 28 groups. The groups ranged in size from 4 to 35 individuals, with averages of 17.3 and 17.4 individuals to a group, according to the year of census-taking. The groups were quite variable in size. These groups contained nine categories of individuals: (1) males, (2) females without infants, (3) infants on mothers' bellies, (4) infants on mothers' backs, (5) infants more or less "on their own," (6–9) miscellaneous juveniles classified according to color, size, and degree of independence. You can tell a male by his beard, his scrotum, his large size, massive head, his vociferousness, and his leading activities in clan movements. There was at least one male in each group and the adult males constituted 15.9 per cent of the total population in 1932 and 16.8 per cent in 1933. The average number of adult males in a group or clan was 2.7 (of course the males come in units, but arithmetical means may not). Females who carried infants or were associated with more or less dependent young were about 16 per cent of the first census and 20 per cent of the second. Such females averaged 7.4 per group. Adult females without young constituted 27 per cent of the first census, but only 19 per cent of the second. These females averaged 4.6 to a group the first year and 3.4 the second year.

Carpenter classified the young howlers according to degree of dependence on mother, size, color, and method of carriage by the mother. Thus he distinguished three classes of infants and three of juveniles. The first class (guessed to be less than one month old) was grayish brown and carried on the mother's belly; the second

<hr>

[4] In case the reader is not familiar with the grim science of statistics it may be explained that the sign ± means plus or minus. The figure that follows it usually is the probable error or the standard error. Roughly, the probable error means that the chances are 50–50 that the true figure would fall between the limits of so much above or below the total stated. The standard error indicates that the chances are about 2 to 1 that the true figure falls between these limits. However, in the present case 398 ± 50 means that Carpenter thinks he ought to allow a margin of 50 above or below for animals counted twice or groups overlooked in the counting.

(about 6 months) brownish black and riding on the mother's back; the third, black, with lower incisors present, was sometimes carried or assisted over hard crossings and was judged to be 18 months; the next class, black, was at the weaning period, associated with the mother but relatively independent; the fifth (about 25 months) was black with a reddish mantle, still seen with mother and siblings; and the sixth (about 3 years) black with a distinctly red mantle and entirely emancipated from mother's apron strings or tail. In the second census the three classes of infants totaled 4.3, 8.9, and 6.5 per cent of the population, respectively, which was an increase over the preceding year. For the 51 groups of the 2 combined years, the percentages of the three grades of juveniles were 7.6, 10.5, and 5.5. In a period of 17 months Group 1 increased in size from 26 to 30. Two adult males joined up, 2 infants were born, and 2 young animals disappeared. Here is Carpenter's typical formula for a howler group: (Males, 3) + (females with semidependent young, 4) + (mothers carrying young, 3) + (infant I, 1) (infant II, 1) (infant III, 1) (juvenile I, 1) (juvenile II, 2) (juvenile III, 1) = 17 + (bachelor males, X).

Of the total of 398 animals in the whole population in 1932, 16 per cent were classified as adult males and 42 per cent as adult females. In the next census the males went up 1 per cent and the females were down 3 per cent. In the entire adult population males varied from 28 to 30 per cent, females from 70 to 72 per cent. Laboratory studies of howlers have shown a similar predominance of females.

MOTHERS AND BABIES

As soon as the infant is born it starts climbing up the mother's abdomen toward her shoulders and she keeps pulling it down toward her breasts. Soon the infant begins to suckle. About this time the mother starts in cleaning the baby thoroughly with tongue and lips. She may hold it up by the tail while she examines and cleans various parts of its anatomy. Females and juveniles look on, and some of the former advance and try to examine the baby. The tail of the very young howler infant apparently is not of much use for the first month, during which the baby rides or rests, clinging to the fur on the mother's abdomen. At the end of this time there is a short transitional period, during which the youngster rides sometimes on the belly and sometimes on the back. Soon, however, its permanent riding position is on the rump, with its tail coiled firmly round the base of the maternal tail. This rump-riding continues for about one year or until the infant weighs 1,500 to 2,000 grams.

On the whole, the mothers seem not oversolicitous toward the young. The latter do all of the demanding, or, as Carpenter says, "behave parasitically with reference to her." However, a mother will break out of the line of march and get down so that her youngster can mount to the saddle; she will retrieve a baby which has fallen to the ground, and will help young ones cross difficult places. The young howlers who are just beginning to achieve independence are those which fall most frequently. When such an accident happens there is a tremendous uproar in the band. All the males yell and everybody looks toward the ground. The mother wails and behaves frantically. All stop feeding and approach the ground. Apparently it is the mother's job to go down and get the youngster. The commonest way for a mother to help a young one to make a difficult crossing is for her to bridge the gap with her own body so that the little howler can walk across over her.

The howler mother seems to do very little teaching of her offspring. She may move away from the infant a short distance to encourage it to try to walk toward her. The young crouch under the lee of the mother at night. Sometimes the young are carried by animals other than their mothers, and in such cases a mother eventually will go and take back her offspring. There is no question of mothers' getting mixed up in the identities of their babies and vice versa. An infant is weaned or partially weaned before the mother bears another, and perhaps during the latter period of her next pregnancy. Mothers wean their infants by cuffing and biting them when they attempt to suckle. The weaning is judged by Carpenter to take place when the infant is between 1½ and 2 years old.

FEMALES AMONG THEMSELVES

The females, with or without young, hang together and get along peacefully. Eight or 10 may feed in the same tree and they respond en masse to disturbing situations. Yet they do not co-operate with each other. They may group around a mother with a new baby and try to touch it, but they do not help her, even when she is crippled. A crippled animal delays the entire group, because it gives cries of distress when left behind, and all stop and wait for it to come up. If the females co-operate not at all, likewise they do not compete.

JUVENILE RELATIONS

Howlers may play with their own anatomy or with external objects, but their most important play is with mates of their own age, or nearly so. One of the favorite types of play is wrestling while suspended by the tail. Another is chasing each other up and down trees, often following a definite circuit. The young howlers spend about as much time in play as in feeding. This activity increases up to the age of 2 or 3 years and then declines. Young howlers are frequently jealous of the new baby and try to pull it away from the mother or wedge themselves between her and it. As they get older, play becomes rougher and rougher and begins to take on the character of fighting. Then they begin to hurt each other and gradually stop playing.

MALE AND FEMALE RELATIONS— MOSTLY SEXUAL

Female howlers have a definite oestrous period (i.e., at certain times they are "in heat"). During this time the female is aggressive in a sexual sense and very provocative. She "solicits" one male after another, taking on the first who is receptive to her advances, or passing on to the next if rebuffed. The response of the males is variable. When a male is first associated with an oestrous female, he is likely to make the advances, but as he approaches satiation, she becomes more and more importunate and aggressive.[5] A precursor to "primary sexual activity" is an exchange of "rhythmic tongue movements between the animals." This exchange, as I understand it, is not kissing but tongue-wagging, in the sense of the animal's opening its mouth, sticking out its tongue, and moving it rapidly in and out and up and down, without contact. These "lingual gestures," if mutual, are a sure sign of sexual readiness and almost certain to prelude copulation. Carpenter says that it seems significant to him "that these gestures are made with the tongue, an organ which is primary in the production of speech."[6] The female may, from time to time, display a preference for this or that male of the group, but on the whole she is promiscuous. Nor are the males jealous or competitive. The howlers appear to conduct their sexual affairs in peace and quietude.

Although there is ample evidence that howlers breed all the year round and young of all sizes may be observed in the summer months,

[5]Carpenter has treated this subject in great detail and with a wealth of statistical elaboration. The data are most instructive but hardly romantic. The present writer, who confesses himself to be a coarse-minded individual, finds some of this material, in spite of the scientific gravity and detachment with which it is presented, quaint. The following is quoted shamefacedly: "For 19 copulations the period of adjustment was 9.7 ± 5.7 seconds; the period of intromission in 25 instances was 21.8 ± 2.8 seconds, and the number of thrusts averaged 16.9 ± 4.8."

[6]Carpenter 1934, p. 89.

there is also a definite oestrous period in the female during which sexual activity is greatly increased.

There is no monogamy among the howlers, since a female in oestrus is not satisfied with a single male, and there are, in any event, no dominant males who would monopolize her attentions.

PATERNAL AND OTHER MALE-YOUNG RELATIONS

Males are generally indifferent toward young howlers, but may occasionally tolerate their attempts to play with them. More rarely they display pugnacity toward their juniors. An adult male may warn younger monkeys of danger by grunting and advancing toward the source of the danger. He may stop play-fighting among the youngsters when it has gone so far that someone is getting hurt. A male may also retrieve a fallen youngster and carry it on his back in the position in which it usually rides its mother. There is no evidence of antagonism of adult males against the growing juveniles.

MAN-TO-MAN RELATIONS

The males of a clan are simultaneously stimulated by any event and react in concert, usually by roaring. When the group is looking for new arboreal pathways, each male explores on his own for a distance and then returns to the clan. If he has found a satisfactory route, he indicates it by a deep clucking sound; then the rest of the males stop exploring and the whole clan falls into line and moves over the route. But there is no stated leadership—no sheep-through-the-gapishness. Nor do the adult males often fight with each other for food, females, or anything else. They are peacefully co-operative and there is neither dominance nor subordination. All of this makes for smooth and efficient communal life.

Solitary, bachelor, or "complemental" adult males are sometimes seen. Usually, or frequently, they seem to be in the position of trying to attach themselves to a clan group. On such occasions the clan males generally intervene and warn off the intruder with defensive roars, but Carpenter has studied certain cases in which a bachelor attempted "to crash the party" over a period of months, and finds that the outsider is gradually adopted into the clan. Such males must have come from other groups and they are not feeble or decrepit animals which have been driven out, but often young adult or active, mature specimens. They serve as cross-breeders between the various clans. Sometimes they are accepted rapidly, sometimes gradually.

MALE BLACK HOWLER (*left*) AND FEMALE RED SPIDER MONKEY, EACH AGED 20 MONTHS

GOVERNMENT AND CONTROL
IN HOWLER SOCIETY

Mothers start out controlling their infants by pushing, pulling, and handling. Soon the infants learn to take certain actions at preparatory signals or movements on the part of the mother. She adopts a certain posture and the young one knows she is going to move and gets on her back or clings to her belly. Thus contact control is eliminated at an early stage. Posturing and gesticulation also serve to some extent for distant signaling. The most notable gesticulation is the tongue-wagging which is a sign of sexual interest. Carpenter describes 9 different types of sounds or vocalizations given by specific animals under definite situations or stimuli, responded to by other animals in a set manner and, apparently, with a well-marked purpose or function. The description of these distinctive vocalizations and the situations in which they occur would occupy too much space in this summary of howler sociology. Actually, Carpenter thinks that the number of different kinds of vocal signals is in the neighborhood of 15 or 20, but he could not describe and analyze to his own satisfaction more than 9. Here may be cited one clear-cut example: a deep, hoarse, clucking sound given by the leading male at the beginning of progression or in the middle of it. It is a directive clue for the rest and is uttered only by the leading animal. Vocal noises may be directive, inhibitory, warning, or they may express distress—for example, the wailing groan given by a mother when her infant falls. But this sound also orients the clan toward the disaster and points the need of recovery.

Howler clans which grow too large for convenient communal direction and progression apparently split up. A large clan may tend toward two or more distinct subgroupings and eventually these may separate. If females and their young should be separated from a clan, it is probable that they would be joined by bachelor males.

Different clans, as a rule, avoid contact, but when they do come close, the males advance and howl at each other. These vocal combats rarely end in real tooth-and-nail encounters. After a while both clans retreat. No sexual activity takes place between clans except through the medium of the loose or complemental males. There is little or no clan competition for feeding places. As far as Carpenter can ascertain, the various species of howling monkeys behave alike.

The principal enemies of the howling monkeys are the ocelot and man. The latter is much more destructive and dangerous than the former. Probably an ocelot occasionally catches and kills a young howler, but most attacks are defeated by the males—mainly, perhaps, by the prodigious noise which they set up.

Groups of capuchin monkeys often occupy feeding trees adjacent to howlers and sometimes mix up with them in the same tree. No international antagonism is exhibited. Capuchins move very rapidly and cover a large range of territory. Howlers move slowly within a restricted area. There is practically no competition for food, since the different kinds of monkeys prefer different diets. Consequently, they get along amicably. No play or other social activity was observed between the different genera.. Capuchin bachelors often hang about with red spider monkey groups. Rates of progression are about the same in these different genera of monkeys and the foods eaten are quite similar. But the howlers flock by themselves. No other monkeys are commonly in contact with the howlers.

CHAPTER VIII

The Over-specialized Spider Monkey

DESCRIPTION

THE SPIDER MONKEY (genus *Ateleus* or *Ateles*) is the New World's closest approximation to an anthropoid ape, both in bodily proportions and in method of locomotion. It has the most perfect prehensile tail of any primate, with the tip always in motion and as sensitive as that of an elephant's trunk. With this tail it can grasp any object firmly and convey it to the mouth. The spider monkey's tail is also used as an organ of suspension. When the animal hangs from it, all other four extremities are free for grasping and exploration. The other New World monkeys which possess prehensile tails enjoy only a limited serviceability of this appendage.

The distribution of prehensile tails in South America is remarkable and mysterious. They occur in the opossum, which is a marsupial; in the raccoon and the kinkajou, which are carnivores; in the armadillo and in certain anteaters, which are edentates; as well as in many of the monkeys—to say nothing of snakes. These various prehensile-tailed animals are very far removed from each other in zoological relationship. Why are prehensile tails endemic in South America? I once asked this question of Dr. W. K. Gregory and he suggested that the frequent floodings of the land surface in the tropical forest area of South America may require special adaptations for arboreal life of the forest-dwelling fauna.

Animals with prehensile tails are not numerous in the Old World. They include some reptiles, such as snakes and chameleons, and the long-snouted phalanger, an Australian marsupial. Some of the Madagascar lemurs appear to have semi-prehensile tails, since the latter are pictured coiled round branches, or, in the case of mothers carrying infants, brought up between the legs of the mother and around the body of the infant which rests across the maternal abdomen. Elliot says that the tail of the spider monkey has 23 vertebrae, flattened beneath and with processes for the attachment of muscles which increase its efficiency as a prehensile organ.

Another outstanding peculiarity of the spider monkey is that the thumb is always reduced to a mere vestige or entirely absent. Since this animal is the only New World monkey which progresses in the trees by arm swings, the four outer fingers are used as a sort of hook and the thumb would be useless in this type of locomotion. Hence it has been the fashion to associate the loss of the thumb with the specialized function of the outer fingers. However, the small anthropoid gibbon, which is a more agile brachiator than any spider monkey, possesses a moderately well-developed thumb, whereas the large groups of colobus monkeys of Africa also have vestigial thumbs, but are pronograde in the trees.

It is evident that the loss of the thumb prevents the development of the hand as an organ of delicate prehension, since an opposable thumb is the most important feature of higher primate manual equipment. To some extent, one supposes, the spider monkey has compensated for the loss of the thumb by developing an especially efficient prehensile tail. In fact, for strictly arboreal purposes the exchange would seem to be advantageous. The spider monkey's tail averages in the adult more than 190 per cent of the length of the head and trunk, but this relationship is individually most variable. The tail is relatively longest before growth has been completed. Schultz in one of his interesting papers has compared the relative tail length of the howler monkey with that of the spider monkey.[1] The former's tail length, relative to trunk height, averages only 148.6 per cent. Relative tail length, however, is not necessarily connected with the grasping function of the tail, or the absence of it, except in so far as the prehensile-tailed monkeys do invariably have both relatively and absolutely long tails. Some of the Old World monkeys and many of the lemurs have relatively very long tails, which are non-prehensile. The highest relative tail length quoted by Schultz, 210 per cent, is that of an American monkey (*Callithrix jacchus*) which has not a grasping tail.

Elliot recognizes 12 species of spider monkeys, mostly based upon variations in coat color. Two of the species, however, have flesh-colored faces, as contrasted with the black faces of the rest. The coat of the true spider monkey is always coarse rather than woolly.

The spider monkey has a long, slender body and relatively long arms and legs. The arms, probably in consequence of this monkey's brachiating habit, are longer than the legs.

[1]Schultz 1926, pp. 286–305.

ADULT SPIDER MONKEY

The spider monkey usually has a relatively long and narrow skull. The cranial length-breadth index in males averages 73.8 and in females 73.9. In the young the forehead is usually high and rounded. Sometimes this high brow is retained in adults, but in others the frontal region is low and receding. The spider monkey has a much bigger·brain case than the howler, although the latter is a larger and bulkier animal. The howler has a relatively broader brain case (cranial index 79.3 in males, 79.8 in females). The face of the howler is much longer and wider.

The snout and jaws of the spider monkey are strongly projecting, but in this respect far behind those of the howler. In 15 per cent of the spider monkeys studied by Schultz the last molars were congenitally lacking, whereas no such case occurred in 110 adult howler monkeys. In the reduction of the jaws and teeth, in the high frontal region, and in certain features of the brain the spider monkey appears to parallel the human course of evolution.

One of the most interesting facts about the spider monkey discovered by Schultz is that there is practically no sex difference in the size of the skull, while the skull of the howler is nearly 10 per cent larger in the male than in the female.

BEHAVIOR OF RED SPIDER MONKEYS IN THE WILD

Dr. C. R. Carpenter has also observed the behavior of red spider monkeys for 48 days in the Coto region of Western Panama, on the border between Panama and Costa Rica.[2] This densely·forested and almost undisturbed country contains perhaps 200 spider monkeys per square mile, as well as fewer capuchins, howlers, squirrel monkeys, and marmosets. Carpenter worked in a reserved sector near camp, in which no hunting was allowed. He studied the geography, pathways, and food trees in this so-called "Yale quadrant" and mapped the area thoroughly. There were 4 groups of red spider monkeys (*Ateles geoffroyi* Kühl) in this quadrant, totaling about 100 animals.

Spider-monkey groups usually awaken at dawn and immediately begin traveling. They feed, move, rest, and play periodically through the day, and at dusk return to one of a number of abode trees and settle down for the night. Sometimes a group may spend 8 or 10 successive nights in the same tree or in neighboring trees. They travel rapidly and scatter over a wide area when moving, so that it is difficult for an observer to follow closely more than one subgroup.

[2]Carpenter 1935, pp. 171–80.

The subgroups may be 400 to 500 yards apart. When a human observer approaches, the monkeys bark in a terrierlike fashion, changing this bark frequently to a rapid metallic chatter. Sometimes the adults growl viciously when closely approached. Usually they come to the ends of the branches, within 40 or 50 feet of the observer, and shake them violently, at the same time scratching themselves vigorously. If the monkey is hanging by its tail, the hands may be used singly or together to scratch the back, and the side and shoulder of the animal opposite to the arm being used. Sometimes both hands may be used to scratch one or both feet, or both feet to scratch an extended arm. If the animal is hanging by tail or arms or both together, running movements of the feet may occur—possibly symbolic escape movements. If the monkey is sitting on a branch, it may sway back and forth and yell. Often these monkeys break off branches and drop them, apparently at the observer. As some of the dead branches weigh 8 to 10 pounds and are dropped from 40 to 50 feet, it is well to look out for them. The branches are not actually thrown, but dropped with a sharp twist of the body or a swinging circular movement of the powerful tail, so that they are launched outward. Often a monkey breaks off a branch and holds it until the man on the ground gets within range. They also urinate and defecate upon or at him.

The red spider monkey displays three characteristic attitudes toward man: first a bluffingly aggressive action; then a flight reaction, during which the group splits up; and finally, if hunted closely or shot at, an immobility and quietude which are very effective in concealing the animal when it gets up in the thick foliage. On the whole, these animals treat man as an enemy.

FOOD

About 90 per cent of the food of the red spider monkeys consists of fruits and nuts. These monkeys may live for considerable periods upon the one or two kinds of fruit which happen to be in season. In June a wild nutmeg is most important. This nut has a mass of red seed-covering beneath the thick hull. As many as 90 of these kernels, which are as large as a small hickory nut and are swallowed whole, may be found in the stomach and intestines of an adult spider monkey. Two beanlike nuts called berba and berbacilla are evidently rich in nutritive value, since the monkeys are fat when they live on these. In February, when these nuts are out of season, the animals are much leaner. They then live on wild figs, "sandi," "guyava," "cainito," and various other fruits of which the names mean nothing to me, but may be found in Carpenter's report.

At times the spider monkeys appear to be searching under bark and leaves and in dead limbs for larvae and insects, but they are not known to eat birds' eggs or young birds, and they consume only insignificant amounts of buds and flowers. The most active feeding period extends from dawn to about 10 o'clock. This is followed by a rest for adults and a playtime for the young. Feeding in the afternoon is more sporadic. It may last until dark.

Locomotion

Normally, spider monkeys travel on all fours on the upper surfaces of limbs, carrying the tail arched over the back. However, when crossing from one support to another they swing by their arms, or brachiate, in a manner approaching that of the gibbon. They also use the powerful grasping tail at this time, making contacts with hands and tail. They have a tendency to keep their heads upward, and back down perpendicular trunks rather than descend headfirst as does the howling monkey. The hands are turned outward when they grasp horizontal limbs, and serve as effective hooks when brachiating. They make long jumps outward and downward, spanning distances of 20 to 30 feet. When jumping, the monkey spreads all of its appendages to increase air resistance and to facilitate making contact with supports on landing. Sometimes an animal will let go and drop 20 to 25 feet from the upper to the lower branches of a tree. Average rate of locomotion is about that of a man walking at top speed.

Real Estate

Each spider-monkey group wanders through a fairly definite range of territory. The territories may overlap to some extent, but on the whole each group moves around and in a definite plot. Shifts of territory probably occur, but are slow. In the quadrant studied by Carpenter the same groups were usually within hearing distance of the camp, traveled over the same routes day by day to the same food trees, picked the same relatively secluded spots for their midday siestas, and returned nightly to their lodging trees.

Social Organization

The large spider-monkey groups may consist of as many as 40 individuals, but they break up in the daytime into subgroups, which may consist of a female or females with young, one or more males and many more females with young, or males only. The subgroups stick together for a whole day or less, and keep within calling distance of the rest of the group and within sight of their fellow subgroup members. The subgroups of "males only" constitute a distinctive feature of spider-monkey social organization. In 181 spider monkeys within his quadrant Carpenter distinguished 19 different subgroups, ranging in number from 3 to 17. All except 3 subgroups contained both males and females. Most of the subgroups contained more females than males. Exclusively male subgroups ranged in number of individuals from 3 to 10 and included males of all ages. In February 1933 Carpenter determined the organization of an entire clan to consist of 34 animals of all classes: 7 adult or nearly adult males, 16 adult females (4 of which carried infants), 7 semi-independent juveniles. This clan repeatedly broke up into 4 subgroups, constituted as follows: (1) 3 mature and one immature males, (2) 4 mothers with infants, 4 females, 5 juveniles, one male; (3) 6 females, one juvenile and one adult male; (4) 2 adult females, one adult male, one juvenile. As in howler monkeys, so in spider monkeys there appears to be a great preponderance of females.

REPRODUCTION

Carpenter did not observe copulation in free-ranging spider monkeys, but he saw plenty of secondary sexual behavior, consisting of the male's manipulation of the greatly developed clitoris of the female, as well as his embracing her, grooming her, and chattering at her.

The red spider monkey has a definite oestrous period, and some females were observed in unusually close association with males. On two such occasions the females were collected and found to have recently formed vaginal plugs, as well as to show the walls and lumina of the vagina greatly enlarged in comparison with those of females who were nursing infants. Wild spider monkeys have no breeding season—a fact evidenced by the observation at the same period of infants and juveniles in all stages of development and by the varying stages of developing embryos found in the pregnant females collected.

RELATIONS OF MOTHER AND YOUNG

For not more than a month the infant spider monkey clings to its mother's belly. Thereafter it rides on her back with its tail coiled around the base of her tail and its hands and feet grasping the hair of the mother's flanks. During the first six months of life the infants are black and begin then to get reddish—a phase which is completed at the age of about 10 months. During the black color-phase the infants are entirely dependent upon their mothers and rarely leave their sides. The period of dependency continues, to some extent, well into the reddish color-phase. It is much longer than that of howling monkeys. The weight of 16 infants captured, varying from the black to the earlier reddish color-phase, averaged 1,579 grams and ranged from 768 to 2,270 grams. One infant spider monkey weighing 2,000 grams was approximately 12 months of age. The largest captured were just cutting their permanent incisor teeth, a circumstance which checks with the fact that a captive animal cut its lower incisors at between 11 and 13 months. This animal had all its incisors at 15 months.

Spider-monkey mothers are more careful of their young than are howlers. Mothers have been seen to travel across several treetops, catch their young, put them on their backs, and carry them away. Spider monkeys often help semidependent young across difficult spots in arboreal pathways. They usually pull together the separated vines or take the young one on their backs, make the crossing, and then put him off again. One female held a vine close to a tree trunk while five young ones, who could not otherwise have crossed, passed from the vine to the tree.

GROOMING AND PLAY

Grooming among wild spider monkeys is apparently not very common. Usually, females pick the hair of their young without using their mouths. They make long, downward, currying movements with their hands, and sometimes part the hair with their hands to make more delicate movements. Captive spider monkeys have been seen to indulge in grooming, much after the manner of other monkeys. This activity is commoner among cebus monkeys and very rarely observed in howlers.

Young spider monkeys play in a variety of ways, but adults do not. Individual play includes running and jumping from one branch to another, swinging from a limb by various combinations of appendages, fooling with sticks and with parts of the animal's body. Most spider-monkey play involves more than one animal and consists of chasing each other over circuitous routes, catching and biting each other, and wrestling. The latter pastime is pursued vigorously, mostly when the youngsters are hanging side by side, swinging by their tails.

SOCIAL CONTROL

A mother seems to control the movements of her infant at first by directing it forcefully and later by teaching it to respond to certain postural cues, especially movements of her body. Thus the infant knows from the movements of the mother that she is about to travel and climbs on her back without requiring her to pick it up. Postures and attitudes of adult animals also signify forthcoming action of specific types, such as flight, aggression, etc.

Data for an adequate discussion of gestures and facial expression in wild spider monkeys are lacking. Captive animals show great expressional variations, which are probably associated with various motivations and call forth suitable responses from their fellows. Carpenter says that protruded lips, wrinkled foreheads, and squinting eyes seem to indicate friendliness. Grunting with a half-open mouth signifies sexual receptivity.

The significance of the varied sounds emitted by these monkeys is insufficiently known. A terrierlike bark indicates the approach of strangers and occasions defensive action or flight. This sound also occurs when strange monkey groups meet. It seems to be a warning signal. Growls are given by adults, generally males, when they are approached too closely and become markedly excited. A third type of sound is like the whinnying of a horse, but of higher pitch and lesser volume. This seems to co-ordinate group movements, since it is often uttered when the subgroups of a clan are separated.

Fighting among the spider monkeys was not frequently seen by Carpenter. The few instances observed involved males, who growled, clinched, bit, squealed, and then separated. Specimens collected showed, on ears, hands, shoulders, and head, evidence of having been chewed from time to time.

There is no obvious centralized control in the spider-monkey group. Leadership seems to fall to the adults, either male or female, but mostly within the subgroups. In leading and defending groups and subgroups the females are active, but usually subordinate. When the entire clan is disturbed, males rush to the leading defensive positions and to the site of the disturbance and appear to show some rudimentary co-operation. However, Carpenter states that female spider monkeys play a more prominent role in group control than do howler females.

INTELLIGENCE TESTS

Apparently, spider monkeys have rarely been used by psychological experimenters. Klüver used two of these monkeys in tests in which they were trained to respond to the lighter of two boxes.[3] The spider monkeys seemed to take up the method of comparisons more quickly than did macaques. One of them became completely proficient in

[3]Klüver 1933.

choosing the lighter of two boxes (one weighing 600 grams and the other 300 grams) in a training period of 9 days. The other took somewhat longer. The spider monkeys did not display the surprising quickness and motor restlessness characteristic of the macaques. Their pulls were slower and more spaced; their comparison methods were more clumsy, since they moved themselves from one side of the cage to the other in making their test pulls. Sometimes they used both hands and feet in pulling in the boxes, and they displayed a good deal of skill and persistence in untangling the strings until that of the correct box was located. They also made more noises and changed facial expression oftener in connection with finding and failing to find food. Instead of testing the relative weights of the boxes by pulling them part way (displacing them), the spider monkeys usually merely tested by pulling the strings taut, and if they moved the boxes, moved them only a few centimeters. They made fewer comparisons per trial. They were inferior to the macaques in speed, but they expended less energy per trial.

The one spider monkey tested for handedness took raisins from a turntable for 4 hours and 3 minutes, until the experimenter ran out of raisins. In 243 successive trials she used the right hand 6 times and the left hand 237 times. Incidentally, the turntable was being revolved counterclockwise. However, in previous trials she used the right hand 16 times out of 16 trials when the table was turned counterclockwise, and the left hand in 10 of 16 trials when it was being rotated clockwise.

The spider monkeys showed no aptitude for the utilization of objects as tools, but they did pay some small attention to moving pictures.

CHAPTER IX

Cebus, the Monkey Mechanic

DESCRIPTION

THE MONKEYS OF THE GENUS *Cebus,* commonly called capuchin monkeys, are the ordinary or garden variety of hand-organ monkeys. They are small animals, with long prehensile tails covered with hair to the tip. Although the extremity is used for grasping, the inner side of the tip is not naked, as in spider monkeys and howlers. Nor is the prehensile function so highly developed as in these other genera.

The brain case of the cebus monkey is moderately well filled and rounded, although the frontal region is poorly developed. The jaws are only medium in protrusion, although the canines are projecting and interlock. As in other New World primates, the premolars are 3 in number, the molars the usual 3, but the third is distinctly reduced in size. The large brain of the cebus monkey is intricately convoluted.

The body of the capuchin is robust, covered with a somewhat woolly fur, which is usually very thick on the head, but comparatively short in this region. The thumb is well developed. Numerous species of this genus of monkey have been recognized, mostly on the basis of variations in coat color and in the presence or absence of a tuft of ¹ ˙ ˙ on the head of the male.

VISION

Grether has found excellent evidence that cebus monkeys are color-blind as far as red is concerned (dichromatic of the protanopic type). Unfortunately, all of the three cebus monkeys investigated were males.[1] The one spider monkey studied was a female who had excellent color vision. Since in man color blindness is virtually restricted to males, it may be that the same is true in the case of the cebus monkey. Two cebus monkeys required an average of 270 per cent of additional red, as compared with man, in a complementary

[1]Grether 1939.

CEBUS MONKEY: QUADRUPEDAL POSTURE

CEBUS MONKEY: TRIPODAL STANCE

mixture to be matched with white. Discrimination of these monkeys was significantly poorer than that of Old World monkeys and man in the red and yellow regions, but about equal in the blue-green region.

There is an interesting suggestion that cebus monkeys, who are red-blind, represent an evolutionary stage below the rhesus monkeys, who have a slightly lowered effectiveness of red in a complementary mixture, as compared with man. Grether's findings of dichromacy (instead of trichromacy) in the cebus afford the first evidence of a blue-yellow stage of vision in any infrahuman mammal.

INTELLIGENCE

Klüver had only one cebus monkey available for the weight-comparison tests. This animal, in working with a 450 grams : 150 grams pair, learned at about the same rate as did the macaques and used the same comparison methods. The principal difference between this American monkey and the macaques lay in her temperament and emotional attitude toward the experimenter. She always objected to being transferred to the experimental cage; she apparently disliked the scientist extremely, and he could not even approach within 2 or 3 meters of the cage without her getting wildly excited and screaming. She would do nothing as long as she knew him to be around. Although hungry, she would not even touch a banana laid before her. Consequently, she worked slowly and with many interruptions. Sometimes she refused to work at all. In spite of these delays, she learned as rapidly as did the macaques.

Another female cebus monkey, which was trained on the discriminations between larger and smaller rectangles, behaved much as did the first and seemed to dislike Dr. Klüver as thoroughly. She also refused to work at all on some days and, when she did work, worked very slowly. Yet she learned just as well as did the macaques. Both cebus monkeys tended to make occasional use of their teeth in pulling in the boxes. Neither used comparisons as extensively as did the macaques.

TOOL-USING

To the writer, at any rate, the most interesting set of experiments which the ingenious and careful investigator, Heinrich Klüver, has conducted were designed to test the tool-using capacity of a female cebus monkey judged to be 7 or 8 years old. Klüver describes 207 problems set for this monkey.[2] To rake in food this American monkey

[2]Klüver 1933, pp. 259–92.

was able to use not only an L-shaped stick, but also sacks, straight wire, wire ring, wire hook, leather belt, rope, floor brush, steel strip, toy monkey, pieces of cardboard, etc. She solved not only problems in which a tool was in close proximity to the food, but also those in which the tool was out of sight (lying on a table or wrapped up in paper), at a considerable distance from the food, or difficult to detect (for example, a green steel strip optically continuous with the green wall of the room). She succeeded in many problems which required using more than one tool. For example, she used a wire hook to get hold of a short T-stick, used the short T-stick to knock down a long T-stick, and used the last to knock down the food. She pulled a sack from a platform and used it to whip in a T-stick, which was then used to obtain food. She solved problems which required the fabrication of a tool, such as tearing off pieces of a newspaper, rolling them and using them to rake in something, or breaking off pieces of a stick. She did fail in a detour problem in which food had to be raked in with a T-stick when the food was ensconced between three steel beams set in the form of a hollow square with the open end away from the cage. She also failed in a problem which necessitated the making of a bridge of cardboard between two tables. She was wholly successful in pulling a box (with her tail) underneath a suspended bit of food, so that she could climb on the box and knock down the food with a stick.

This animal showed extraordinary perseverance and concentration. She often worked for an hour or more on a problem and stopped not from lack of interest but through sheer exhaustion. It was very rarely that she did anything halfheartedly. She pushed, pulled, tore, struck, or threw objects with speed and definition. The experimenter was greatly impressed with the quickness of her solutions and the speed of her motor reactions. Apparently, she far exceeded anthropoid apes in ability to solve similar problems. Often she indulged in a good many circuitous movements and irrelevant actions on the way to the solution of a problem, but these were not trial-and-error movements, but merely "monkeying" with things on the way to the goal. Obviously, she looked upon an object as of interest and use in various ways—as a tool, as a plaything, etc.

Another cebus monkey tried upon these tool problems was also able to utilize objects as tools, but his techniques were very inferior to those of the first.

Three years after Klüver performed the tool-using experiments with the female cebus monkey which was mechanically so gifted, he made a re-examination of her capacities in this line.[3] During the interval she had not been used in experiments of any kind. She was now about 10 or 11 years old and in fairly good health, but she was not so strong as in 1931 and could not move, break, or tear up objects as easily as in the previous series. The second series consisted of 120 experiments, mostly the same as in the early work, but with some new and interesting variations. The most important of these innovations were the introduction of live animals and the presentation of two joined sticks to be used as a flail. She seemed incapable of solving only two kinds of problems: the "detour beam" problem and the problems involving straightening a piece of bent wire or using two joined sticks as a flail. She failed to complete some problems because she was no longer strong enough or energetic enough to manipulate the objects as vigorously as in the days of her prime. Yet she was able to utilize effectively the objects offered as tools in 10 of 12 major classes of situations. In both series she showed the same quick utilization of chance variations which developed in the course of the experiment. She showed the same ability in repeating a problem to solve it much more quickly. She solved all the problems which she had solved 3 years before and made the same failures. Some of the problems were solved more quickly and efficiently in the second series, especially the two-handed problems in which she had to pull both ends of a piece of loose string run along a crossbar and attached to a lever. She also improved in the tasks which involved pushing a pole through a long, narrow box to poke out food placed in the middle, and in removing a ring from a peg in order to get and use a stick which was attached to the ring. I cannot refrain from a lengthy direct quotation describing the way in which this monkey utilized a live animal as an implement.

Exp. 70. PROBLEM: Food a few centimeters beyond reach on floor; live albino rat tied by means of string (length 130 cm.) to heavy box; heavy box within reach of monkey and about 85 cm. from food; rat can run to points beyond food.

RESPONSE: At once grasps string and pulls rat toward her; lifts rat by means of string, then throws it away; rat runs toward wall AD; pulls rat within reach, picks it up, opens mouth as if to bite head of rat but does not injure it, rat squeals; lets rat run away, then pulls it in again and carries it to point opposite food, attempts to throw it over food; drops rat, runs to wooden box, bites into it; picks up rat and energetically throws it several times in direction of food; preparatory to throwing grabs into fur of rat or gets hold of string near point of contact with body of rat; after throwing does not always pull back immediately but watches movements

[3]Klüver 1937, pp. 347–97.

of rat; pulls back quickly, either straight or diagonally, when position of rat is such that rat, food, and hand holding string form a straight line; if after throwing, rat runs quickly away to a point not in line with the food, monkey pulls back immediately; finally succeeds in pulling in food by means of rat (3 min., 10 sec.).[4]

Klüver notes that a cebus monkey definitely kicks or pushes objects away from himself. He actually throws objects and does not merely drop them as does a macaque.[5] Furthermore, he throws them *at* something; he does not merely throw them around. A cebus monkey also uses various objects (carrots, nuts, food pans, pieces of wood, metal, etc.) with which to hammer on the floor or on other objects. He molds clay into long cylinders. He often uses his index finger alone to examine or touch an object.

A macaque characteristically tears an object to pieces as quickly and thoroughly as possible, but a cebus monkey takes it apart, apparently more interested in its construction than in its destruction. He seems to learn much more about the objects handled and dismembered.

The emotional, or as the psychologists call them "affective," expressions of cebus monkeys seem to be much more differentiated than those of macaques. The most trivial incident may cause a cebus monkey to take up a permanently hostile attitude toward a person or object.

This same female monkey genius made "drawings." It was observed that, when she had difficulty in solving problems, she used objects such as a nail or a wire to draw upon the floor. She was then given a piece of white chalk. Her drawings on the floor consisted mostly of groups of curved lines made by broad sweeping movements from right to left or vice versa. All the curves drawn at one time were made by movements in the same direction. The chalk was held in either right or left hand. The lines were usually bunched in groups. After getting tired of one "drawing," the monkey would move to another part of a room and do another. Some lines were almost straight; some crosses and S-shaped lines were produced. As she became accustomed to the use of the chalk, the lines became heavier. Given a piece of red chalk, she applied it more or less evenly to an area, which was later surrounded by configurations of yellow, blue, and green lines. She liked to draw on cardboard and wood as much as upon cement, but she never could be induced to try to copy the drawings of the experimenter.

[4] Klüver 1937, p. 374. NOTE. I read this experiment aloud to my wife, expecting her to exclaim with surprise at the intelligence and ingenuity of the monkey, but all that she said was that "it was rough on the rat." So much for the humanitarian attitude!

[5] Klüver 1933.

YOUNG CEBUS MONKEY

CEBUS MONKEYS

Photograph Zoological Park

Courtesy The Zoological Society of Philadelphia

EMOTIONS

Klüver tried the effect of showing moving pictures to his monkeys, presenting such subjects as *Canines and Felines, Reptiles and Monkeys,* films showing children at play, and the record of the cebus monkey using tools. A lemur did not react at all to the pictures, but only to the sound of the projector. Klüver was not certain that the macaques even directed their attention to the place on the walls upon which the pictures were projected. However, all the American monkeys—cebus, spider, and squirrel—certainly reacted to at least some of the pictures. Yet only in the cebus monkeys were there definitely recordable reactions. These included eye movements, vocalization, changes in position, approach and retreat, urination and defecation. The cebus monkey who was the gifted tool user was greatly interested in *Reptiles and Monkeys.* She talked at the picture, and showed extreme fear when a python was shown; she uttered sounds, defecated, and retreated into a corner of the room from which the picture could not be seen. She was even more strongly affected by the close-up of a lion. Whereas normally her attention shifted with great rapidity, she became so "absorbed" in pictures that she paid no attention to anything else for 20 minutes or for whatever space of time the projection occupied.[6]

Other New World Monkeys

THE WOOLLY SPIDER MONKEY

(Genus *Brachyteleus*)

The woolly spider monkey belongs to a different genus from the true spider monkey in that its fur is fine and woolly, its body build is thicker and heavier, the canines are smaller, the head more rounded, the snout less projecting, and the hinder angles of the jaw deeper. The fingernails and toenails are compressed and clawlike.

THE WOOLLY MONKEYS

(Genus *Lagothrix*)

These are heavy-bodied, woolly-haired monkeys with long prehensile tails. The limbs are moderately long and both the thumb and great toe are well developed. The canines are large. These animals are said to be

[6]Klüver 1933, pp. 305–06.

gregarious, slow in their movements, and amiable and tractable in captivity. In the cranium of a woolly monkey figured by Elliot the hinder angles of the mandible are very deep and inverted.

SQUIRREL MONKEYS

(Genus *Saimiri*)

The squirrel monkeys are small, brilliantly colored animals which range from Nicaragua through the valley of the Amazon into Bolivia and Peru. They are stated to be strictly arboreal and the commonest of the ordinary American monkeys. To the anthropologist the most remarkable feature of this animal is the extraordinarily elongated, dolichocephalic skull with the frontal bone projecting backward in a V-shaped point between the parietals, and the foramen magnum, through which the spinal cord passes up to join the brain, situated far forward on the base of the skull. The hinder part of the skull or occiput projects backward and is bun-shaped, as in no other monkey. The eyes are very large and the orbits are close together, the face short, but the canine teeth projecting and interlocking. The nostrils are widely separated and directed sidewise. This is a diurnal type of monkey in spite of its very large eyes. The tail is long, nonprehensile, and short-haired.

The common squirrel monkey is about the size of the rodent from which it takes its name. The general coat color is grizzled gray, tending to blackish, but with some tinges of gold in the back region. The outer sides of the forearms are yellowish; the paws whitish; the long and slender tail tipped with black. Humboldt says this little monkey has the physiognomy of a child, an innocent expression, a playful smile, facile transitions from joy to sorrow, eyes suffused with tears when afraid. All of this seems a trifle imaginative. It is easier to believe Humboldt when he says that his squirrel monkey was extremely fond of spiders and insects; attempted to seize uncolored pictures of wasps, etc., in a work on natural history, but was utterly unmoved by pictures of the heads and skeletons of mammals.

Bates says that the squirrel monkeys live in large groups and, when on the move, take flying leaps from tree to tree.

Intelligence Tests

Klüver trained a squirrel monkey (which had not been previously used in laboratory tests) to react positively to the larger of two figures.[7] In the beginning, when a piece of potato was attached to a string, she immediately pulled in the string. The difficulty was to get this monkey to look at the stimuli before pulling in the strings. She made her first comparisons on the seventh day and from that point on errors decreased until she made virtually errorless trials from the fourteenth day on. The error-

[7]Klüver 1933, pp. 178, 187.

less performances on the fifteenth and sixteenth days were made upon a pair of 63.6 sq. cm. : 4.9 sq. cm. white circles pasted on black backgrounds.

Thereafter it was found possible to replace the circles by rings, by dotted outlines, or by areas differing in color and brightness without upsetting the reaction. Even the outlines of semicircles were able to elicit responses to the larger of the two stimuli in 67 to 77 per cent of cases. However, when only the vertical lines representing the diameters of the circles were presented, chance reactions occurred.

A male squirrel monkey (not the animal whose achievements have been described above) was used by Klüver for experiments in the choice of colors. In the very beginning this calm and deliberate animal utilized the method of comparisons and on the fifth to ninth days inclusive made practically errorless performances in a large number of tests in which he was to respond positively to violet-red in preference to yellow. Various other color tests were made, not, however, with the set purpose of determining the presence or absence of color vision. Yet the consistent reactions to pairs of 2 colors are best understood in this animal by assuming the efficacy both of brightness and of color properties. This squirrel monkey reacted successfully to 6 other color pairs which were equivalent to the original violet-red shade No. 2 : yellow pair. However, the discriminations broke down when two shades of violet-red were presented together and when violet-red was contrasted with blue.

The squirrel monkeys showed no tool-using aptitude.

THE SAKIS (Genus *Pithecia*)

The sakis are long-haired, coarse-haired monkeys with bushy, nonprehensile tails and buck teeth (incisors which lean forward). The hinder parts of the lower jaw are greatly expanded, but not so markedly as in the howlers. Most of the sakis have long hair on the crown of the head, sometimes parted down the middle, sometimes radiating from the center. Their whiskers also may have a central parting. The sakis are found principally in Guiana and in the valley of the Amazon. They are said to be delicate and difficult to keep in confinement. Little is known of their habits in the wild. Elliot distinguishes eight species of sakis—six of large size and two of small size. Half of the large sakis have long head hair projecting forward over their faces, but in the other three species the head hair is short and does not so project. Coat colors are varied.

A typical example of this genus is Humboldt's saki, also called the hairy saki (*Pithecia monacha*). This animal has purplish brown face and ears, face and head usually covered•with short hairs, white on the face and up to the crown, black and white on the crown and sides. On other parts of the body the coat color varies from black to brown and yellowish white.

Humboldt describes the red-backed saki (*P. chiropotes*) as "a robust, active, fierce, and untamable animal." When it is irritated it rises on its hindquarters, grinds its teeth, pulls its beard, and attacks. It is melancholy except at mealtimes, and is supposed to drink by conveying water to its mouth in the hollow of its hand. It is also said to live in pairs and to give vent to a disagreeable grunting sound. If these saki monkeys are as dull and cheerless as the accounts of them, we need not repine because so little is known about them.

UAKARI MONKEYS (Genus *Cacajao*)

The uakari monkeys are small animals with long silky hair and short to stumpy tails. In fact, their tails are shortest of all New World monkeys, although they are exclusively arboreal owing to the fact that the ground is usually flooded in the forest areas which they inhabit. The hinder part of the jaw, as in the case of the sakis, is somewhat enlarged. The brain is well developed and complicated in pattern. Two of the three species of this monkey have bright scarlet or vermillion-colored faces; one has a black face. In the red-faced types it is stated that the color deepens when the animals are excited—evidently a blushing monkey. Each of the three species is restricted to a certain district and the animals are never known to mingle, although the ranges may approximate each other.

The bald-headed uakari is found in Brazil in the angle formed by the junction of the Japura and Amazon rivers. The face is naked and scarlet, the sides of the head and hairs below the chin cinnamon to chestnut, top of head, neck, back, and outer sides of limbs gray, under parts and insides of 'mbs cinnamon-rufous to whitish, hands and feet yellowish brown. Although the tail is short, the number of vertebrae in it ranges from 15 to 20. This animal is only about 18 inches long and is stated to have reddish yellow eyes. The young are lighter in color than the adults.

Bates says that the bald-headed uakari is found only on the banks of the Japura River, in an area of swampy woods of about 60 miles in extent. These animals go in small troops in the tops of the highest trees and subsist upon fruits. The uakari runs along nimbly on all fours but does not leap. The young are carried on the backs of the mothers. The natives capture them alive by shooting them with darts tipped with diluted urari poison, blown from a blowpipe. When the animal is overcome by the poison and caught, it is revived with a pinch of salt, which is an antidote to the poison. In captivity the uakaris are sulky and untamable, often refuse food, and frequently succumb, apparently to respiratory ailments.

THE DOUROUCOULIS (Genus *Aotus*)

These small American monkeys have round heads, short, thick bodies, short ears mostly hidden in fur, very large eyes, nostrils separated by a broad septum, very abbreviated snouts, bushy non-prehensile tails of moderate length. The most notable feature of the skull is the enormous orbit

Zoological Park

Courtesy The Zoological Society of Philadelphia

SAKI MONKEY

MARMOSET

ALLEGED GIA
SPIDER MONK

which lodges the eyeball. The hinder angle of the jaw is enlarged. The great toe is said to be weak and the thumb only semi-opposable.

The douroucoulis are nocturnal and strictly arboreal. The large size of the orbit is connected with night vision. In the daytime they hide themselves in thick foliage or in holes in trees. At night they are active and noisy. The sound they emit is described as "caterwauling." They live upon insects, fruit, and small birds, when they can catch them. There are several species, varied in coat color and markings. With the exception of possibly one species, these monkeys are found only in South America.

THE FAMILY HAPALIDAE

The family Hapalidae includes the smallest and most primitive of the monkeys. It is divided by Elliot into two genera, the marmosets and the tamarins. The latter have longer hands. Otherwise the differences are small. A description of the common marmoset, *Hapale jacchus,* will suffice for the entire family, which is found in the tropical forests of South America, Central America, and Mexico.

THE COMMON MARMOSET

The common marmoset is a species said to be restricted to the island of Marajo at the mouth of the Amazon.[8] This animal is about the size of a squirrel. The hair on the face is black, with a white spot at the root of the nose and round the eyelids. In front and behind the ears are tufts of long, black hair tipped with white. The rest of the scalp is covered with brownish black hairs. Neck, chest, and belly are pink-skinned with varying amounts of short brown hair, in some places almost none. The anterior surfaces of the arms and legs are similarly sparsely haired. The back is covered with hair, which is black for 7 or 8 mm. at the root, then golden brown for the same distance, then black, and finally tipped with white. The underside of the tail is almost bare, the sides and upper surface covered with the black, white-tipped hair. The tail ends in a tuft.[9] The numerous species of marmosets differ markedly in coat color and distribution. These variations are interesting to see, but tiresome to describe They are neglected here.

The ears of the marmoset are large and flaplike. Feelers are well developed on the face, and there is a wrist pad with a group of vibrissae, or feelers, arising from it. The long tail is not prehensile. The head is egg-shaped, the jaws only slightly projecting, the mouth wide, with no mucous membrane showing on the lips. The oval nostrils are widely separated and are directed sideways. There is a groove down the middle

[8]Beattie 1927, pp. 593–718. This animal has been selected for treatment here because it is the subject of an admirable monograph by Dr. J. Beattie, Conservator of the Museum of the Royal College of Surgeons. All of the description of the common marmoset here set forth has been derived from Beattie's work.

[9]Most writers say that the common marmoset has a banded, black-and-white tail.

of the nasal tip and a slight ridging of the nasal bridge. The eyes look forward, although the axes of the orbits are directed laterally. The female has two nipples in the pectoral region; the male has none. The forelimbs are short, and there are six pads on the palm with the usual papillary ridges. Flattened pads also occur on the last segments of the digits. The thumb and all the fingers are provided with sharp, hooked claws. The legs are longer than the arms and more powerful. The long, narrow foot is provided with pads similar to those found on the hand. The great toe has a flattened nail, but the other toes bear claws.

The thumb is not opposable to the other digits, although it can be moved weakly toward and away from the palm. The great toe is widely divergent and is used for obtaining a grip on the tree trunk, in addition to the support obtained from the clinging claws.

The eyes of the marmoset probably do not move much in their sockets during lifetime. By way of compensation, the head is very flexible and can be turned upon the spinal column more than 90°, but it cannot be rotated back a full half-circle as in *Tarsius*. The face is very short and the orbital cavity is almost completely walled off behind, as in *Tarsius* and in all higher primate forms.

In general, American monkeys tend to have 2 incisors, one canine, 3 premolars, and 3 molars on each side of the upper and lower jaws. However, the marmosets have only 2 molars—a fact which may be connected with the shortening of their snouts.

The brain of the marmoset is relatively very large, since, according to Hrdlička, it is one twenty-ninth of the entire body weight. Another authority has stated the brain of the marmoset to be one fifteenth of the body weight. If this is correct, the marmoset is relatively the largest-brained of all primates. The olfactory parts of the brain are reduced. The cerebral hemispheres extend far back, covering the cerebellum, as in higher primates, but the fissures and grooves are very poorly defined and the general surface is primitively smooth. The muscular system is very primitive—more so in many ways than that of *Tarsius* but similar to that of the latter "in so far as they both approach the primitive insectivore condition."[10]

There is a marked difference of opinion as to the position of the marmoset, and the entire family Hapalidae, among the primates. Beattie regards this animal as the most primitive form of monkey, representing one stage of evolution above the tarsier. On the other hand, Professor W. K. Gregory thinks that the Hapalidae are secondarily specialized animals—that the claws, for example, are not retained primitive features, but rather degenerative, bent-up nails. He notes that the fibula (the outside bone of the leg) shows a tendency to be fused at the bottom with the tibia—a condition present also in the tarsier and certainly far from primitive. The problem of the marmoset—whether primitive or de-

[10]Beattie 1927, p. 712.

generate—cannot be solved here. It is sufficient to indicate that this little animal is by all means the lowest type of monkey to be found in the New or Old World.

The marmoset is the only monkey which habitually produces two or even three young at a birth. This reproductive habit allies it with lower forms. Beattie states that the common marmoset is a diurnal and arboreal animal which lives upon fruit and insects. Other observers say that it will raid the nests of birds and devour newly hatched chicks. One authority asserts that marmosets will eat flesh and are especially fond of fish. In captivity Beattie states that marmosets are playful, gentle animals and, if kept in warm places with ultraviolet light irradiation every day, they will breed in captivity. They are active on branches, but clumsy when moving on a floor. When at rest they dig their claws into the bark of the branches. The great toe is maintained at a right angle with the rest of the foot, but its grip is weak. The forelimbs are used for grasping food, as in other primates, but the hand serves mainly for fixing the piece of food and not for conveying it to the mouth. The arms can be extended fully at the elbow, but the hind limb is permanently flexed, so that the thigh is against the abdomen and the knee is also bent.

In feeding, the marmoset does not use its lips to surround the food, but retracts them so as expose a considerable area of the teeth and gums. The canines bite deeply. Lydekker quotes an account of the common marmoset published in *Loudon's Magazine of Natural History* for 1829.[11] This animal was procured at Bahia and for a while on shipboard was so fierce that it could not be approached or touched. It had very acute hearing and was constantly turning its head from side to side, eyeing everyone with a most suspicious and angry look. It made sharp, shrill, disagreeable sounds which could be heard all over the ship. The native name, *ouistiti,* is said to be an imitation of these characteristic noises. This animal was not playful. It ate nothing but fruit as long as the fruit on board held out. It was then discovered devouring cockroaches, and for 4 or 5 weeks it fed exclusively upon them and fairly well cleaned up the ship. It frequently ate a score or more of the larger cockroaches which ranged from 2 to 2½ inches in length, in addition to a great number of smaller ones, 2 or 3 times a day. The marmoset held a cockroach in his paws, nipped off the head, pulled out and cast aside the viscera, and then devoured the rest of the body with the exception of the legs and wings. When the ship began to get into the cooler latitudes he refused cockroaches, and the hair on his tail fell out until it became almost naked. (This may explain Beattie's description of the partial nakedness of the marmosets which he studied in London.) The animal was then kept in a warm room and rolled itself up in a piece of flannel. After reaching England it was revived in a warm room and recovered its agility. There it would not eat insects, but subsisted on milk, bread, jelly, and ripe fruit.

[11]Lydekker 1893–94, pp. 190–91.

The Tamarin

The naturalist, Bates, describes the negro tamarin (*Midas ursulus*) which is found in Guiana and the lower part of the Amazon Valley. This animal, which is really just another kind of marmoset, belongs to a group in which both forehead and face are hairy, the ears large and naked, the color nearly a uniform black, except on the hinder part of the body, where the fur is mottled with grayish white. Bates says that this animal does not occur in troops, three or four being the largest number observed together. Its mode of progression in the trees is said to resemble that of a squirrel; it does not take the flying leaps made by the monkeys with prehensile hands and tails. Rather it confines itself to the larger boughs and trunks of trees, clinging securely to the bark by its claws. It has its share of curiosity and will stop and stare at human beings passing by under the trees. It is often tamed in Para. The body of the full-grown animal is about 9 inches long, and the tail 15 inches. It is very timid and irritable, always in a querulous humor. It utters a twittering, complaining noise, and observes keenly and distrustfully with its dark eyes. When it is well acquainted, it is tame and playful. It feeds on fruits, such as the banana, but also likes insects. Its countenance is very expressive and intelligent in appearance—an effect enhanced by the small projection of the jaws and the quick movements of the head.

Bates saw a brown-headed tamarin miss its grip when passing from one tree to another and fall to the ground—a distance of at least 50 feet. However, the animal lighted on its feet, turned round, gave him a good stare, and bounded gaily up another tree. Of another species (*Leontocebus rosalia*), Bates gives the following stock anecdote:

A tame specimen observed by him was very playful and intelligent and would climb about the person of everyone who entered the house. When he first came in, it climbed upon his shoulder and looked into his face, showing its teeth and chattering as if to say, "Well, and how do you do?" It kept climbing upon the head of its master, searching for parasites.[12] Incidentally, Zuckerman reports that a species of the genus *Pediculus,* which are lice, have been found on marmosets as well as upon other South American monkeys. The spider monkey is said to be the true host of these lice, but, in the case of marmosets and capuchin monkeys, these parasites are regarded as "stragglers." Thus it would appear that if the marmoset failed to find lice in the hair of its master, the lice, nevertheless, found the marmoset. Zuckerman also reports that Clark and his co-workers in Panama have found *Leontocebus* to harbor a spirochete which is identical with the local species of relapsing human fever. This organism can be passed from one monkey to another, to white mice, rats, guinea pigs, and human beings.[13]

[12]Bates 1863, p. 59.
[13]Zuckerman 1933, p. 85.

Of the same louse-hunting species of tamarins, Isidore Geoffrey-Saint Hilaire is said to have known a tame individual which distinguished between objects in engravings. It was much frightened of pictures of cats and wasps, but when it saw the representation of a grasshopper or beetle, it pounced on the picture and tried to seize them. The reader is not required to believe this tale.

Anecdotal natural history of this type is not a satisfactory substitute for detailed scientific investigation. It is perfectly apparent from the foregoing rambling account of the marmoset that, whereas the details of the structure of a single species are well known, we are appallingly ignorant of the animal's habits in the wild.

The Alleged South American Anthropoid Ape

One of the most persistent zoological legends which I know relates to the existence of a South American anthropoid ape, tailless and of large size. I first heard it in 1915, or about that time, when a student in one of my Harvard classes, who was an Ecuadorian, confidently asserted that I was incorrect when I stated that there were no anthropoid apes native to the New World. He had repeatedly heard, from substantial authorities, of the existence of a huge, tailless ape in northern Colombia. Then came a report in 1929, which, in 1930, I summarized as follows:

"Last year there appeared in various popular periodicals accounts of the discovery of a new anthropoid ape in the forests near the Tarra River, in the Motilones districts of Colombia and Venezuela, South America. A Frenchman, Dr. Francis de Loys, was travelling in this region in 1917 when his party was attacked by two great tailless apes, who advanced to the assault defecating in their hands and hurling this disagreeable ammunition at their foes. One of these apes, an adult female, was shot. The other escaped. The body was said to measure more than five feet in height (157 centimeters) and its weight was guessed to be more than 112 pounds. Unfortunately the skin and bones were not brought out. The cook used the skull for a salt box and the salt is said to have dissolved the bones! A picture alleged to represent this anthropoid shows it sitting on a box. It looks suspiciously like a spider monkey and seems to have rudimentary thumbs. The tail is either missing or behind the box. There is no scale in the photograph. We shall have to secure better evidence than has been presented before we receive this scatological relative into the anthropoid family."[14]

Sir Arthur Keith, writing in the year of the first published accounts of this supposed discovery, came to the conclusion also that De Loys's phony anthropoid was nothing more than a spider monkey.[15]

Late in 1932 I received a letter from A. James Durlacher, an American engineer employed by a petroleum company, relative to the De Loys find.

[14]Hooton 1931, p. 23.

[15]Keith 1929, pp. 135–36.

Mr. Durlacher was in charge of his company's field work on Rio de Oro, Colombia, farther in the bush than the Tarra River, in 1927. At this time he made inquiries of men who had been on the De Loys expedition, and discovered that the specimen De Loys shot was, indeed, a spider monkey, known in that region as the "marimonda." Durlacher said that the flesh of this animal was considered quite a delicacy. Earlier in the same year in which I received the first communication from Durlacher, I had a letter from W. D. Prior, of London, Ontario, another engineer who had worked in the same area in 1910. Mr. Prior stated that he himself had on one occasion seen a large ape, covered with long, chestnut-colored hair and about as large as a small man. He described this animal as bounding or leaping from tree to tree, covering 50 feet at a spring, and moving with the utmost ease and agility. He watched it for half a mile, but never saw another specimen. As a result of these communications I was inclined to conclude that some very large and hitherto undescribed type of spider monkey probably exists in this area. Mr. Prior's letter made no reference to the presence or absence of a tail. Subsequently, I had a correspondence with Mr. Durlacher which extended over a period of years. On January 1, 1934, he sent me a postcard from Catumbo, on which were a New Year's greeting and a picture of a spider monkey sitting on a tree trunk with its long tail in plain sight. In the right hand the animal held an egg, the size of which, compared with that of the hand, was the only indication of the scale of the photograph. On this postcard Mr. Durlacher wrote that the animal "is a spider monkey, called 'marimonda' here, and is used by Indians and natives as food. It measures 3 feet 6 inches high and weighs 72 pounds." Mr. Harold J. Coolidge then wrote Durlacher, asking him to secure specimens and giving him directions for their preservation and shipment to Harvard. Early in 1936 Mr. Durlacher wrote Coolidge that he had been unable as yet to get a specimen, but that some of his men were still on the lookout for one. At the same time he reported that he had seen the notes and drawings of a Captain Deming who had killed one of these giant monkeys, which weighed 65 pounds.

There the matter rested until July 6, 1941, when another American, writing from Caracas, Venezuela, accused Durlacher of faking the whole story of the giant spider monkey. This individual states that Durlacher got the picture of the monkey on the stump from a Shell geological party which had been working in the Rio Tarra region and made the picture for a joke. The egg was not a hen's egg but is stated to have been probably the egg of a gallineta, which is about half the size of a hen's egg. This person claims that Durlacher took the photograph, made a greeting card of it, and "told everyone about the good one he was putting over on the folks in the States." Our correspondent reported that his informant, who is a scientist, felt that the joke had been carried too far.

I myself have carefully reread the entire correspondence and can find no internal evidence of frivolity or faking on the part of any one of the engineers or other persons who have written us. I am inclined to let the matter rest with the tentative conclusion that a giant spider monkey with the usual long, prehensile tail may possibly range this area of South America and that some inveterate tellers of tall tales almost certainly frequent the same region.

Anatomy of the Cebidae

The family of New World monkeys called the Cebidae is said to be diversified to such an extent in its minor adaptive radiations that a general description of its anatomy merely furnishes a sort of composite from which actual individual species vary widely in one direction or another.[16]

EXTERNAL CHARACTERS

Thus, in texture of coat there is a range from coarse and shaggy to silky and woolly, in hair pattern no uniformity, in coat coloration a variation from sober black and other dull tones through bright yellow and red. However, Wood Jones states that no platyrrhine monkey has any tinge of green in its fur. Skin color on the face, which is naked in many species, is black or dark brown in the woolly monkeys and the spider monkeys, usually flesh-colored in the cebus or capuchin monkeys, and often bright red in the uakaris. There are no ischial callosities, but the skin of the perineal region is often naked and somewhat specialized. In those species which have prehensile tails the undersurface near the tip is naked and pigmented. The howling monkeys have beards. Feelers, or facial vibrissae, are reduced to the mustache and supraorbital sets.

The Cebidae have small oval or nearly circular ears, flattened to the sides of the heads and highly sculptured in a very human manner. The helix is rolled over most of the periphery of the ear, and such features as the antihelix, the tragus, and the antitragus are well differentiated. There is no lobe, but the ear is more or less naked, contrary to its hairy condition in the marmosets.

The eyes are enlarged only in *Aotus*. In all species the pupils are circular and the iris is usually some shade of brown. Eyelashes are well developed.

The nails are narrow, curved, and often sharply pointed, thus resembling claws. The thumb is small, "fingerlike," according to Wood Jones, and shows very limited opposability and a restricted range of movements that are independent of those of the fingers. Wood Jones says that a completely opposable thumb can be rotated on its own axis so that it is placed in the palm of the hand with its nail facing directly upward from the palm. I have little doubt that the New World monkeys are unable to accomplish this feat, since I cannot do it myself, although I

[16]Jones 1929, pp. 195ff.

insist that my thumbs are opposable to my finger tips. Wood Jones asserts also that the great toe in these monkeys is far more individualized, has a wide range of abduction and adduction, but is incapable of true rotation. According to this author, the grasping development of the hand has two stages: that in which large objects can be grasped for support; that in which small objects can be picked up between the thumb and finger tips. He considers that this second stage is never fully achieved in New World monkeys.

In most of the Cebidae the hind limbs are said to exceed the forelimbs in length, but the contrary is true in the case of the spider monkeys. In the woolly monkeys the limbs are of almost equal length. The tail is short only in the genus *Cacajao* (the uakaris); it is usually long and often prehensile, the exceptions to the latter being the teetees, the douroucoulis, the sakis, the uakaris, and the squirrel monkeys.

THE SKULL

The facial portion of the skull is generally reduced, the brain case well rounded, and the postorbital constriction small. The palate is usually short. The orbits have their axes directed forward and slightly outward and are cut off from the temporal fossae by a bony wall, a large portion of which is derived from the jugal or malar bone. This jugal element articulates over a wide area with the parietal and cuts off the wing of the sphenoid and the temporal from any contact with the frontal bone. The arrangement is thus very different from that found in Old World monkeys, in anthropoid apes, and in man. However, within the orbits the lachrymal bone articulates with the ethmoid. Usually the articulation of the nasal bones with the frontal occurs above the level of the fronto-maxillary suture. Wood Jones states that sometimes, as in certain examples of the *Callicebus*, the lachrymal articulates directly with the nasals, thus excluding the frontal from contact with the maxillaries. The premaxillae usually reach about to the lower level of the nasal bones on either side of the nasal aperture. A bony swelling or bulla is found in the auditory region of the temporal bone. The tympanic ring or annulus lies outside this bulla and is not developed into a well-marked external auditory meatus. Auditory bullae, together with the tympanic annulus and the absence of a tubular bony auditory meatus, are characters which the New World monkeys, including the marmosets, share with the lemurs and the tarsier. The external pterygoid plates are large, the internal small. Within the skull notable features are the ridgelike ossification of the tentorium cerebelli and a cerebellar fossa of the petrosal.

Gregory summarizes the stem characters of skull and teeth of the New World monkeys as follows: "Dental formula $I\frac{2}{2}$ $C\frac{1}{1}$ $P\frac{3}{3}$ $M\frac{3}{3}$; face short; brain case expanded; orbits relatively small, well-rimmed, directed partly forward; lachrymal mostly within orbits; nose wide, flat; auditory bullae expanded; tympanic bones large, ringlike; front teeth not rodent-like, but 'normal,' dental arches pointed; lower jaw short, deep; canines small, no bony chin; zygomatic arches stout, pitching sharply downward in front; all three upper pre-molars bicuspid; upper molars tritubercular, with small hypocones and reduced proto- and metaconules; lower molars with trigonid but little elevated above talonid, the latter large but not excessively widened, paraconids reduced or absent, hypoconulids present."[17]

ALIMENTARY SYSTEM

In the Cebidae the stomach is simple, but it has been pointed out that there is some tendency to sacculation in the spider monkeys and the howlers as in the Old World Semnopithecinae. Sonntag says that the colon is long in the douroucoulis and the marmosets (Hapalidae), but short in other forms. There is no vermiform appendix. The 4-lobed liver is stated to be intermediate between that of the lemuroids and that of the Old World monkeys.

RESPIRATORY AND CIRCULATORY SYSTEMS

The left lung has 2 or 3 lobes and the right 4, including the azygos lobe. In many species the branches of the aortic arch are as in man. The heart is more vertical than in the apes and the azygos lobe of the right lung lies immediately beneath it. There are no air sacs communicating with the ventricles of the larynx, but the spider monkey is said to have a large membranous sac behind the cricoid cartilage. In the howlers the hyoid bone is ballooned to form a resonating chamber.

UROGENITAL ORGANS

The spider monkey agrees with man in having a kidney which is divided into 5 papillae, but in other American monkeys the kidney is a single papilla, although it may be subdivided into as many as 5 or 6 pyramids.

Wood Jones says that the glans penis and the urethral orifice are distinctly human in the teetee and squirrel monkeys, but less so in cebus, the howler, and the spider monkey. The penis bone is found only in cebus. A scrotum is present, but the inguinal canals often remain open in adults, as in the marmoset. The female has a well-developed uterus with short, stout Fallopian tubes. The clitoris is enlarged, especially in the spider and woolly monkeys, and may have a bone, but is never traversed by the urethra.

[17]Gregory 1922, p. 226.

NERVOUS SYSTEM

The brains of the Cebidae are voluminous, and, relative to body weight, may greatly exceed the brain of man. The cerebrum extends well back over the cerebellum. The overhang in the squirrel monkeys equals or surpasses that of man, but in the howler there is some recession of the occipital projection of the cerebral hemispheres. Olfactory bulbs are relatively smaller than in the lemuroids. Fissuration of the cerebrum is well developed. The central sulcus is stated by Sonntag to be better marked in the Cebidae than in the Lemuroidea. The Sylvian fissure exists in typical primate form. In the occipital region a simian sulcus may or may not be present. The cerebellum is large, but the floccular lobes, according to Wood Jones, are still conspicuous in most types.

Dr. Gerhardt von Bonin has described the cerebral cortex of the very gifted female cebus monkey, designated as P-Y (Princeton-Yale), which Klüver used in experiments upon the use of objects as tools. This monkey died on April 29, 1934, at the age of about 11 years. Her weight at death was only 1.022 kilos. Apparently she was greatly emaciated. Most of Von Bonin's description of this cebus brain is far too technical for the comprehension of anyone except an anatomist who has specialized upon the structure of the brain. The prefrontal cortex of the cebus, according to Brodmann, covers only 10 per cent of the whole cortex in the brain as compared with 29 per cent in the human brain. In the particular brain examined by Von Bonin the visual area was well differentiated, but less so in the somesthetic and even less in the auditory areas. The parietal and frontal lobes showed much simpler structure than in the human brain, but differentiation was foreshadowed. There was an especially high degree of specialization in the operculum of the insula, where human "speech centers" seemed already discernible.[18]

[18]Von Bonin 1938, pp. 181–227.

PART IV

Backward Primates of the Old World

CHAPTER X

The Retarded Tarsier

THE MOST VOLUMINOUS and acrimonious discussion about any of the primates, except man, has been devoted to one of the tiniest and rarest of that zoological order—the animal called the spectral tarsier (*Tarsius spectrum*). This little creature inhabits some of the islands of the East Indian Archipelago: Borneo, Java, the Philippines (here and there), and probably others. Interest in the tarsier is aroused by the fact that it is not really a lemur, certainly not a monkey, but assuredly a primitive primate which has affinities with both. It is often placed by itself in a separate suborder of the primates—the Tarsioidea. There is a strong body of orthodox zoological opinion which considers that some very early and generalized ancestors of the present tarsiers gave rise to all the higher primate forms, including man. Eventually we shall have to grapple with some of these arguments, but, for the moment, we may confine ourselves to description of the animal and its habits, so far as known.

DESCRIPTION

Clark measured 10 adult tarsiers and found the average body length to be 154 mm. and the tail length 216 mm.[1] The head length averaged 42 mm. and head breadth 33 mm. The upper limbs are less than half as long as the legs, the upper arm being particularly short. The foot is longer than the leg or the thigh, and the hand longer than the arm or the forearm. The average weight of the 10 adult specimens was 114 grams. There was no sex difference in size. Newly born babies weighed about 24 grams and had body lengths of roughly 100 mm., but tail lengths inferior to body length. The tail is long and ratty with little hair on it, except at the end, which is tufted. The

[1] Clark 1924, pp. 217–24.

body is well furred in most places, but the inner sides of the thighs are only sparsely covered, and the greatly elongated tarsal or ankle region is naked. The general fur color is reddish brown, with the underside of the body more of a grayish white, and the face rufous. The facial feelers, or vibrissae, are well developed. Cutaneous glands have not been observed.

The tarsier differs from all lemurs in that it has only a narrow strip of naked skin around the nostrils and not a moist muzzle with a central prolongation dividing the upper lip. Also the nostrils of the tarsier are set far apart and are not slit upwards and sideways. The whole of the upper lip is covered with hair. Although the upper lip is not closely tethered to the gums, the animal drinks by lapping. The tarsier, being a nocturnal animal, has perfectly enormous, round eyes. The iris is yellow-brown in the adult, but said to be bluish at birth. The eyelids are fringed with fine lashes. The ears are big and upstanding, with the hinder rims flattened, not rolled. The snout is short and blunt, the skull rounded.

The tarsier has five digits on both hands and feet. These digits are tipped on the underside with expanded, disklike pads, which are useful in gripping the boughs. All the nails on fingers and toes are narrow and pointed—rather clawlike—but the second and third toes on the feet bear definitely sharp and recurved claws—presumably toilet accessories. The thumb is short, but the great toe is long; both of these digits are opposable to the outer series.

The anatomy of this animal has so many important and distinctive features that it is desirable here to say something of its skeleton and its viscera.

The bony sockets which lodge the eyeball—the orbits—are of tremendous size and directed somewhat laterally so that the eyes look outward as in lemurs. The space between the orbits is very narrow. None of the lemurs has any back wall to the orbit, but in tarsiers, as in monkeys, apes, and man, there is a complete bony partition between the eyeball and the side of the skull where the temporal muscle —one of the most important chewing muscles—is attached. The lachrymal bone, which is a small bone inside of the inner lower corner of the orbit in monkeys, apes, and man, is large in the tarsier, as in lemurs, and extends over the lower orbital rim onto the facial surface. As in the aye-aye (a specialized lemur), the halves of the lower jaw are not fused together in the middle line of the chin.

Some other skeletal details about the tarsier will be found at the end of the chapter. One or two more bony features must be mentioned here. The lower leg, which in other primates has two more or less parallel bones—a smaller outside bone called the fibula and an inner large bone called the tibia or shinbone—has been modified for hopping. The lower half of the fibula is fused with the tibia. The heel and ankle bones are tremendously lengthened and the whole ankle region appears dried up and fleshless.

The teeth of the tarsier are simple and primitive. There is but one incisor tooth on each side of the lower jaw and these are erect, not raked forward as in lemurs. The upper jaw has the ordinary two pairs of incisor teeth and the middle pair are not widely separated as in lemurs. The canine teeth are not tusked, but small. There are three premolar teeth and three molars, as in most lemurs and in New World monkeys. The stomach and the intestinal canal are simple in form and arrangement; there is no vermiform appendix.

The brain of the tarsier has the olfactory lobes (seat of the sense of smell) much reduced as compared with lemurs, whereas the visual areas of the cerebrum are greatly enlarged. The cerebral hemispheres extend back and overhang the cerebellum to some extent—a feature associated with the higher primate forms and absent from lemuroid brains. The animal is intermediate between lemurs and higher primates in that the sense of smell is less developed than in the former, and more than in the latter. The reduction of the snout has been accompanied by a swiveling forward to some degree of the planes of the orbits, so that the visual fields of the two eyes overlap. Nevertheless, this animal does not possess stereoscopic vision, although it is, so to speak, just around the corner.

HABITAT, POSTURE, LOCOMOTION

The Philippine tarsier is reported to frequent abandoned clearings where new growth has sprung up to the height of some 20 feet and, in the island of Samar, places where the ground is covered with ferns and plants to the height of 3 feet or more. Such spots afford easy concealment for the animal during the daytime.[2] Mr. John Whitehead, one of the few persons who have seen this animal at large, found one in Samar clinging to the stem of a small tree just above the fern growth, awake and watching his movements intently.

The tarsier is not known to make nests. This little animal is a notable arboreal acrobat. All observers agree that it may be seen at one moment clinging to a bough and in the next instant clinging to another a yard or more away, in precisely the same position, having translated itself with such extreme rapidity that the onlooker has

[2] Elliot 1913, I, 10-11.

scarcely caught a glimpse of it flying through the air with its tail streaming out behind. Galagos are also very good at this sort of "presto! change boughs!" business. Conservative observers estimate the space cleared in these hops or leaps at 2 feet to a yard, but the tarsier can probably do better than that. The animal, like the galago, can spring vertically upward, as well as outward and downward. Professor Le Gros Clark, who has made some of the most detailed and accurate studies of the living tarsier, says that the animal at rest clings to a vertical branch with the palms of the hands and the soles of the feet closely applied to the bark, the great toe opposed to the outer digits in grasping the branch, but not the thumb. In this vertical position the lower surface of the tail is pressed hard against the branch below and serves as a considerable support. On a flat surface Le Gros Clark says that the tarsier progresses in froglike jumps, landing sprawling. The implication is that the animal jumps from its hind limbs but lands on all fours.

Cook says that tarsiers progress by high, but short, hops, with the body in an erect position.[3] One that is pursued may make hops about 6 feet in length, rising in the air about 4 feet at each hop. The tail is used as a prop when the animal is sitting. The clawlike toenails on the second and third digits are aids in climbing very smooth surfaces. When the animal is urinating or defecating the tail is held in a rigid arch with the tip resting on or near the crown of the head. Fur is kept immaculately clean and the animals lick each other as do cats. The tarsier holds its legs out, supporting them with its hands, so that it can lick them more conveniently. The two claws on the feet are used for scratching. The animal doubles up its toes in such a way that only the two claws are left protruding.

DIET AND FEEDING

Little or nothing is known of the diet of the free tarsier. Lasker has compiled existing information from many sources.[4] He states that the only suggestion about the diet of the animal in the wild is derived from the fact that Cook reports a tarsier seen perched upon the remains of a wild hog, as yet untainted. Lasker suggests that this position would be advantageous for catching insects. It is agreed that the captive animal rejects all vegetable food, including leaves and fruit. The one dissentient is a Father Camel, who made some observations on the tarsier in 1706 or 1707. According to him, the tarsier

[3]Cook 1939, pp. 173–78.
[4]Lasker, I, 48, 49.

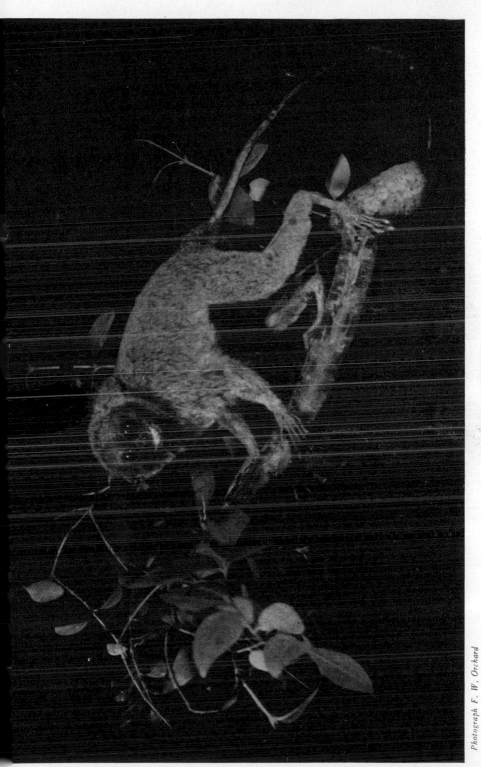

THE TARSIER

Photograph F. W. Orchard

eats the fig and other fruits. But this good father also reported that the tarsiers were said to live upon charcoal. Whitehead mentions this native belief in the Philippines and ascribes it to the fact that the animal often lives in plantations that have been cut and burned. This unfortunate misconception has resulted in captive tarsiers being fed on a diet of charcoal, upon which, of course, they quickly starve.

The tarsier sits up on its hindquarters and eats with its hands. Le Gros Clark gives the following description:

On being offered a grasshopper, the animal stares at it for a moment or so, drawing itself up and adjusting its position so as best to spring on the insect. This it does with both its forelimbs, seizing hold with its long fingers, and raking the morsel to its mouth, which is protruded as far forward as possible to assist in the capture. The animal screws up its eyes very tightly when seizing its prey, and in the daytime it appears to find great difficulty in accurately locating the grasshopper, for it will often seize and bite the fingers or forceps which hold the insect. The latter is crammed into the mouth and scrunched up, protruding portions being helped in by one of the hands.[5]

Whitehead reports a similar manner of eating grasshoppers, but says that the tarsier held the kicking legs of the grasshopper with both hands while the body was passed through the sharp teeth. When the insect had been killed, the tarsier would open its eyes, bite off the legs and wings, and chew the rest up thoroughly.

The favorite food of Cook's tarsiers was grasshoppers, next lizards, and, lastly, fresh-water shrimps and small fish. But insects other than the grasshopper were eaten with almost equal relish, including mantes, moths, butterflies, and the larvae of the coconut beetle. Lizard eggs were refused at first, but eaten at night. The field lizard, which is 3 to 5 inches long, is about the largest living prey which the tarsier can handle. Four or 5 grasshoppers at a time are all the tarsier can eat and a supply of 8 is sufficient for 24 hours.

GENERAL BEHAVIOR

Tarsiers spend the greater part of the day in sleeping, preferably in dark places.[6] They struggle with each other over food, but never in a serious fashion nor with ill temper. These struggles are more in the nature of wrestling bouts than fights, and the teeth are not used. One may pull a half-eaten grasshopper away from another and prevent the

[5]Clark 1924, pp. 217–23.
[6]Cook 1939.

original owner from recovering it by grabbing a handful of hair on the crown of his head.

Two of the tarsiers which escaped one night were found the next morning on top of a post not 15 feet from the cage. They had their arms about each other like a pair of frightened children. Another which had escaped at this time was found among the rocks of the beach, dripping wet. Apparently it had swum across a small river some 200 yards from the point of its escape.

Tarsier couples apparently stick together even when herded with others and Cook states that the male will allow the female to take food away from him, almost without effort.

A very unlemuroid and monkeylike trick of the animal is its habit of staring at a person for a long time without moving a muscle and then grimacing and showing its teeth. Tarsiers often bite viciously, but are capable of being tamed without great difficulty. Cuming says that the tame specimens like to be caressed and will lick the faces of human friends.

SENSES

In the daytime the pupil of the tarsier's eye is reduced to a mere pin point and vision is poor. In order to recognize a grasshopper, for example, it seems necessary for the animal to hold the insect up so that a horizontal line across the eyes is parallel to its length. At night the pupils enlarge enormously and probably the tarsier sees very well. In order to look at an object directly overhead this animal twists its extremely mobile head until the nose is over the middle line of the back.

The sense of smell seems to be very obtuse, since a food morsel dropped on the floor in the daytime has nearly to be touched by the nose before it is discovered, the eyes meanwhile being tightly closed.

The hearing of the tarsier seems to be more acute. The upper part of the ear can be reduced in size by folding. Then the entire ear is laid against the side of the head. However, when the animal is listening intently, the ears are opened widely and are moved back and forth, one pointing to the front and the other to the rear, alternately.

In the cage Cook's tarsiers made no noise, but one at liberty in a shed near by frequently uttered a high, clear, twittering musical note, repeated at intervals of a few seconds. The noise was made with the mouth half open, but without perceptible mouth movements. Cook says that the respiration of the tarsier is about 82 per minute.

BREEDING SEASON

The available evidence indicates that tarsiers live in pairs with their young. Le Gros Clark ascertained the breeding season of the tarsier in Sarawak to correspond with that of the northeast monsoon—from October to March. He secured embryos of various sizes and newly-born tarsiers which indicated that impregnation might take place as early as October and as late as December. The young are born, as a rule, in the early months of the year. However, the extensive data of the Hubrecht collection, including nearly 1,000 specimens, have been determined by Zuckerman to show no significant seasonal variation in the birth rate of this animal. Very little is known of the reproductive cycle of the tarsier, but certain observations of Van Herwerden indicate that this animal is continuously polyoestrous, when not pregnant, and that successive cycles are separated by uterine hemorrhage. In having a menstrual cycle the tarsier thus appears to resemble man, the apes, the Old World monkeys, and the New World monkeys (bleeding observed by Carpenter, Wislocki, and Hammett), and possibly to differ from lemurs. Only one baby is produced at birth.

MATERNAL CARE

The newborn tarsier clings to the fur of the mother's abdominal wall with its hands and feet and is not held by the mother. At birth the eyes are open and the animal can cling to a branch and scramble about in a hesitating way. During the first month of life it can progress along the ground by short jumps, but is not able to leap from branch to branch.

ANATOMY

SKULL

The outstanding features of the skull of the tarsier are its very short, pointed snout, enormous orbits, and rounded brain case. The orbits are so enlarged that the space between them is reduced to a very thin septum. Duckworth states that the cribriform plate of the ethmoid does not exist as such and quotes Burmeister to the effect that the olfactory nerve filaments pass to the nasal fossa by a single canal on each side.[7] Within the orbit is a lachrymo-ethmoidal articulation. The postorbital wall is complete. The large lachrymal bone extends onto the face. The alisphenoid articulates with the parietal. The glenoid fossa is said to be deeper than that of the lemurs. The auditory bulla is inflated, but the tympanic annulus

[7] Duckworth 1915, pp. 103ff.

is not enclosed within it as in lemurs, but forms a short, funnel-shaped bony auditory meatus as in higher primates. The carotid canal is situated on the ventral aspect of the bulla. The premaxillae extend upward to overlap the lower margins of the nasal aperture. The halves of the mandible are not synostosed.

The upper central incisors are long and pointed, and the lower incisors are small cones. The upper molar teeth have only 3 cusps, whereas in the lowers the 3 cusps are supplemented by a heel or talonid.

ORGANS OF DIGESTION

According to Duckworth, the lips of the tarsier have large sebaceous glands, and thus differ from those of the lemurs and the apes. The hard palate is marked by transverse crests crossing the roof of the mouth through its entire extent. The tongue has frenal lamellae as in all primates except man and the orang-utan, but the sublingua is represented by a plica fimbricata, devoid of a horny, dentate margin specialized for toothcleaning. The stomach is a simple dilatation of the alimentary canal, and the duodenum is not strikingly enlarged. The arrangement of the entire intestinal canal, according to Wood Jones, is excessively simple. The small intestine is arranged in simple loops. The large intestine is but little longer than the caecum and is without flexures or coils. The caecum is well developed, but there is no vermiform appendix. The liver has 3 main lobes in addition to a caudate lobe. Duckworth discusses the liver of *Tarsius* in detail and concludes that it is of a lemurian type and generalized.

ORGANS OF RESPIRATION

Wood Jones says that the rings of the trachea in *Tarsius* are incomplete on their dorsal side. The left lung has 4 lobes and the right 5 or 6. Duckworth says that the free portion of the vocal cord is small, and the extensive musculature adjacent to it is relatively undifferentiated.

URO-GENITAL SYSTEM

The left kidney is farther back than the right. Wood Jones and Woollard found a single pyramid and papilla, but Burmeister found 4 in his specimen. The penis is well developed in the differentiation of its various parts. It contains no bone. The testes are usually descended into the scrotum, although they were abdominal in the specimen dissected by Duckworth. The bicornuate uterus has a single undivided body, considerably larger than the cornua. Wood Jones says that the urethra opens in front of the vaginal orifice and some distance from the small clitoris. The labia are well marked and conceal the orifices. The external genitalia of the female thus resemble those of man and contrast with those of other primates. Woollard has also stated that the spermatoza of the tarsier closely resemble those of man.

CENTRAL NERVOUS SYSTEM

The shape of the brain is peculiar because of the encroachment of the orbits upon the cranial cavity. The cerebrum is broader than it is long and devoid of fissures, with the exception of one on the lateral surface which has been identified by some anatomists as the supra-Sylvian sulcus and by Wood Jones as the Sylvian. The cerebral hemispheres overlap the cerebellum, and, according to Wood Jones, a posterior cornu is developed. The visual cortex, which is very extensive, tends to ally *Tarsius* with the higher primate forms. The corpus callosum is very short and small.

According to Duckworth, the cerebellum of *Tarsius* approaches the form characteristic of the Insectivora more closely than does that of any other primate. But in the higher degree of folding and the more massive "middle lobe" the cerebellum of *Tarsius* has advanced beyond the lowlier stage of the insectivores. The same anatomist states that the pituitary consists of a median non-glandular portion with two lateral glandular lobes.[8] This arrangement recalls that of the reptiles. On the whole, the brain displays a mixture of very primitive and advanced characters.

[8] Duckworth 1915, p. 115.

CHAPTER XI

The Ghosts of Linnaeus, or Night Life in Madagascar

MADAGASCAR AND THE LEMURS

THE ISLAND OF MADAGASCAR lies in the Indian Ocean some 300 miles off the southeast coast of Africa. It is shaped like the print of a left human foot with the big toe pointing northeast. From the tip of the big toe to the heel is 1,000 miles and the ball of the foot is nearly 360 miles across. The island is the third largest in the world (not counting Australia and Greenland). It is not quite four times the size of England and Wales. The interior is rugged and mountainous, but between the elevated central plateaus and the coast are broad belts of luxuriant tropical forest. The climate here is not salubrious. Probably the island was once a part of Africa, but its isolation has been protracted and the animals which inhabit it, together with certain features of the ocean floor, suggest that Madagascar is the remnant of an archipelago which once connected Africa with Asia. The human fauna (to the number of some two and three-quarter millions) seems to have come mostly from islands of the Indian and Pacific oceans, although there is some African mixture. The subhuman animals also have more Asiatic than African relationships, but they are strongly individual, not to say peculiar. Few tourists visit Madagascar, which is deficient in harbors, cities, characteristic tropical forms of life, and civilization, although a French colony. However, it is rich in hot springs and earthquake shocks and is headquarters for the chameleons, in which we are not interested, and for the lemurs, in which we are interested—passionately.

Dr. Linnaeus was an eighteenth-century Swedish naturalist who undertook to bring order out of the chaos of plants and animals left around by the untidy creative experiments of Nature. He classified these living things and named a good many of them. Some curious animals indigenous to Madagascar he called lemurs, from the Latin *lemures,* which means "ghosts," or "spirits of the departed ancestors."

Whether Linnaeus gave them this name because they are active mainly at night and are silent and stealthy, or whether he regarded these animals as the pallid shades of ancestral types, I do not know. Incidentally, this same classifier and copious bestower of names is responsible for calling the great group or "order" of animals which includes man, apes, monkeys, and lemurs "Primates," from *primus,* "first."

As a matter of interest, Madagascar is not only the home of about 39 out of 50 existing groups or species of lemurs; it is a haven for these almost defenseless animals, since there are on the island no large carnivores except one kind of a ferocious civet cat. Indeed half of the mammalian fauna of Madagascar is made up of lemurs. Alfred Grandidier, who wrote a classic work on Madagascar consisting of some 28 quarto volumes, says that the lemurs are so numerous that you can find one in every little copse in the island. We may then get out flashlights, since most lemurs are nocturnal, and go out to study a few kinds of lemurs, but without any native guides, since it is said that the natives are superstitious about molesting them.

It would be foolish to go stumbling about in the dark of the jungles of Madagascar searching for lemurs without knowing how to recognize them when found. In the first place, how big are lemurs? The smallest, called mouse-lemurs, are no bigger than a small rat, with a head and body length of 4 inches, and an extra half-foot of tail. The largest, which belongs to a group named *Indris,* is about 2 feet from snout to rump, not including a rabbity stump of a tail.[1] Of course the young ones come small and grow larger. Lemurs are quadrupeds, although the older writers usually describe them as quadrumanous, because all of their four extremities look like hands rather than feet. Nevertheless, anatomically, the fore pair are hands and the hind pair feet. There are five digits on each extremity, flat-nailed, except the second toe of the foot, which usually bears a claw. In some lemurs, however, the index fingers are reduced to stumps. Both thumb and great toe are well developed and can be rotated so as to oppose the

---

[1] My big, black alley cat, Ham, measures about 24 inches from snout to rump, and has a good 12 inches of tail. His weight, as of Sunday morning, September 21, 1941, is 13 pounds 7 ounces. He is roughly 2½ years old and looks huge. He eats a pound of tinned salmon in 2 days, in addition to other oddments. I doubt if any lemur would equal him in weight, but lemurs are not carnivores, or, at any rate, do not live upon canned salmon in Madagascar. My little yellow cat, Shem, is about 5 months old, weighs 7 pounds 2 ounces, and has about 15 inches of body length in addition to 9 inches of tail. He may be about the size of the average of the larger lemur species. I compare lemurs with cats, partly because they look more like cats than any other animal except foxes, and, in case of little ones, squirrels. Also, I have no foxes or squirrels about the house.

tips of the outer digits. This statement is a technical way of saying that lemurs have grasping or prehensile hands and feet; so do all other primates except man, whose foot has been perverted. Some lemurs have long, bushy tails, some long, ratty tails, some short, tufted tails, and some no tails at all. Thus the kind of tail, if any, does not help one to recognize lemurs in general, but only in particular, in the case of different types already identified as lemurs. All lemurs have hairy or furry coats, but these vary in a bewildering fashion in color and distribution. One suspects that a great many of the different species (one of the smaller and more intimate zoological classifications) have been established mainly, if not entirely, on the basis of differences in coat color and arrangement.

All lemurs have pointed snouts, usually long and sharp, but sometimes short and blunt. Every one of them, however, has nostrils like those of a cat or dog, shaped like inverted commas and set in a naked, moist muzzle, which has a strip of bare skin extending down the middle of the upper lip. This corresponds to the vertical furrow in the middle of the human upper lip, which is called a philtrum. The upper lip of the lemur is tethered so closely to the gum of the upper jaw that the animal has to drink by lapping and not by sucking. The ears are usually pointed, leaflike, and prominent, but in some kinds of lemurs they are short and folded and partly concealed by the hair. Most lemurs have big, round eyes; in the case of nocturnal species they are enormous. The foregoing ought to be enough in the way of external characters to enable us to pick out lemurs, especially in Madagascar, where nearly every other animal is a lemur. One might add, for good measure, that there is always a gap between the upper middle incisor teeth and that the lower front teeth are small and lean forward, so that they look like a comb. The conventional explanation of this arrangement, which zoologists in their simple language call "procumbent inferior incisors," is that the lemur uses these teeth to comb his hair, as if he were *die Lorelei*. However, Dr. Russell Stein, an iconoclastic student of odontology, experimented with the teeth of the alleged lemuroid comb, and found that they were so close together that not even fur could pass between them.[2]

The one long, pointed claw on the second toe of the foot is also supposed to have been retained for "toilet purposes." Whether this means scratching, or picking the lower teeth when the hair gets snarled in them, I am unable to say. Professor Wood Jones, one of our most brilliant and perversely original students of primates, thinks

[2]Lowther 1939, quoting Dr. M. Russell Stein, "The Myth of the Lemur's Comb," *Amer. Nat.*, Vol. LXX, Jan. 1936.

that the elaborate pattern of tracts and whorls which can be traced out in the hair of the lemur is due to the fact that the animal spends a large part of his time doing his hair with his teeth and his toilet toenail.[3] But Wood Jones would not subscribe to my frivolous suggestion that the toenail is used to pick the teeth. On the lower part of the lemur tongue is a horny denticulated fold, which is said to be used as a rake for cleaning the toilet teeth after the fur-combing process.[4] Thus before we have really come to close quarters with the lemurs we find them profoundly resembling man in that they spend an inordinate time in combing their hair and brushing their teeth— that is, if they really do.

However, we have not yet stated where one must go to look for lemurs, except, vaguely, in the island of Madagascar. Nearly all lemurs live in trees; that is to say they are "arboreal."[5] So are most of the other subhuman primates.

LEMUROIDEA–CLASSIFICATION

The lemurs belong to a separate suborder of the primates, called the Lemuroidea. Informally this suborder may be divided into the lemuriforms and lorisiforms. The former include the family Lemuridae, consisting of ordinary or true lemurs, gentle lemurs, sportive lemurs, and the hattock (genera: *Lemur, Hapalemur, Lepidolemur, Myoxicebus*); also the mouse lemurs, dwarf lemurs, and fat-tailed lemurs (genera: *Chirogale, Microcebus, Opolemur* or *Allitilemur*). All of

---

[3] Jones 1929, p. 83.

[4] Jones 1929, p. 101.

[5] The word "arboreal" intrigues me, because I do not remember encountering it before I began to concern myself with anthropology, apes, etc. Of course, *arbor* is Latin for tree. In my youth an arbor was a sort of trellised arrangement of trees or vines, trained over a latticework to make a leafy roof. One sat underneath and was bitten by insects. Then, again, there was "Arbor Day" which the Oxford Dictionary snootily defines thus: "1872. A day set apart, orig. in Nebraska, U.S.A., for the planting of trees." The same ultimate etymological authority gives for "arboreal": "Connected with, haunting, or inhabiting trees 1834" (*sic*). "Hanging about" or even "hanging out" in trees might be more suitable as the adjective applies to primates. Pursuing these philological researches farther, I found in the Century Dictionary a remarkable quotation exemplifying the use of the word "arboraceous" which is roughly a synonym of "arboreal." Here it is: "Not like Papuas or Bushmen, with *arboraceous* habits and half-animal clicks. *Max Müller*, India, etc., p. 133." This little sentence contains one orthographic and three anthropological errors. See if you can find them. None of them has anything to do with lemurs.

A few human groups build houses in trees as did the Swiss Family Robinson, but I should hesitate to call them "arboreal." Zacchaeus was not "arboreal" because he only climbed a tree and then climbed down again. However, I suppose that Simeon Stylites, who passed the last 30 of his years on a pillar, might be described, in a cultural rather than a zoological sense, as "stylitic."

these live in Madagascar. The second family of the lemuriforms is the Indrisidae, including avahis, sifakas, and indris (genera: *Avahis* or *Lichanotus, Propithecus, Indris*). The third family consists only of the aye-aye (family Chiromyidae, genus *Chiromys* [*Daubentonia*]). The lorisiform lemurs are of two families, the Lorisidae, residents of the oriental region, and the Galagidae, which dwell on the African mainland. The lorises are of two types, slender and slow (genera: *Loris, Nycticebus*). The Galagidae consist of galagos or bush babies, pottos, and awantibos (genera: *Galago, Perodicticus, Arctocebus*).[6]

THE GENUINE LEMURS

The true lemurs live not only in Madagascar but in the Comoro Islands, which are halfway between Madagascar and Zanzibar. The four outside toes of the feet are not webbed as in the indris and the lemurs of that group; the snout is longer and there is an extra premolar or bicuspid tooth on each side of both jaws. All the true lemurs have long tails and much longer arms than the avahis, sifakas, and indris. Consequently, on the ground they go on all fours.

There is a number of species of true lemur, including the ring-tailed lemur, the red-fronted, black-fronted, white-fronted, mongoose, black and ruffed types. Merely to describe the coat colors of all of the species would involve us in many pages of dreary writing which most readers would skip. We shall then select one species for description and pass over the rest with a bald statement as to any peculiarities of physique, habitat, or habit, which may seem either of importance or of interest.

THE RING-TAILED LEMUR (*Lemur catta*)

This animal, which is about the size of an average house cat, but looks more like a fox, has a black-and-white ringed tail, but is mostly ash-gray on the back, with white on the undersides and around the eyes and cheeks.

The ring-tailed lemur inhabits a part of the central tableland of Madagascar, especially the south and the southwest, where the country is rocky and almost treeless. This lemur is stated to be entirely absent from the adjacent forest belts. It is possibly more diurnal than nocturnal, although it takes a long siesta in the middle of the day. The ring-tailed lemur goes about in small troops. The palms of the hands and soles of the feet are said to be particularly adapted for lo-

[6]Jones 1929, pp. 81–82.

comotion over smooth and slippery rocks, being long, hard, smooth, and leathery. The great toes are less developed than in the tree-dwelling species which use the feet for grasping boughs.

Since lemurs of this entire genus are common in zoos, something is known of their reproductive habits. Zuckerman, for example, has charted the percentage monthly distribution of births for 66 lemurs of various species of the genus *Lemur,* all born in the London Zoological Gardens.[7] Over 55 per cent were born in April, with nearly all of the rest appearing in March, May, and June. The implication is that the lemurs have a definite breeding season and do not make love all the year round, contrary to the habits of the allegedly higher primates. The actual duration of pregnancy in lemurs is not well known. Away back in 1824, E. Geoffroy and Cuvier estimated it at 111 days for the species *L. albifrons* (the white-fronted lemur), but in 1882 Schmidt observed two specimens of the black lemur (*L. macaco*) and stated that the period of gestation was 145 days. Four to 5 months seems a good guess. Female lemuroids are not known to menstruate and they have a primitive two-horned form of the uterus. The afterbirth, or placenta, is diffuse and bell-shaped, rather than discoidal as in higher primate forms.

The number of young produced at a birth in the genus of true lemurs seems ordinarily to be one. The species *L. macaco* repeatedly produced living offspring in the London Zoological Gardens, and of 7 consecutive records, 5 births were of single offspring, and 2 cases were twins.[8] All the records of *L. mongoz* and *L. brunneus* are of single births, but the ring tailed lemur and the white fronted lemur are known to have produced two at a birth.

The different species of the genus *Lemur* readily interbreed. Zuckerman alone has reported 8 interspecific hybrids among the true lemurs.[9]

When the lemur baby is born, it clings tightly to the fur of the underside of the mother's body, although later it may be carried on her back. In 1885 P. L. Sclater gave an account and published a drawing of the manner in which the black lemur carries her young.[10] In this picture the baby lies across the abdomen of the mother, with its long tail passed around her back and looped around its owner's neck. Another observer has stated that the lemur mother supports the baby

---

[7] Zuckerman 1933, p. 32.
[8] Jones 1929, p. 114.
[9] Zuckerman 1932, pp. 1059–75.
[10] Sclater 1885, p. 672.

with her own tail by curling it between her legs over the infant's body and around her back. Yet general zoological opinion denies that any of the long tails of lemurs are prehensile or grasping. Several of the plates of Milne-Edwards and Grandidier, however, show various lemurs with their tails coiled around boughs.

Lemurs apparently suckle for a prolonged period. In the case of a white-fronted lemur and her baby observed by Cuvier, the infant was not weaned for 6 months, although food placed in the cage was taken by the infant during the fifth or sixth week. Wood Jones says that the lemur mother does not nurse or handle her offspring; the latter clings to the mother. He asserts that it is very difficult to dogmatize about maternal affection in these animals. They all will bite savagely if any interference with the young is attempted; but they will bite just as hard if interfered with in any other way. The fathers are said to be perfectly indifferent to their offspring.

True lemurs are mixed feeders, eating both animal and vegetable materials. They are very fond of insects. Wood Jones says that many species will kill and eat birds and nearly all will take meat in captivity. The mongoose lemur is said to be fond of birds' brains, which are sucked into the mouth after the skull of the bird has been cracked with the teeth. The rest of the bird is not eaten. The lemurs kill living prey by pouncing upon it with forelimbs and mouth, killing with the teeth. Ordinarily, food is taken by mouth, although it may be grasped by hand through the bars of the cage, in case of a captive animal. The hands are used, both together, not so much for putting food into the mouth, as for holding it so that the jaws and teeth may get at it. Whether wild or captive, lemurs will eat almost any kind of fruit, but Wood Jones says they are not sufficiently vegetarian to enjoy cabbage or lettuce, as do many monkeys. The ring-tailed lemur uses its long upper canines to strip off the outer cover of the thorny prickly pear. This fruit is the chief food of ring-tailed lemurs, since it grows abundantly in rocky crevices and around the foot of rocks. Natives say that the ring-tailed lemur does not drink at all, and, in captivity, it has been observed to abstain from water for a whole month, living upon bananas. Wood Jones thinks that most lemurs drink very little, and when they do drink, they lap rather than suck. Shaw reported that the western Madagascar lemurs appeared to subsist without drinking, whereas those in the east generally or invariably drank with their meals.

The gentleness of lemurs seems, like Mark Twain's death, to have been exaggerated. Ring-tailed lemurs are said to depend more upon the hands in fighting than upon their teeth. Scratching and striking

BLACK-FRONTED LEMUR

ANOTHER TRUE LEMUR

THE SLOW LORIS

with the hands, a male lemur has been seen to whip a dog larger than itself. Wood Jones says that lemurs in fighting lay back their ears, bring both forelimbs into action, and attempt to get the adversary within reach of their canine teeth. Lying on back or side with eyes tight shut and teeth drawn back, they will grapple with anything which comes within reach of their hands and feet, and fight with utmost ferocity and tenacity. Cuvier mentions a case of a ruffed lemur which tore to pieces a mongoose, with which it had formerly lived upon terms of armed neutrality. The mongoose is an unusually pugnacious animal. Even the little mouse or dwarf lemurs fight fiercely.

Wood Jones attests also the tenacious hold upon life which is characteristic of lemurs. He claims that no lemur gives up the ghost either in fighting or in resisting disease "till it has reached the limit of resistance of the least specialized of animal tissues."[11] He relates a long medical history of a L. fulvus which was brought in, apparently dead, but was resuscitated by artificial respiration several times in the course of 2 days. When it finally succumbed, the post-mortem showed septicemia with "extensive focal necrosis of the nasal chambers and abscess formation within the orbits and around the base of the skull." Evidently a tough animal.

Thanks to the accurate records kept by the London Zoological Gardens, we have some idea of the life span of captive lemurs. According to Zuckerman, 119 lemurs belonging to 4 genera or species averaged 10 years and 6 months of life.[12] The oldest age attained was 26 years. These are impressive figures, indicating that even these lowly primates are decidedly long lived.

The blood of the lemur does not react to anti-human sera as do the bloods of all higher primates. There are nearly twice as many red cells and white cells per cubic millimeter in lemuroid blood as in human blood.[13] The crystallography of lemuroid blood indicates that these animals have orthorhombic blood crystals, as have also most of the lower primates which have been examined, together with man.[14] The blood groups present in the anthropoid apes, monkeys, and man are definitely lacking in eight lemurs examined, all of the genus of true lemurs.

The eyes of all lemuroids are set sideways in the head, so that the fields of vision do not coincide. In fact, they probably overlap very little, except in the short-snouted galagos. The retina conforms to a

[11]Jones 1929, p. 112.
[12]Zuckerman 1933, p. 27.
[13]Zuckerman 1933, p. 49, citing Ponder, Yeager, and Charipper.
[14]Zuckerman 1933, p. 50, quoting Reichert and Brown.

nocturnal type and lacks a fovea and a macula. From these considerations it is agreed that lemurs do not possess stereoscopic vision. Lemurs are probably color-blind and able to discriminate between differently colored disks only on the basis of variations in brightness.

It seems probable that the relatively large size of the olfactory lobes of the brain in lemurs indicates that the sense of smell is more important to these animals than to any of the higher primates. Arm glands and anal glands, probably scent glands, are found in most species of the genus *Lemur* and in some other lemurs.

The facial musculature of the lemur is comparatively simple and undifferentiated, much like the head musculature of lower mammals. Correspondingly, facial movements are few and there is little or nothing of facial expression. Zuckerman observes that the only changes of expressions conveyed are by means of flinching, which may involve the entire body, movements of the eyes and upper eyelids, and sometimes slight movements of the ears.[15] Movements of the mouth are made, as a rule, only when the animal is eating, licking, lapping, or fighting.

The grooming habits of lemurs have attracted the attention of various observers from Cuvier on. Most of them agree that these animals indulge in a good deal of licking and raking of the fur with the comblike lower incisors. This comb is stated to be cleaned by the natural toothbrush on the underside of the tongue. Parts of the body which cannot be reached with teeth and tongue are cleaned by scratching with the one claw on the hind foot; the right foot serving to scratch the left side, and vice versa. Animals often indulge in mutual grooming, using mostly the teeth and tongue. The hands are employed only to hold the fur of the animal which is being cleaned. Wood Jones says that lemurs are very particular about keeping their hands clean, so that the easiest way to induce a sick lemur to take medicine is to smear it on the hands and then allow it to lick them off.[16]

VOCALIZATIONS

The true lemurs are not, as a rule, noisy animals, but they apparently have a wide range of vocalization. Wood Jones describes their ordinary noise as a deep grunt, subject to very few inflections, although the intervals between the grunts may be marked by widely different emotional phases. Pleasure is expressed by almost continuous grunting, which impressed Cuvier and Linnaeus as similar to the

[15]Zuckerman 1933, pp. 68–69.
[16]Jones 1929, p. III.

deep purring of cats. True lemurs also have a chorus call, which is uttered only occasionally by captive animals during the dusk of summer evenings. This call seems difficult to describe but is said to be loud, harsh, and powerful, audible at a.long distance. The indri emits "doleful, doglike howls" and another lemur, *Hapalemur simus,* sometimes utters a cry either resembling the quack of a duck or loud and piercing. The big *Propithecus* lemurs are silent unless alarmed, when they make a clucking sound. Madagascar lemurs are described as noisier than African and Asiatic lemurs.

INTELLIGENCE

Klüver worked with an ordinary ring-tailed lemur (*Lemur catta*) in tests involving the selection of the lighter of two boxes (1,200 grams and 300 grams).[17] This animal differed from all the monkeys in that she had to be trained to pull in the string. She persistently reached for the banana when it was quite out of range. The strings of the two boxes had to be placed nearer together in order to decrease the difficulty of "making comparisons." (Was this connected with the lack of stereoscopic vision in the lemur, as contrasted with higher primates?) In the course of 16 days this lemur learned to respond positively to the 300-gram box in the 300 : 1,200 pair. She persisted in pulling in the wrong box after she had pulled in and eaten the food from the correct box. This lemur also succeeded in differentiating between 900 grams : 300 grams, but lost ground when the differences in weight were reduced. The lemur did not recognize as quickly as did the monkeys the advantage of using successive comparisons as a means of making a correct choice. She made fewer comparisons. She worked faster than the spider monkeys and was exceeded in speed only by the macaques. A curious fact is that the animal usually lost the banana slice when it fell out of the box during the tilting process. Although it was in plain sight, directly in front of her, she sniffed around and sometimes gave up the search without locating it. She may have been confused or disoriented.

MOUSE LEMURS

The mouse lemurs are miscalled because they are all bigger than mice, although it is stated that some are smaller than a rat. At any rate, they are not large. There are 3 genera (*Chirogale, Microcebus,* and *Opolemur*). All have the bones of the ankle and heel considerably elongated; all have short snouts and rounded skulls, large eyes, long

[17]Klüver 1933, pp. 92ff.

hind limbs, and very lengthy tails. They live in Madagascar, are nocturnal, and mainly vegetarian. However, insects and small birds are
also eaten by these little creatures.

The most interesting feature of this group is the habit of estivation
which is characteristic of certain species. Estivation is the opposite of
hibernation, in that the animal remains dormant during the hot, dry
season rather than in the winter. The physiology of hibernation has
been investigated, but little is known about estivation. The latter is
assumed to be similar. During the period of hibernation starvation
and the wasting of tissues are avoided by the absorption of quantities
of fat which have been previously accumulated in various parts of
the body. Alimentation and excretion ceases; the body temperature is
lowered virtually to that of the surrounding medium; respiration is
totally or completely suspended; circulation continues.

The mouse lemurs which estivate are said to accumulate a great
mass of fat, mainly at the base of the tail, during the rainy season
which precedes their estivation. During this period the tail and hindquarters become enormously swollen.

There are some interesting parallels to the fat-buttocked condition
found in these lower primates. The most obvious are among sheep.
The Bokharan or Astrakan dumba, which occurs on the Asiatic
steppes and in the Near East, has a fat tail which weighs about 10
pounds, whereas the entire carcass will not weigh more than 50 or 60
pounds. The Persian fat-tailed sheep has a tail measuring 10 inches
across and weighing from 20 to 30 pounds. Fat-tailed sheep were introduced early into North Africa and have a wide distribution there.
Fat-rumped sheep are closer to the condition found in the mouse
lemurs. These are widespread in Europe and Asia. The tail is vestigial
and is embedded between two vast cushions of fat on the buttocks.
There are breeds of these sheep in many of the drier parts of southern
and central Africa, and they are also found in Madagascar. Both of
these types of sheep thrive in steppe, mountain, and desert regions
where change of seasons involves alternate periods of plenty and
scarcity of food. Undoubtedly the sheep live, to some extent, upon
the reserve of fat during the lean season. However, I am not aware
that any of these creatures estivate.

Among the primates the only parallel to the fat-rumped condition
of the mouse lemurs is found in man. The Bushmen and Hottentots,
inhabitants of the Kalahari Desert in South Africa, are notorious for
accumulation of fat on the buttocks, called steatopygia. This condition is less marked and more sporadic among some of the other
African peoples, including the Congo pygmies and the Somalis. On

the evidence of Paleolithic cave drawings and figurines dating from the last phases of the glacial period, it is certain that many of the Upper Paleolithic peoples, who flourished in Europe between 25,000 and 20,000 years ago, had these enormous mounds of fat on the buttocks.

The question is naturally raised as to the possibility of some of these ancients having developed the ability to hibernate. That would have been an admirable way of getting through the glacial period. In northern Russia, when the harvest has been insufficient, it is stated by Volkov that entire districts and villages settle themselves down for a winter sleep, in which the families are so disposed that their bodily heat is conserved and all movements are reduced to a minimum.[18] Darkness, silence, and lethargy descend upon the households. However, this is only pseudo-hibernation. Many years ago I attempted to find some evidence that the Bushmen and Hottentots went in for some sort of estivation. I did find that these peoples gorge themselves in an incredible fashion for several days at a time, when they have plenty of game or when certain fruits are in season, and then sleep, fast, and remain torpid for protracted periods. There is little doubt that the fat on the rump serves as a reserve larder to be drawn upon in hard times. On the other hand, there is no physiological evidence of actual estivation or hibernation. One of the difficulties in the way of accepting such an attractive hypothesis for the Bushmen and for ancient breeds of cave man is that the steatopygia is really well developed only in the females. It must be, to some extent, a secondary sexual character. It is hard to see how his wife's steatopygia would help a husband survive a glacial winter.

A reliable authority tells of a mouse lemur which he captured in the eastern side of the Betsileo province in Madagascar.[19] He kept it in a small box, but allowed it to run round the room and exercise at night. It went on all fours but sat up to eat its food with its hands. One evening in the winter (June) he opened the box and found the animal asleep and quite cold. He warmed it by the fire and rubbed it, and it came to life. This happened a number of times. Previous to this, the tail of the animal had become enlarged. This lemur made for itself a nest of grass and leaves, scooping a hole large enough for its body and covering itself over with loose material. Apparently, all the mouse lemurs make nests of this sort, ordinarily in trees.

The same zoologist, Shaw, gives information about the dwarf lemur, which belongs to the same group. It lives in the treetops and

[18]Volkov 1900, pp. 67ff.
[19]Elliot 1913, I, 94.

makes a nest of dried leaves. In captivity it feeds upon fruit and insects. Among themselves these lemurs are said to be quarrelsome, fighting fiercely and uttering shrill, whistling cries. Their small teeth are sharp and they hang on like grim death. They run along the branches nimbly on all fours and are good jumpers. They often hang by their feet, reach down for food, and then pull themselves up to the branch again. The tail is said to be used for balancing but not for grasping. Shaw particularly admired the beautiful eyes and perfect hands of these little animals.

THE AYE–AYE

The aye-aye (genus *Daubentonia*) is a Madagascar lemur so aberrant, eccentric, and generally peculiar that he was finally elected to the primates only on the basis of a slim plurality of physical characteristics. His teeth are virtually those of a rodent. A round head with a short, pointed muzzle is featured by a single pair of enormously long, curved incisor teeth in each jaw. These chisel-like teeth are enameled in front only; their bodies are formed of comparatively soft dentine. The wear on such a tooth, if used for the rasping and gnawing of hard surfaces, quickly produces a chisel edge, and it is obvious that the tooth would wear away entirely, were it not for the fact that the lower end remains open and it keeps on growing out from a persistent pulp as it is worn down. This condition is characteristic of rodent incisors. Back of these rodentlike front teeth are large gaps in the dental arch—no canines at all and only one small premolar, heading a series of 3 rather degenerate grinding teeth. The halves of the lower jaw are not fused together in front, but merely united at an acute angle by elastic tissue. The animal has big round eyes which are notable for a nictating membrane—a third eyelid which can be wiped across the eyeball transversely in some birds. This membrane is found in the inner corner of the eye. I do not know to what extent it functions in the aye-aye. A remnant of the nictating membrane occurs probably in all primates, including man. The aye-aye has large, naked ears, studded with small protuberances and protruding, handle-like, from the sides of the head. It is about the size of a cat and has a long and extraordinarily bushy tail.

The general color of the aye-aye is black, with yellowish white spots here and there, especially on the face and neck. The hands and feet are black. The foot differs from that of an ordinary lemur in that all the toes except the big toe are provided with pointed claws. The great toe has a flat nail and is opposable to the other digits.

The hands are most strange. All the fingers are long and thin, provided with compressed claws. The middle finger is so long and so attenuated that it looks like a piece of bent wire. In spite of the clawed thumb, that member can be rotated so as to oppose the finger tips.

The aye-aye is found in the forests of the east coast of Madagascar, in a restricted area between the Bay of Antongil and Mahanaro—practically the same region in which the indri lives. It was first discovered in 1780 by Sonnerat, a French traveler, who at the same time found the indri. There is some argument about the origin of the name, aye-aye, which is said by some to be the Malagasy natives' expression of surprise at seeing the animal, and by others to be an imitation of the cry of the animal itself. In any event, the natives of Madagascar call this lemur by a name somewhat resembling this nautical term of assent.

The aye-aye is said to be nocturnal, prowling about in pairs—male and female. It builds a nest of leaves and twigs, about 2 feet in diameter, in the upper branches of trees. The entrance is a hole in the side and here the animal (or married couple?) spends the day in sleep. At night the aye-ayes go about their business, seeking food.

What little is known of the habits of the aye-aye has been learned from the few animals which have survived in captivity. Some of the most important observations were made by H. Sandwith, Colonial Secretary of the island of Mauritius, who kept a specimen for some time in captivity. He tried feeding it on bananas and dates with success, but wondered about the possible use of the chisel incisors and the bent-wire middle finger. As the animal chewed the woodwork of the cage every night, so that he had by degrees to line it with tin, Sandwith put some straight sticks over the woodwork, hoping that the aye-aye would be satisfied with chewing them. It happened that these sticks had been extensively bored by a large and destructive grub. The following occurred when the aye-aye woke up at sunset:

Presently he came to one of the worm-eaten branches, and applying his nose close to the bark, he rapidly tapped the surface with the curious second digit, as a Woodpecker taps a tree, though with much less noise, from time to time inserting the end of the slender finger into the worm-holes as a surgeon would a probe. At length he came to a part of the branch which evidently gave out an interesting sound, for he began to tear it with his strong teeth. He rapidly stripped off the bark, cut into the wood, and exposed the nest of a grub, which he daintily picked out of its bed with the slender tapping finger, and conveyed the luscious morsel to his mouth.[20]

[20]Elliot 1913, I, 4.

This observation explained simultaneously the chisel teeth, the bent-wire finger, and, probably, the large ears. Sandwith also discovered that, when the aye-aye was given water to drink, he stretched out his hand, dipped a finger into it, and drew it obliquely through his mouth, repeating the movement so rapidly that the water seemed to flow into his mouth. He also lapped water like a cat, but Sandwith guessed that the first method was that employed for reaching water in deep clefts of trees. An aye-aye which lived in the London Zoological Gardens was stated to feed in the following manner. The fourth finger of the left hand was thrust into the food and drawn between the lips, the head of the animal held sideways. This method seems to correspond to the finger drinking. Mr. Bartlett, the superintendent of the zoo, stated that the animal would sometimes lap food from a dish, but not often. This aye-aye would never look at the food in the dish, but merely keep on dipping and wiping it into his mouth until there was nothing more on the spooning finger. It would eat food in a fluid state, and was ordinarily fed upon a nauseating mixture of milk, honey, and eggs. After this it would make a dessert from portions of wood and bark—roughage, no doubt. Curiously (from a lemuroid point of view), it refused meal worms, grasshoppers, and the larvae of wasps.

This aye-aye, incidentally, was a female and gave birth to one infant on its voyage to England. The baby lived only 10 days and the mother was in poor condition when she arrived.[21] She slept on her side all day, with the body curved and the bushy tail spread over it as a comfort. Some authorities state that it is the female who makes the nest. This naturalized British aye-aye used to hang by its hind legs while performing its toilet. The wirelike finger was used to clean and comb the tail. The same finger was used to clean other parts of the body, and pick at the corners of the mouth, eyes, and ears. Whether this was also done with the animal upside down is not clear from the description.

One may wind up this account with some folklore about the aye-aye. The natives in whose country the animal is chiefly found had occasion long ago to open a tomb in which an ancestor had been buried. Out jumped this animal, which was obviously a reincarnation of said ancestor. "Aye-aye!" exclaimed the surprised natives. Thus the aye-aye has become the embodiment of departed ancestors and the natives will not touch it, or even disturb its nest, for fear of death. When they

[21] It is reported that the young aye-aye is born with the bent-wire finger fully developed but with lemurine teeth. "Believe it or not!"

find a dead aye-aye they bury it with all formality. That is why it is so hard to obtain a specimen of the aye-aye.

THE BUSH BABIES

All the lemurs described up to this point live in Madagascar. The bush babies, or galagos (genus *Galago*), dwell on the African continent and a couple of adjacent islands—Zanzibar off the east coast and Fernando Po off the west coast. They are small animals about the size of a rat, but otherwise unlike that disagreeable rodent.

The bush babies have thick, woolly fur and very bushy tails which are considerably longer than the body. The eyes are very large, for all these lemurs are nocturnal. One of their most obvious distinguishing characters is the very large, naked ear, which is unique among the primates because its owner can fold the hinder and free part of the ear back at will so that it lies nearly flat to the side of the head. Some opine that the purpose of this ear-folding is to protect the organ when passing through dense, wet foliage. Others say the galagos fold their ears when they sleep. These animals have high, broad skulls and short muzzles, the usual long and slender fingers and toes. Galagos resemble somewhat the Madagascar mouse lemurs, but differ from them in their ears and in some details of teeth. In the mouse lemurs and most other lemurs the 3 premolars each have 3 points or cusps, of unequal size, but the bush babies sometimes have 4 cusps on the last premolar, which is thus nearly square.

On the ends of the toes and fingers are flat disks of thickened skin, which are probably useful in grasping boughs. Most characteristic is the elongation of that part of the foot called the tarsus, which includes the instep, ankle, and heel. The heel bone in the galagos is actually one-third or more of the length of the shinbone and the entire foot is said to be longer than the forearm. This tarsal enlargement is an adaptation for a hopping gait.

There are at least 2 genera and 30-odd species of these bush babies, according to Elliot. The majority of them are found in the eastern half of the continent, from the White Nile on the north to Mashonaland in the south. On the west side, they range from Senegal to Angola, and some are probably to be found in the Congo forest area.

The few records available concerning births in the genus *Galago* suggest that these animals, like the true lemurs, may have a restricted breeding season. They are stated ordinarily to produce two or three young at a birth—certainly a lower-class reproductive habit, and very uncommon among the primates, except perhaps among some French Canadians.

The bush babies sleep in the daytime, either in hollows in trees, or, according to some reports, in old squirrels' nests. Some of the smaller species perhaps make their own nests. Ordinarily, these animals are found in family parties with three or four or more huddled together in the same hollow asleep, clinging to each other with the arms or to the branches of the tree, when they are outside. Bates says that a West African species (*G. elegantulus pallidus*) makes a shrill chirping or squeaking at night in the treetops. The natives say that this noise is heard oftener near morning, and that then the father is calling the rest of the company together for the daytime huddle.

Galagos live on a mixed diet including fruits, insects, small birds, and birds' eggs. Sir John Kirk fed a captive upon biscuit, rice, orange, banana, guava, and a little cooked meat. Du Chaillu fed his on cockroaches, bananas, and corn. The largest galago (*G. crassicaudatus*) has been reported by Kirk to be, even in a wild state, regrettably addicted to alcoholic beverages. It robs the pots of palm wine which the natives set out for it, and then gets drunk and is easily captured. Thus drunkenness seems to extend down to the humblest of the primates.

Galagos hop on their hind legs like miniature kangaroos. Tall stories are told of their jumping prowess. Sir John Kirk describes the great galago as jumping from one palm tree to another with marvelous agility, "adhering to any object as if it were a lump of wet clay." Here the terminal disks on fingers and toes probably help, and may even act as sucker disks. A captive animal in the London Zoo, turned loose in the superintendent's apartment, hopped about, clearing several feet at a spring and easily mounting tables and other articles of furniture. Bates, the West African naturalist, was impressed with the jumping power of a galago observed by him in the Cameroons. He says that, whereas a monkey can leap downward and outward and catch a branch, this galago could jump out and up and catch a branch.

Dr. Florence de L. Lowther, of Barnard College, Columbia University, kept a tame *G. crassicaudatus* for 14 months, and for more than 3 years she has made a study of a pair of Senegalese galagos which were obliging enough to produce twins in captivity. Dr. Lowther's admirable papers upon these lemurs are a godsend to the student who is looking for something more than descriptions of pelts and skulls.[22] All of the following account is derived from this excellent authority.

[22]Lowther 1939, pp. 477–80; 1940, pp. 433–62.

THE BIG-TAILED GALAGO

The big-tailed galago kept by Dr. Lowther was a young male, about the size of a gray squirrel. He was allowed to roam the house and the screened-in porch. He slept all day in some dark, high spot, with his neck arched and head tucked in between his hind legs. He preferred grasshoppers to any other food, and, during the summer months, his owner would turn loose on the porch each evening a dozen or more grasshoppers and moths. The galago would jump, catch the insect with both hands, and put it in the side of his mouth, holding the morsel in his hands. He ate everything but the wings, which he pushed out over the lower incisor trough with his tongue. He also ate cut-up bits of raw vegetables, fruit, bread, and milk. The milk was lapped. Other food was smelled carefully, and, if acceptable, would be conveyed to the mouth with the hands and a piece bitten off, with the upper canine opposing the incisiform lower first premolar. He once astonished Dr. Lowther by leaping to her shoulder with a half-consumed young mouse in his hands. He depended very much upon his sense of smell in investigating food and also in other ways, such as testing whether or not a radiator was too hot to land on. This animal used the shelving lower incisors not as a comb, but as a scraper. With this scraper he would dig down into his fur to remove dead skin or foreign objects. The toilet was finished by a thorough licking of the fur. The claw on the hind foot was used only occasionally for scratching.

FAMILY LIFE OF THE BUSH BABIES

The Senegalese galago male kept by Dr. Lowther was 6½ inches long from head to tail and had a long tail (8½ inches), used for balancing. The female was slightly smaller. The front limbs were much shorter than the hind limbs. The feet had greatly elongated ankle and heel bones. For two winters these animals were kept in a cage in Dr. Lowther's room. In the evening, for a period of several hours, they were turned loose in the room, during which period all damageable articles had to be covered with sheets, and, from time to time, the walls of the room had to be washed down. The implication of devotion to the duties of scientific observation on the part of Dr. Lowther is clear. In the summer, the galagos lived in a screened porch. The third winter they were removed to a part of a heated greenhouse in Barnard College.

Galagos are muscularly incapable of facial expression. They cannot draw the lips up in a snarl or grimace. Smelling is a most important guiding sense. The entire surface of the large, round, bulging eye is a homogeneous light brown. None of the cornea shows. The pupillary slit is vertical, not horizontal as in the tarsier. At night the pupil expands to cover nearly the entire iris. The large eye cannot be moved by the eye muscles, so the entire head is turned. It is extraordinarily flexible; it can be twisted so that one eye is directly above another, and, as in the case of *Tarsius,* can be swiveled around 180° so that the snout points backward over the spine. This ability is thought to be an adaptation to the habit of perching, so that the animal can look round without changing its position.

The large and almost naked ears have four transverse ridges terminating in an outside vertical ridge. The animal can move the whole ear forward, laterally, or upward. It can also fold the ear on the transverse ridges, accordionlike, and press the whole member against the head so that it does not project. In sleep it uses the accordion fold, and also in anger. The complete flattening takes place when the galago is entering an enclosed space or when it is seeking food held out in a cupped hand.

The lower incisor scraper is not used for biting off fruit or leaves. It seems to be primarily a toilet utensil, although probably not used for combing, since Stein has pointed out that the teeth are too close together to allow the fur to pass between them.

The index finger is very small and sometimes divides with the thumb in grasping, but is just as likely to go with the outer fingers. When the animal puts its hands and feet on flat surfaces the toes and fingers are semiflexed so that the first phalanges are off the ground. Grasping food with the hands involves the flexing of the two outer joints of the fingers. The food is held against the first phalanges, not against the palm. The palms and soles are provided with large pads, and there is a disklike pad at the tip of each digit. The strength of the legs and feet is great. A galago can hang itself head down in a jar, holding on by its feet, and lift itself up again without using the hands or arms. Pressure on the interdigital pads and the tip pads makes them veritable sucker disks, so that an animal can climb up a glass pane or any vertical surface that offers an edge upon which the thumb and great toe can get a purchase. The adhesive effect of these pads is enhanced by moistening. The galago reaches down and gets a drop or two of urine, rubs the palms and soles, and is then ready for difficult climbing over smooth surfaces. In climbing and perching it often uses all four members, but on a horizontal surface it hops. These hops cover as much as 6 feet horizontally, and this lemur can jump as high as 5 feet vertically, landing on a small perch with unerring pre-

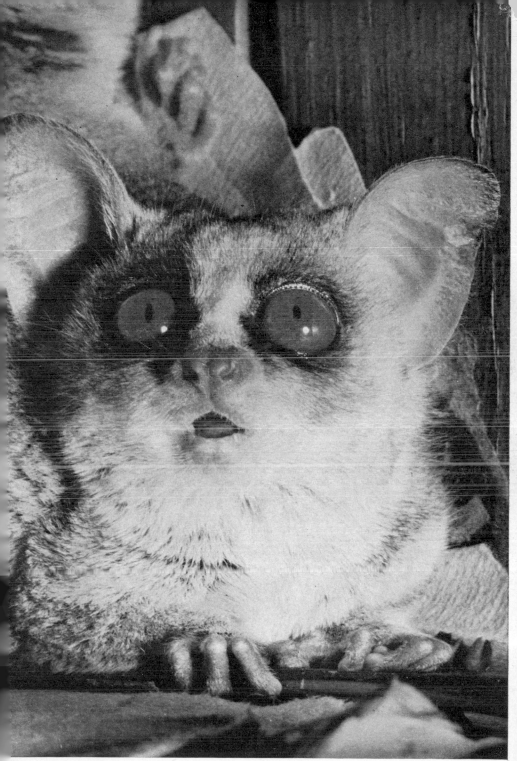

raph Dr. Agnes Townsend   Courtesy Dr. Florence de L. Lowther

A GALAGO OR BUSH BABY

cision. Jumping downward, much larger distances are covered. One of the adults sprang from a balcony rail of a studio room to the top of a door 20 feet below, landing with precision. The galago gauges the distance before jumping and can do a diagonal or backward leap with ease, turning in the air so that it lands facing the perch. The tail is used for balancing in jumping and when the galago stands upright.

The galago is a quick-moving, nervous animal and will spring away at lightning speed when startled. It is truculent toward human beings and resents handling. It will jump from its haunches, striking out with both hands and biting. During the attack it gives vent to a "querulous chatter." But the galagos do not fight among themselves. Those born in captivity are not afraid of human beings, provided that they do not make noises or quick movements. They are most inquisitive and will investigate strange objects by smelling rather than by handling.

The young are very playful with each other, chasing, grappling, hanging by their hind feet from a horizontal stick, and striking at each other with their hands. Food in another's hands is much more attractive than the same food free in a dish; they try to acquire the former by capture rather than taking the latter without competition. If one galago gets another's food, the latter shows no resentment but immediately goes after it in turn.

Feeding habits are similar to those described in the case of *G. crassi-caudatus*. Galagos are wasteful eaters and will take a bite and drop the rest. In spite of personal cleanliness, they evacuate bowels and bladder frequently and anywhere except in the sleeping box.

Grooming, already described, is frequent throughout the active period and is often mutual.

Dr. Lowther describes some eight different kinds of calls used by the galagos. These are: a shrill alarm note ending in a whistle; a piercing automatic cry, which has a high and low pitch and may go on for an hour while the animal continues its various activities; a low, clucking note when annoyed; a soft, questioning, two-noted call of the male when pursuing the female; similar conversational notes between male and female when separated; a chattering sound made by the female when annoyed by male attentions; a soft, caressing sound made by the mother to the young; the squeaky chirp of the young.

The female accepts the male only during oestrus, which may last 5 or 6 days. Then copulation occurs 3 or 4 times a night and also in daytime. At other times the male still pursues, but the female rejects, keeping one jump ahead of him. She may get angry and turn upon him, so that he takes to his heels. Ordinarily, they are an affectionate couple and spend a good deal of time grooming, wrestling, embracing, and nose-rubbing. When the female is pregnant she is bad-tempered and repulses the male with violence.

Probably the galagos make nests in a wild state, for in captivity they were in the habit of gathering string, paper, flowers, leaves, and almost any sort of soft object. Before the birth of the young ones, the prospective mother was actively engaged in making a lining for the sleeping box.

Data gathered upon the reproductive activities of this pair indicate that the period of gestation is 4 months and the time for the birth of the young is limited between the months of April and November. During the period of pregnancy the female showed no unusual behavior until the first 2 months had passed. She then became increasingly irritated at the attentions of the male; her pelt became patchy between the shoulders; she looked thin and in poor condition. It was found advisable to put the male in a separate cage. The female stopped jumping up to high places and was inclined to hug the radiator. She was enormously interested in food and ate a good deal more than usual. One evening Dr. Lowther, returning to the room a half-hour after the animals had been liberated for exercise, found the mother perched on the edge of the sleeping box with an infant dangling from her mouth. She was uttering a strange, protesting cry, apparently directed at the male, who had entered her cage and was watching the scene with great interest. The mother jumped from the cage on to a portiere and from there to the picture molding, still carrying the young one in her mouth. Thence she made a downward leap 10 feet to the bed, and finally retired to a dark corner of the room, where she deposited the squeaking infant. Upon investigation of the sleeping box, a second infant was found clinging to its perpendicular side. The pelt of one baby was wet, but there were no signs of the afterbirth in the box. Probably the mother had eaten it.

The young were about the size of a woman's index finger and nearly as slender. Their eyes were partly open; they were sparsely covered with a gray pelt, and their tails were curled in a loose spiral. They were able to stand on all fours and to cling to the perpendicular sides of the box soon after birth. They clung to the mother with all four feet when she was in the nest, but never as she moved about. When she wanted to move them, she carried them in her mouth. Ordinarily, when nursing, the infants clung to the mother with their forelimbs, while their legs were free and protruding beyond the body of the mother. They were often found sitting on the back of the mother or the father when the adult animals were quiet or sleeping. The female has two pairs of breasts, one pectoral and the other inguinal. She nursed the babies for 3½ months, during which period she displayed a great interest in food and consumed about twice as much milk as ordinary. She kept the young clean by grooming their fur.

The mother displayed great maternal solicitude. She was much agitated when the babies were taken out of the cage and handled. As soon as they were laid down, she took them in her mouth, one by one, and returned them to the nest, giving them a thorough licking and smelling. The male was kept apart in another cage for 3 weeks. During this time his attention was concentrated upon the activities in the other cage to such an extent that he ate relatively little. Whenever he was liberated he went over to the other cage and tried to open the locked door. After 3 weeks the family was reunited with satisfactory results. At first the mother often made a soft, caressing sound to the young, who obeyed her calls up to the age of 9 months. Just before sunrise the mother would give a call, summoning the family to rest. This was immediately answered by all, including the father. In 5 minutes all four would be asleep in the box. It was the mother who assumed the main responsibility for the safety of the young and who gave warning cries of the approach of danger, as, for example, when a cat was lurking about the steps leading to the porch. It was a very affectionate family, and the mother continued to caress her offspring, even when they were a year old. When they became far too heavy to be carried in her mouth, she still attempted to lift them back into the nest when they were molested. After someone had handled the babies, she would lick them solicitously.

In 2 weeks the babies not only walked, but began to take small leaps of 4 and 5 inches and attempted clumsily to balance on their hind legs and climb on the struts of the cage. Between the second and third weeks they began to groom themselves and each other. At 4 weeks they could jump from the sides of the cage a foot or more to the floor and back again, could walk a horizontal bar, and balance on their hind legs. They were now as playful as kittens. At about 6 weeks they began moistening the pads of hands and feet for better climbing. They could then jump 2 or 3 feet horizontally and were greatly interested in the vertical leaps made by their parents from the window sill to the picture molding. At the age of 7 weeks one managed to jump to the top of the window trim. A parent immediately jumped up beside it and licked it. By the eighth week they began descending vertical surfaces, holding on by the edge. At the end of the second month they could stand upright with considerable confidence.

The babies began to eat solid food after a month. By the end of the second month, although still nursing, they were so large that they had to be suckled one at a time. They did not attempt to catch flying insects, but would try to get them away from a parent who had captured a specimen. By the twelfth week they were getting their own moths and would sometimes have to relinquish them to a hungry parent. After 3 months and a little over they stopped nursing, but still were permitted to take moths from the mother.

At the age of 20 months the young male was sexually mature, and both males were accepted by the mother. Thus this interesting account ends on a note of incest.

The Eye of the Galago

The retina of the vertebrate eye, and especially that of man, possesses two types of visual cells, which serve different functions. The rods are probably concerned with colorless vision at low intensities and the cones with the perception of color and with vision at high intensities. It is possible to predict the visual ability of an animal and something of its habits from a histological study of the retina. Most reptiles are rodless and the forms with pure cone retinae are diurnal and have little capacity for vision in dim light. On the other hand, crocodiles, which have rod-rich retinae, are particularly adapted for nocturnal life. In the monkeys and apes both rods and cones are found in the retina. They are diurnal. Woollard has described the retina of *Tarsius,* which is nocturnal and apparently has no cones. Detwiler has studied the eyes of a galago, which, with the potto and the loris, belongs to the lemuroid groups that are nocturnal in their habits.[23] The retina of the galago's eyes is entirely composed of rods. The cornea is markedly curved and constitutes approximately one third of the bulb. The anterior chamber in relation to the vitreous is about 6 times as large as that of the marmoset and of man. So is the lens. The marmoset has both rods and cones, as has man.

LESS-KNOWN LEMURS

The Indri or "There He Goes!" (Genus *Indris*)

If we wish to study the largest of the lemurs, we must visit the forests of a belt which occupies the middle half of the eastern coastal slope of Madagascar, stretching from Antongil Bay in the north to the Masura River in the south. The indri is found nowhere else, although the regions to the south and the north are precisely the same in climate and geograph-

[23]Detwiler 1939, pp. 129–45.

ical features. The high, unforested mountains form an effective barrier to the west. Another but closely related lemur, the diademed sifaka, lives in the same belt, and outside of the indri belt the sifakas belong also to different races.

If there is no particular environmental reason why the indri should be confined within this belt, it is possible that we have encountered here, for the first time among the lowlier primates, what is compendiously called the principle of "territoriality." This is the tendency for a certain group to stay in its own bailiwick. Territoriality has been established for howler monkeys, spider monkeys, and gibbons.

Indri is the corruption of a native word, which means, some authorities say, "There he goes!" Others contend that it means no such thing, and, anyhow, the natives of some districts call this lemur babakoto, or "little old man." The indri is first of three lemurs which belong in the same family. All of them have much longer legs than arms, and the four outside toes are webbed up to the end of the first joints. The muzzle is not big and is nearly naked; the skin is black, the eyes large, the ears small and almost concealed by hair. The members of this group differ from some other lemurs in that the females never produce more than one young at a birth. The number of the teeth is reduced in the adult to 30; 3 molars on each side above and below, 2 premolars (what your dentist calls bicuspids), one canine or eye tooth, 2 upper incisors, and only one lower incisor.

The indri himself rejoices in the scientific name *Indris brevicaudata,* on account of his stump of a tail. This big lemur is brilliantly colored; hands, feet, face, ears, back, and shoulders are usually velvety black; forearms and legs are whitish on the front surface and gray behind, but large black bands extend down the front of the thigh. The sides of the trunk are yellowish; the apology for a tail is white, and is set in the middle of the base of a white triangle which covers the buttocks and extends up the middle of the back to a sharp point. The magnificent colored lithographs of this lemur and others in Grandidier's great work, published in 1875, remind us that the art of illustration has declined dismally in our mechanized age.

The indri is said to be purely vegetarian in diet; details are lacking. It differs from many lemurs in being active in the daytime and not mainly nocturnal. Not much is known of the social life of this animal; it is said to occur in groups of four or five, but in the daytime solitary individuals go off "on their own."

There is, however, a certain amount of amusing and incredible folklore about the indri, which I recount here with much gusto and equal skepticism. Here first of all are a few obstetrical and natal details. The Betsimisarakas (a human tribe of Madagascar) say that the immediately expectant indri mother descends from her tree and takes her position up at its base "in a secluded spot." Her companions of her own sex lavish care upon her, while the males of the band sedulously forage around for the vegetable delicacies she fancies. After the birth she climbs the tree with the young on her back, and when the infant *"veut teter"* she slides it around under her armpit and applies its mouth to the breast.

But here is a better one. "They say," too, "that after birth the mother throws her young one to the male who throws it back again, and when this has been repeated a dozen times without accident, the little one is taken up and carefully nursed. If, however, it falls to the ground, it is left lying."[24] I suggest that this is a test of legitimacy; if the father muffs the catch, the baby is "out."

Talking about the proficiency of the indri in catching, the natives say that it is dangerous to hurl a spear at the animal, since it catches it and chucks it back at the aggressor. We need not believe these romances, but it is certain that many of the natives entertain a superstitious veneration for the indri, for varying reasons. One group claims that these animals, by unaccustomed daytime yelling, warned their ancestors of the approach of a sneaking band of human enemies. Another has a tale of an ancestor who fell out of a tree and either had his fall broken by landing on an indri in the lower branches, or, better, by having the animal catch him in the lower branches before he hit the ground.

Grandidier thinks that the veneration the natives have for the indris is probably ultimately referable to plaintive, mournful, and very human cries which these animals emit from time to time.

Finally, here is an important postural note. Grandidier claims that the indri walks erect when on the ground, but he adds that it rarely descends to the ground, but spends its time leaping prodigiously from bough to bough and tree to tree, since it is in the trees that it obtains food.

THE PROPITHEQUES OR SIFAKAS (Genus *Propithecus*)

Allied to the indris is the genus *Propithecus,* which, however, includes three species. The indris belong in a genus by themselves, and together with a third genus, the avahis, make up a larger related group which is usually called a subfamily. The sifakas, as the natives of Madagascar call the propitheques, are easily distinguishable from the indris by their long tails and smaller ears, largely concealed by fur. The skin is black and the face is bare, but the fur is white or yellowish white, although in some individuals and on certain parts of the body it passes into gray-black and even red.

These sifakas have short arms, terminating in long, slender hands. The thumbs are short and are little used in movements of opposability. At any rate, Grandidier says that the animals pick up a banana or a potato with their mouths and not with their hands. When the hands are used for prehension the object is held between fingers and palm, yet the

[24]Craig 1897, pp. 103–04.

long fingers are used in climbing with great efficiency. These lemurs are stringently adapted for arboreal life. The hind limbs are very large and strong, so that it is said that they easily leap 10 to 12 yards in passing from bough to bough. A membrane unites the upper arms to the axillary region in such a way as to form a sort of parachute. When the animal takes its prodigious jumps from bough to bough, it appears to be flying. On the ground the sifakas cannot well adopt a quadrupedal gait because of their disproportionately short arms. They hold the body in a semierect position and hop, with their arms forward and their long hands dangling.

In the trees the sifakas are likely to sit in the fork of two branches with their long legs drawn up so that their knees touch their chins, and their hands resting on their knees. In the hottest part of the day they stay in the shadiest part of the treetops. When resting or asleep, the head is dropped upon the chest or rested upon the arms, and the long tail, which ordinarily hangs down straight, is rolled into a spiral between the legs. They are entirely diurnal, but given to the tropical habit of taking siestas in the middle of the day.

Sifakas are asserted to be completely vegetarian, living upon leaves, blossoms, and fruits. Their shelving lower incisors allow them to cut a hole in the rind of a fruit and spoon out the interior; they do not eat the skins. Also they like their fruit green rather than ripe. Or perhaps, like small boys, they cannot wait for fruit to ripen.

Little is known of the social and familial life of the sifakas. They are said to go about in bands of six to eight, and, apparently, the females bear but one young at a time. Grandidier thinks that the period of gestation must be 4 or 5 months, since pregnant females are often shot in April, but one never sees mothers with infants until September. The males apparently engage in sex fights on occasion, since their ears are often observed to have been considerably chewed. As a rule, however, the sifakas are gentle and do not bite, but if they do bite, the wound inflicted is not serious. They make little noise, contrary to the custom of many lemurs. It is only when alarmed or angry that they give vent to sounds somewhat recalling the clucking of a hen. The natives of Madagascar claim that, when these animals are wounded, they chew up certain leaves and plaster them over the injuries, thus affecting a prompt cure. So we have the genesis of medical science in the lowliest primates, if anyone can credit this statement.

The most interesting fact (as contrasted with fiction) pertaining to these sifakas is their alleged distribution according to coat color. Grandidier says that the black varieties are found only in the damper regions of southern Madagascar, whereas the white forms are confined to the drier, colder regions of the north. These racial differences in habitat involve us in the necessity of describing the physical distinctions between the three species of sifakas.

The largest of the sifakas are called diademed, because of a fringe of white hair running across the forehead. The diademed sifakas are stockier in body build, with shorter tails and rounder or more brachycephalic heads, than the other species. They also have smaller frontal sinuses, broader noses, and larger upper middle incisor teeth. It is not worth our while here to enter into an elaborate description of the pattern and color of their coats. Gray, brown, orange, and black are strikingly combined on various parts of the body. The orange is usually on the forearms and around the buttocks and tail. Apparently, these diademed sifakas are found only in a strip of the east coast of Madagascar between the Bay of Antongil in the north and the river Masura in the south—the same area which is the home of the indris. However, in the northeast of Madagascar the sifakas tend to be white, yellowish white, or gray. They are separated from the ordinary variety of sifakas only by a certain river, and are bounded to the north by another river only some 23 miles distant. This region is a little hotter and drier than the strip in the middle where the diademed sifaka lives. A short strip of the southeastern coastal forest to the south of the river Masura is inhabited by a black race with yellowish flanks. This region is a little cooler, but just as damp as the central strip. The white race in the north, the particolored in the middle, and the black in the south raise interesting questions of the relationship of coat color to environment.

Two other species of sifakas, smaller than the diademed type, are Verreaux's sifaka and the crowned sifaka. There are two types of the former, one yellowish white with a brown head, the other white with patches of bright red on the arms and the thighs. These sifakas of Verreaux live in the occasional thick patches of forest which are found here and there amid the sandy wastes of western and southern Madagascar.

The crowned sifaka, the third species, inhabits a small area of the northwest coast. It has a crest of blackish hair on the forehead, and the crown and cheeks are blackish brown, the rest of the body white, with occasional rosy tints. The skull and muzzle are supposed to be unusually large. There seem to be more races and species of these sifaka lemurs than a sensible Nature would produce and they are more highly localized than one would expect. The idea of crossing a river and finding the sifakas on one bank belonging to different races, if not species, from those on the other bank is difficult to accept. However, Madagascar is a peculiar place.

THE WOOLLY AVAHI (Genus *Lichanotus*)

The woolly avahi is the third genus of the subfamily which includes the indri and the sifaka. These lemurs are much smaller than either of the other two. The total body length averages in the east coast specimens only 30 cm., whereas the tail is 39 cm. long. Milne-Edwards and Grandidier insist upon the extremely spherical shape of head and the shortness of the snout. The canine or eye teeth are not tusklike, but small. The forelimbs are about 18 cm. long and the hind limbs 40 cm. The face is not naked, but covered with reddish hair everywhere except at the tip of the nose. The small, folded ears are buried in fur. The fur is very thick and woolly rather than silky as in the indri and the sifaka. The hair, in most regions, is gray at the roots, red in middle, and black-tipped. The tail is usually red, but the other parts of the body vary from reddish to yellow-white and gray tones. The flanks and the loins are generally lighter than the back, and there is a reddish white triangle on the rump with its base at the tail. Hands and feet are also reddish in color. There is a great deal of individual variation in coat color among the avahis. Some are reddish all over; others have white fur on the backs of their thighs. The hair on the hind limbs grows in tufts.

The avahis are found in the forest belts along the east coast of Madagascar, but not in the plains of the south and west, which have a different climate and fauna. These lemurs also occur in a restricted area of the northwestern part of the island, where they differ somewhat from east-coast specimens in coat color and are nearly one tenth smaller and even more brachycephalic or round-headed.

Avahis are stated to be exclusively nocturnal animals. In the daytime they sleep curled up in the forks of branches, but they are active at night in satisfying the demands of their exclusively vegetarian appetite. They are rather slow-moving in the trees and rarely go to the ground. It is stated that, on the ground, they hop on their hind feet. In the avahis, as in the other lemurs of this group, the hand is not a very effective prehensile organ except for grasping branches.

The avahis are not gregarious; they are found solitary or in pairs. The female produces but one at a birth.

Other Madagascar Lemurs

THE GENTLE LEMURS (Genus *Myoxicebus*). To finish off the Madagascar lemurs, brief mention must be made of three other genera which cannot be grouped with true lemurs, propitheques, indris, or mouse lemurs.

The gentle lemurs are smaller than true lemurs and have rounded heads, short muzzles, short ears, and broad noses, with very small upper incisor teeth. On the front surface of the forearm above the palm of the hand is a bare area covered with spines. These lemurs are purely nocturnal and are found chiefly in bamboo jungles, since they feed upon the shoots and roots of the bamboo. The grinding teeth are serrated or saw-toothed. The gray gentle lemur lives in the bamboo forest of northwestern Madagascar, sleeping during the day among the shoots of the highest bamboos, with the back curved, the head between the thighs, and the tail covering the back. At night it is very active.

Shaw describes a captive broad-nosed lemur which belongs to this genus, but to a distinct species. This animal had no wrist spines. Its shelving lower incisors were used for scraping rather than biting. The interlocking serrations of the upper teeth enabled the animal to scissor off and mince up bamboo shoots and stalks and blades of grass. This lemur was kept chained on the lawn for several months and usually ate grass from morning to night. It would not eat fruit, but was fond of meat and sugar cane, and finally settled down to a diet of cooked rice.

THE SPORTIVE LEMURS (Genus *Lepidolemur*). The sportive lemurs are also called weasel lemurs and include several species. The adults have no upper incisor teeth, or, at most, a single pair of minute and vestigial upper incisors. They are all nocturnal, and nest in leaves during the daytime. At night these lemurs, which are small, are prodigiously active. They are said to live entirely upon leaves. Coat color varies greatly.

THE SLOW LEMURS

The lemurs which live outside of Madagascar, either in Africa, in Asia, or in the Indo-Malayan Archipelago, all belong to a great general group which is often called lorisiform, after the Asiatic lorises. By some zoologists the galagos, or African bush babies, are separated from the lorisiforms, and indeed they seem distinct because of their large, naked folding ears, their elongated tarsi, and other characters.

Apart from the galagos, or bush babies, the lorisiforms include the Asiatic lorises and the African pottos, which are often called slow lemurs. They are all slow-moving, nocturnal animals without tails or with merely the rudiments of tails. The skull is broad and rounded, the muzzle short and pointed; the eyes are very large, the ears small but erect, the limbs nearly equal in length, and the tarsus of the foot short.

THE AFRICAN POTTOS (Genus *Perodicticus*). The pottos (*Perodicticus potto* and other species) are found in the tropical forests of Africa, three species in the west and one in the east. These African slow lemurs have very short, but distinct, tails, large feet and hands, with rudimentary index fingers devoid of nails. Usually the spines of the vertebrae, especially in the neck region, stick out above the general level of the back, making a series of humps covered with skin. The purpose of this structural peculiarity is unknown. As a rule, these pottos are rather heavy and sluggish animals, although they are quite small.

The most famous of the African slow lemurs is Bosman's potto, first described and drawn by a Dutch naturalist in 1704. The description given by Bosman is so amusing that it warrants partial quotation, whether or not it is scientifically accurate.

"Draught of a creature, by the *Negroes* called *Potto,* but known to us by the name of Sluggard, doubtless from its lazy, sluggish nature, a whole day being enough for it to advance ten steps forward.

"Some writers affirm, that when this animal has climbed upon a Tree, he doth not leave it until he hath eaten up not only the Fruit, but the leaves entirely; and then descends fat and in very good case in order to get up into another Tree; but before his slow pace can compass this he becomes as poor and lean as 'tis possible to imagine; and if the tree be high, or the way anything distant, and he meets nothing on his journey, he invariably dies of Hunger betwixt one tree and the other. Thus 'tis represented by others, but I will not undertake for the truth of it, though the *Negroes* are apt to believe something like it.

"This is such a horrible ugly Creature that I don't believe anything besides so very disagreeable is to be found on the whole Earth."[25]

As a matter of fact, P. T. L. Putnam brought two live pottos to this country a few years ago and they were kept in the Harvard Biological Institute for a couple of days, during which time we made some moving pictures of them. The most notable features of these animals were the strong hands with the index fingers reduced to mere stumps, and the bony ridges along the back of the neck made by the projecting vertebral spines. In order to get shots of the potto climbing, we allowed one of them to ascend the handle of a garden rake, which he did fairly rapidly, hand over hand and foot over foot. When he reached the top of the handle the rake was reversed and the animal started over again. The grip of the hands and feet was very powerful, but Putnam was most impressed with the grip of the teeth, since one of the pottos managed to get hold of his thumb and bit right through the nail. When we put these animals on the ground, they started off deliberately, on all fours, for the nearest tree, with a most peculiar rolling gait, covering the ground fast enough to force an accompanying human being to move at something more than a stroll. We took some shots of them lying on a small garden table. Since it was bright afternoon, they had to be poked in order to get them to open their eyes. Each seemed to be trying to cover himself with the other, or perhaps to roll himself up in the other.

Mr. Bates observed some pottos of a different species in the Cameroons. He stated that they are found in the daytime curled up asleep in the trees, tightly clinging to a branch. In fact their grips were so tenacious that specimens brought to him frequently had their hands mutilated, because the natives said that they could not break the animal's hold without cutting the fingers.

The angwantibo, or Calabar potto (genus *Arctocebus*), is more slender than ordinary African pottos, has an even shorter tail, and somewhat longer snout. A web unites the lower joint of the fingers—although the thumb is free—and of the toes, except the great toe. The index finger is a mere tubercle, without a nail. The angwantibo is nocturnal; thus its habits seem to have escaped notice in the dark.

THE LORISES—SLENDER AND SLOW (Genera *Loris* and *Nycticebus*). The loris is at home in a zoological area which Wallace called the Oriental Region. India, Indo-China, and the Malay Peninsula are included in this area, together with the islands of Java, Sumatra, Borneo, and the Philippines. Lorises are small, furry animals with short, pointed snouts, enor-

[25]Elliot 1913, I, 40.

mous eyes, rounded heads, and no tail whatsoever. They are nocturnal and slow. The Dutch colonists in the East Indies called this type of lemur *loeris,* which means "clown."

The slender loris (genus *Loris*) lives in the forests of Ceylon and southern India, not far above sea level. This small animal is only about 8 inches long and has very skinny and attenuated limbs. Its enormous eyes are separated only by a very narrow space, marked by a white stripe which spreads out on the forehead. The fur around the eyes is darker than on most parts of the body. The general coat color is an earthy gray with the under parts paler, and with some ruddy tinges and silvery washes showing here and there. Young specimens are supposed to be reddish. The index finger in the loris is a stump and, as usual in lemurs, the second toe bears a claw.

In the daytime the slender loris sleeps on a branch, rolled up in a ball, with its head between its legs and its hands grasping the bough. At night it comes to life and pursues its food quest, moving slowly, but silently. Tennant had a captive loris which ate rice, fruits, and leaves, but preferred insects. It was very greedy for milk and for the flesh of birds. The natives of Ceylon claim that it will attack peacocks at night, choke them, and suck the brains. One Wood gives a highly romantic account of the slender loris out hunting:

"Alas for the doomed bird that has attracted the fiery eyes of the Loris! No Indian on his war-path moves with stealthier step or more deadly purpose than the Loris on its progress toward its sleeping prey. With movements as imperceptible and silent as the shadow on the dial, paw after paw is lifted from its hold, advanced a step and placed again on the bough, until the destroyer stands by the side of the unconscious victim. Then, the hand is raised with equal silence, until the fingers overhang the bird and nearly touch it. Suddenly the slow caution is exchanged for lightning speed, and with a movement so rapid that the eye can hardly follow it, the bird is torn from its perch, and almost before its eyes are opened from slumber, they are closed forever in death."[26]

One wonders how the narrator could have seen all this in the dark. Tennant asserts that the Singalese, attracted by the large and brilliant eyes of the slender loris, make amulets and love charms from them, holding the creature in the fire until its eyeballs burst.

The slow loris has a wider distribution than the slender loris. It is placed in a separate genus, *Nycticebus,* which includes some 11 species. It is a larger and more heavily built animal than the slender loris. It is roughly the size of a smallish cat, head and body measuring 13 to 15 inches and more in length. Its head is broad and flat, with a short, pointed muzzle and perfectly round eyes. The pupils of the eyes can be completely closed by contraction of the iris. When the pupils are half closed, they are stated to form a transverse slit. The ears are short, rounded, and buried

---

[26]Craig 1897, p. 111.

STANCE OF THE POTTO

HANDS AND FEET OF THE POTTO

in fur. The hind limbs are only slightly longer than the forelimbs. The index finger is vestigial and the second toe has the usual claw.

The body is covered with long, close, woolly fur. Coat color varies considerably in the different species, but there is always a dark, chestnut-colored stripe running down the middle of the back; the eyes are surrounded by dark rims with a white streak between them. The ears are brown, the back ashy gray, sides more silvery, and rump often reddish. However, this is only a very general and rough description. Details can be found in such works as D. G. Elliot's *Review of the Primates*, which describes the coat patterns of the various species at great length, but tells almost nothing of interest to anyone who is not a taxonomist, concerned merely with pawing over dusty and moth-eaten skins of dead animals in museum collections.

Whatever the species, the slow loris is nocturnal and arboreal and feeds on leaves, shoots, fruit, birds' eggs, birds, and insects.

Most of the data on the diet of the loris have been gathered from experience with captive specimens. One account from Loudon's *Magazine of Natural History* states that a tame loris was very fond of small birds, which, "when put into his cage, he kills speedily; and, plucking the feathers off with the skill of a poulterer, soon lodges the carcase in his stomach. He eats the bones as well as the flesh; and though birds, and mice perhaps, are his favorite food, he eats other meat very readily, especially when quite fresh; if boiled, or otherwise cooked, he will not taste it. He prefers veal to all other kinds of butcher's meat; eggs, also, he is fond of, and sugar is especially grateful to his palate; he likewise eats gum-arabic. . . . When food is presented to him, if hungry, he seizes it with both hands, and, letting go with his right, holds it with his left all the time he is eating. Frequently, when feeding, he grasps the bars in the upper part of his cage with his hind paws, and hangs inverted, appearing very much intent upon the food he holds in his left hand. He is exceedingly fond of oranges; but, when they are at all hard, he seems very much puzzled how to extract the juice. I have, upon such occasion, seen him lie all his length upon his back in the bottom of the cage, and, firmly grasping the piece of orange in both hands, squeeze the juice into his mouth."[27]

Wood Jones says that a loris, if given a strange fruit such as a Cape gooseberry, will rub it on the floor of its cage so as to abrade the surface, and then smell it and lick its fingers before trying to taste it.[28]

The loris is stated to inhabit the densest forests and never to leave the trees by choice. In the trees the slow loris climbs deliberately but surely. Lydekker also says:

"When he climbs he first lays hold of the branch with one of his hands, and then with the other. When he has obtained a firm hold with both

[27] Lydekker 1893–94, pp. 230–31.
[28] Jones 1929, p. 117.

hands, he moves one of his hind paws, and, after firmly grasping the branch with it, he moves the other. He never quits his hold with his hind paws until he has obtained a secure grasp with his hands."

Major Tickell, who observed an Indian species of loris (*Nycticebus tenasserimensis*), states that its gait on the ground is a "wavering kind of trot, the limbs placed at right angles." This reptilian type of gait, in which the elbows and knees are thrust out from the body, is similar to the walk of the African pottos which we had for a short time here in Cambridge. The orang-utan on the ground manages a little better, but holds the arms in somewhat the same way.

The slow loris sleeps rolled up in a ball, with its head and hands buried between its thighs.

It bears but one young at a time. Zuckerman has data from a large number of the uteri of *Nycticebus coucang,* in the Hubrecht Collection, Utrecht, which indicate that this loris breeds throughout the year.[29] Maternal care seems not to be excessive. Wood Jones say that the baby clings tight to the mother, but the latter makes little effort to handle it. She will bite if any attempt is made to remove the baby from her fur, but all observers agree that these beasts are given to biting savagely on any or no provocation. Captain Flower, reporting on a Siamese slow loris, says that the young are carried under the mother's belly, hanging on by all four extremities until they almost equal the maternal size. Wood Jones reports a disillusioning case of maternal indifference on the part of the slow loris. A female escaped from her cage, leaving her nursing baby to its fate. The baby was reared on the bottle and raised its voice each evening, but the mother, who was living in the trees well within earshot, never returned. Her voice was heard on rare occasions, but it was 5 years before her actual home was discovered, although it was within a few paces of the spot where she escaped. Meanwhile the young one had died.[30]

The cry of the loris is sometimes described as a feeble croaking sound, a tolerably loud grunt or groan, or a shrill plaintive cry. Possibly these different vocalizations express different moods, mostly of complaint or annoyance.

Craig states that the circulation in the limbs of the slow loris is reminiscent of that of the sloth, in that the vessels, instead of entering the limb in one treelike trunk which gives off numerous branches, are divided into a great number of cylindrical vessels lying close to each other for some distance and then giving off tubes to different parts of the limb.[31] Wood Jones refers to this tendency of the limb arteries to be "plexiform" as a peculiarity perhaps in response to some habit.[32] Craig hazards a guess that this habit may be that of "silent movement and slow patience." This

[29]Zuckerman 1933, p. 33.
[30]Jones 1916, p. 185.
[31]Craig 1897, p. 110.
[32]Jones 1929, p. 103.

multiple division of arteries, according to Sonntag, is found not only in the lorises and sloths, but also in the whale and in the cerebral arteries of the carnivora.[33]

The Siamese are said to attribute to the slow loris, dead or alive, in parts or whole, the power of affecting the lives of human beings and even of domestic animals. If a man commits an unpremeditated crime, it may be because some enemy has buried a part of a loris under his threshold, which has compelled him so to act. The fur has a curative effect upon wounds. A ship which carries a live loris is never becalmed. But the loris is unhappy; it is always seeing ghosts. That is why it hides its head in its hands.[34]

ANATOMY OF THE LEMUROIDEA

EXTERNAL CHARACTERS

VIBRISSAE. Full sets of tactile hairs, "feelers" or vibrissae, are present in many lemurs. They consist in true lemurs and in the mouse lemur of the usual specialized, elongated hairs on the chin, cheeks, upper lips, and above the eyes. These feelers occur in certain other places, notably on the wrist. In the lorises the development is not so complete.

SKIN GLANDS. In *Lemur catta* there is a well-developed glandular area on the front of the forearm just above the wrist, and another gland on the inner side of the arm just below the shoulder. Wood Jones thinks that there may be another glandular area on the breast. In general, scent glands are reduced in these animals, possibly in connection with the diminution of sensory stimuli resulting from their arboreal habits.

EAR. The root and anterior branch of the helix are well developed in lemurs, but the upper part of the ear expands into a flattened, leaflike tip. The antitragus and helix are also well developed. The ear of the galago is said to be capable of being folded in sleep.

HANDS AND FEET. In lemurs, on hands and feet, the digital length in descending order is 4-5-3-2-1. Pads on the finger tips, between the bases of the fingers, at the base of the thumbs, and on the heel of the palm are well developed and bear fine papillary lines.

INTERNAL CHARACTERS

SKULL. Elongation of the facial portion of the skull in lemuroids is extremely variable. The longest snouts are found in the true lemurs and the most abbreviated in the galagos. The elongated snout projects in the axis of the cranio-facial base and is not bent down as in many higher primate forms. In all lemuroids the bony orbital ring is complete, but there is no back wall to the orbit. The orbits are directed somewhat laterally, although the degree depends, apparently, upon the elongation

[33]Sonntag 1924, p. 23.

[34]Flower 1900, p. 322.

of the snout. The orbits are typically large, in connection with the nocturnal habits of most of these primates. On the inner wall of the orbit the orbital process of the frontal bone articulates along its lower border with the lachrymal, the palatine, and the orbito-sphenoid. The maxilla forms no part of the orbital margin. The lachrymal is very large and extends onto the facial surface.

The nasals are large bones, wider above than below; the premaxillae are small and meet the lower margins of the nasals. The wing of the sphenoid articulates with the parietal over a wide area, but the squamous element of the temporal bone is very small. The glenoid fossa is shallow and has a large postglenoid tubercle on its hinder margin.

In the auditory region is a large, inflated, spherical bony chamber or bulla, which incloses the tympanic ring. The latter is free in the cavity in the true lemurs, but adherent to the outer wall in the lorises.

TEETH. The dental formula is typically $I\frac{2}{2}$; $C\frac{1}{1}$; $P.M.\frac{3}{3}$; $M\frac{3}{3}$ in lemurs. The Indrisidae have only two premolars. In most lemurs the lower canines have taken on the form and function of the shelving haircomb (if it is a comb). They have ceased to be tusklike and the anterior premolars have become caninelike. Some writers have regarded the incisiform canine as a third incisor and the tusklike anterior premolar as a canine. Thus they have given the dental formula as $I\frac{2}{3}$; $C\frac{1}{1}$; $P.M.\frac{3}{2}$; $M\frac{3}{3}$. This view is probably incorrect.

POSTCRANIAL SKELETON. The typical vertebral formula is 7 cervical, 12 thoracic, 7 lumbar, 3 sacral, and 27–28 caudal.

There is usually an entepicondylar foramen in the humerus. An os centrale is present in the carpus.

ALIMENTARY SYSTEM. Among the true lemurs *L. varius* has a simple tubular stomach suspended in a U-shaped loop; the lorises tend to have more globular stomachs. The caecum is generally well differentiated and tapers off into an appendix.

REPRODUCTIVE SYSTEM. The glans penis in lemurs is armed with horny, thornlike spines; there is always an os penis and the testes are descended into the scrotum. The uterus of the female is of the lower mammalian, bicornuate type.

CENTRAL NERVOUS SYSTEM. The brain is relatively large, the olfactory lobes well developed, and the cerebral hemispheres small. A considerable part of the cerebellum is left exposed by the failure of the cerebral lobes to overhang. The convolutions of the cerebral hemispheres are but feebly marked. They are simplest in some of the little galagos and most complex in the Indrisinae.

PART V

Man and His Primate Peers and Inferiors

CHAPTER XII

Sex and Society, Antics and Semantics

THE UTILITY OF PRIMATE SOCIOLOGY

I MAY BE CONSIDERED an apostate from anthropology when I assert that it seems to me that the study of individual and group behavior among the infrahuman primates may offer nearly as much to the student of man as does the investigation of the social life and psychology of contemporary savages. The supposedly simple peoples of today have usually evolved institutions so intricate and so divergent from our own, and their mental processes are so bound up with these alien and remote social manifestations, that the civilized sophisticate is likely to misunderstand and misinterpret both primitive culture and its producers. One of the main ideas of social anthropology is that the savage offers a simplification of human culture and behavior which we can understand and analyze more readily than the complexities of domesticated man. If we can get back to first principles in primitive human behavior, perhaps we shall be in a position to understand our own. I am afraid that this hope has proved somewhat illusory, because the savage is not simple and his institutions are not so much primitive as different.

Partly because apes and monkeys have no articulate language, no material culture, and possibly nothing which can be called social institutions, we are not misled linguistically and semantically when we attempt to observe their behavior. No doubt many errors are made by the psychologist who attempts to test the mental and temperamental qualities of our poor relations, and unquestionably even such carefully objective students of primate sociology as Carpenter and Zuckerman may misinterpret the social phenomena which they observe, hampered as they are by the inability of monkeys to furnish articulate informants who will explain simian institutions. However, by the same token, the apes and monkeys are not able to mislead the men who are studying them by giving erroneous information.

323

We have nothing approaching an adequate knowledge of the behavior and social organization of primates in the wild below the
monkey level. The corpus of satisfactory information on the social life
of the primates includes excellent data on the howling monkey, the
red spider monkey, and the rhesus monkey by Carpenter, good material on the hamadryas baboon by Zuckerman, more splendid information on the gibbon by Carpenter, with some valuable but incomplete notes on the wild life of the chimpanzee by Nissen. There are
no other really substantial contributions to the subject, as far as I am
aware. On the other hand, a great deal is known of the family life of
captive animals and, pre-eminently, of the chimpanzee. Further, much
insight into the variations of individual animals in temperament and
disposition has been derived from experimental psychological investigations. All these data have been presented in a moderately full form
in this book under the discussions of the various types of primates.
Nothing more than a brief commentary on this subject matter need
be attempted here.

The most important aspects of the social behavior of primates are
included under the categories of sexual relations and dominance.
Topics of subsidiary interest are altruism and food-sharing, play activities, parent-young relations, group co-ordination, and "territoriality." The subject of individuality or personality is perhaps more
important than any of the others except sex and dominance. A few
remarks on each of these subjects may serve as some sort of synthesis
of the detailed information presented in earlier parts of the book.

SEXUAL RELATIONS AND DOMINANCE

Although sex is the basis of primate social organization, there is an
astounding contrast in its apparent importance between the New
World and Old World monkeys which have been carefully studied up
to the present. This difference seems to be inextricably bound up with
similarly great contrasts in what the primatologists call "dominance"—
the extent to which individual animals get the upper hand of, or
knuckle under to, the fellows of their group through the exertion of
physical force and by the use of wiles, bluff, aggression, and intimidation. Thus the rhesus monkeys and baboons seem not only to be
obsessed by sex,[1] but also to show in both sexual and non-sexual activities a sadism which is nothing short of appalling. In the rhesus monkeys vicious attacks by the male are the regular preliminaries of sexual

[1]Dr. Carpenter, however, states that during the month of June following the study of
oestrus on Santiago Island, he observed no copulations, whatsoever. Thus, rhesus sex
obsession would appear to be intermittent.

intercourse, while oestrous females, although varying individually, seem, in general, to be veritable nymphomaniacs, no gentler than the males, but merely less powerful. Baboons are, if possible, even nastier; witness the sexual fights between males and the sex murders of females which occurred on Monkey Hill in the London Zoological Gardens. When Zuckerman first published the description of this hamadryas baboon society, one was inclined to discount this history of rape and massacre because of the artificial conditions of confinement on Monkey Hill and the insufficient number of females in the colony. Some allowance must undoubtedly be made for these factors, but Carpenter's observation of free-ranging macaques on Santiago Island, near Puerto Rico, suggests that the normal behavior of some of these groups of Old World monkeys may not differ markedly from that described by Zuckerman.

In these baboon and macaque societies dominant. individuals are ruthless in their cruelty and apparently devoid of any of the tenderer emotions and of the least semblance of altruism. There is such utter selfishness that the animal which has the ascendancy will nearly starve to death. subordinate animals, even when the overlord has stuffed himself to utter repletion. All but a few monkeys live in a constant state of intimidation and panic, but, if the downtrodden beasts in some way or other achieve a mastery over their still weaker fellows, they treat them with even more cruelty and ruthlessness than they themselves have suffered from other monkeys. Prostitution, either heterosexual or homosexual, seems to be the orthodox way of propitiating aggressive animals. Loyalties or attachments between pairs of animals, on any other basis than that of sexual activity, are generally conspicuous by their absence. Homosexuality is an apparently normal phenomenon in groups composed exclusively of one or the other sex, and the barbarity of dominance behavior is scarcely mitigated in such unisexual groups. Not only is paternal care lacking, but frequently the father is an active menace to the very existence of his offspring, even when constantly consorting with the mother. This picture is perhaps overdrawn, and there may be families and troops of baboons and macaques which live in comparative peace and harmony and display occasionally the qualities of co-operativeness, tolerance, and friendliness for each other which one might suppose would be the prerequisite of group cohesion and perhaps even of social survival. Yet one gets little or no impression from the works of Carpenter and Zuckerman that such decent primate behavior is ever evinced by these particular monkeys and baboons.

In sharp contrast with the sort of Nazi regime which seems to hold sway among the baboons and the macaques is the very peaceable and almost communistic organization of the howler monkeys, described by Carpenter, and the apparently similar society of the red spider monkeys, which the same observer has studied, but in far less detail. Among these American animals the females also pass through a period of oestrus in which they are sexually desirable to the male and extremely demanding of his services. Perhaps there is as much primary sexual activity among howlers as among rhesus monkeys, but it is attended with no such fighting and bloodshed as among Old World monkeys which have been studied. The howler female in oestrus is not satisfied with a single male but solicits and is accepted or rejected by one after another. She is, generally speaking, promiscuous, and no one cares. The males do not fight over females or, to any extent, over anything else. Sexual jealousy seems to be quite absent. Either males or females get along quietly and peaceably among themselves, because there is virtually no dominance. Animals do not attempt to bully and browbeat their fellows. Corresponding to the lack of dominance among these animals is the feeble development of leadership and of group co-operation. There are, of course, clan groupings and the disposition of the clans to stick together and to repel the incursions of rival clans. They do combine for mutual defense and they come to the assistance of members of their group which are in distress. But, on the whole, individual monkeys tend to pay little attention to each other. They flock together, but seem not to establish relations of intimacy or of hostility. Howler adult males are generally indifferent to young animals, but may play with them occasionally or help them out when they are in tight places. They certainly do not attack and intimidate them. How far the spider monkeys resemble the howlers in these respects is uncertain, because of the rather abbreviated account of the former given by Carpenter. This foremost student of primate sociology did not observe sexual intercourse even once in his field study of red spider monkeys. Nor did he see any fights, although specimens collected showed evidence of having received wounds which probably resulted from combat.

There is then a most astonishing variation in type of social and individual behavior between Old World and New World monkeys, if we can rely upon present data as fully representative. It is wholly possible that further field studies of the monkeys of both hemispheres may reveal gradations and approximations of the two families so that the sharpness of the distinction in behavior may be blurred. But with the data now in hand it seems at least tentatively established that Old World monkeys are vicious, cruel, domineering, hypersexual, and given to tyrannical social groupings, whereas the Cebidae show a diminution in degree of such behavior which may amount to a difference in kind. These findings should make the students of human behavior sit up and take notice—especially those who steadfastly adhere to the dogma of the essential psychological unity of all mankind, irrespective of marked physiological and anatomical differences, such as are usually found between its main physical divisions.

The only anthropoid ape for which we have adequate field information with respect to behavior is the gibbon, studied by Carpenter. The social unit is here the monogamous family and between the adult male and the adult female there is little size difference and no fixed dominance. Dominance not only is a matter of individuality, but also shifts according to circumstances. Carpenter does not think that the sexual drive in these animals is nearly so strong as in macaques and baboons. He observed very few instances of primary sexual activity in the gibbon groups he watched. There is a dominance gradient between individual animals, but in no wise so striking and of such an unpleasant character as in baboons and macaques. Probably very little intra-group fighting goes on, although families may be dominant or subordinate to other groups in the matter of territory and in occupying feeding trees. Carpenter saw no actual conflicts between groups, although plenty of aggressive and threatening behavior. Yet gibbons are not invariably gentle and peaceable animals. On the contrary, many of them are vicious and dangerous, and attempts to confine a considerable number of them in one large cage have had lethal results. Carpenter thinks that the monogamous family among the gibbons is maintained by the very strong antagonisms which adults of both sexes develop for individuals of their own sex and age. Maturing males are almost certainly driven from the family group by their fathers, and, probably, nubile daughters by their mothers. Thus it would appear that large social groupings of gibbons are prevented by the types of behavior of individuals of both sexes which are probably genetically predetermined.

The social life of free-ranging chimpanzees is too little known to permit many conclusions as to sexual behavior and dominance. However, this great ape has been studied so carefully in captivity that it seems probable that a fairly accurate picture of its natural status in these respects may be reconstructed. In the first place, it seems clear that the chimpanzee, and probably any other great ape, represents an enormous advance in what may be called personality development over the gibbon or any lower primate. Chimpanzees are surely more highly individualized and more richly variable in their temperaments and in their behavior than are gibbons or monkeys. Thus it seems probable that the social life of the great apes may be far less stereotyped than that of lower primates.

We seem to encounter here, perhaps for the first time, the development of personal attachments between animals that are to some extent disinterested and independent of sexual motivations. Simultaneously, there are to be observed dislikes and antagonisms which seem to be more or less unaffected by sexual status. Sexual activity is, of course, rich and fairly pervasive in chimpanzee life, but except upon occasion and between potential mates it may not be the predominant social factor. There can be no doubt that the female chimpanzee frequently uses her sexual attractions to improve her position with the naturally dominant male.

Yet the accounts of Yerkes and other observers of the manner in which female chimpanzees get their way by wiles and coquetry in dealing with adult males do not create the disagreeable impression of treacherous whorishness which is given by the descriptions of sexual behavior of female baboons and rhesus monkeys. When the lady chimpanzee trades upon her sex, she trades legitimately and does not appear to be a despicable cheat. Frenzied hyper-eroticism does not seem to figure in the detailed descriptions of chimpanzee primary sexual activity which I have read. The animals are, in general, highly sexed, and a certain amount of homosexuality appears to be a constant phenomenon, but the entire social life of the chimpanzee seems not to be regulated by forms of sexual approach. Presentation, a sort of symbolic sexual submission, is not, so far as I am aware, the conventional method of social greeting between these animals, as it is in hamadryas baboons. Sexual activity may be somewhat more to the fore than in human society, but, on the whole, sex seems to be relegated to its proper place in the social order. Dominance, too, although present and clearly defined in all chimpanzee groups, is strongly mitigated by friendship, affection, sympathy, and co-operation, so that it ceases to manifest itself in brutally sadistic activities. Subordinate chimpanzees apparently do not lead a miserable and panic-stricken existence, unable to call their souls their own and literally afraid to eat, as do the downtrodden among some of the nastier Old World monkeys. The dominant chimpanzee in a pair is a friend, a protector, and a cherished leader, rather than a ruthless overlord. Jealousy is probably not so violent and so productive of bloody combat as in baboons. Of course, the conditions under which captive chimpanzees are allowed to mate preclude the possibility of observing what would happen if a number of vigorous adult males were allowed to work out their sexual and social salvation in company with an insufficient number of mature females. It is to be doubted that the issue of such an experiment would be the sort of Kilkenny cat-fighting which happened among the hamadryas baboons on Monkey Hill in the London Zoo. One gains from the many and varied accounts of all phases of captive chimpanzee life that these animals are sufficiently intelligent to manage their group affairs peaceably and with a fair degree of independence and some measure of happiness for each individual member.

It is very unfortunate that, in spite of the number of orang-utan matings which have taken place in captivity, no trained observer has either had the opportunity or has taken the trouble to give any reasonably full description of familial and individual relationships in this great ape. More extensive field studies of all the great apes are sorely needed, but it would appear feasible to secure as rich a store of knowledge of the habits and behavior of the orang in captivity as has been gleaned by students of the chimpanzee. An orang-utan laboratory comparable to the chimpanzee laboratories developed by Yale University is one of the first desiderata of primate studies.

The gorilla is the fascinating enigma of the higher primates. The few human beings who have had the opportunity to know intimately one or more gorillas seem to be unanimous in according to this animal the most human personality and the richest intelligence, however inferior it may be to the chimpanzee in mechanical facility, social adaptability, and general capacity for making its way in a human world. The insufficient hints we have of sexual activity and dominance in the gorilla do not suggest that either of these phenomena bulk inordinately large in the social life of the animal. But, in point of fact, our knowledge of these matters is virtually nil.

ALTRUISM AND FOOD-SHARING

The quality known as altruism is scarcely susceptible of objective recording. Interpretations of actions performed by the infrahuman primates as altruistic are all too likely to reflect the emotions and notions of the human observer. Thus, many instances of highly subjective, idealistic, and anthropomorphizing accounts of ape behavior may be culled from the popular books of the women who have raised apes as members of their own families. It is possible that many of these interpretations may be correct, but it is difficult for the skeptical scientist to accept them as factual. That selfless, altruistic behavior does occur sometimes in monkeys is a priori probable, although we ought to exclude from this category the activities of mothers relative to their offspring, which are directed by some instinct or drive which removes from them any element of free will.

Observations of food-sharing have been hit upon by the psychologists as the most objective method of studying something which may be called altruism. Unfortunately, systematic studies seem to have been limited to the chimpanzee. In the case of this ape, animals which are attached to each other undoubtedly exhibit a considerable amount of this type of behavior. It is more ordinary, however, for dominant animals to take all or nearly all of food offered, even when they are associated with congenial cage mates. If the howlers and the spider monkeys do not squabble over food and do not attempt to deprive their weaker fellows of any share, it is probably safer to attribute such actions to lack of dominance and to indifference rather than to altruism. It is certain that voluntary food-sharing is rare and perhaps non-existent in baboons and macaques. Animals may be friendly to each other, manifest apparent sympathy and affection, and yet continue to exercise dominance and extreme selfishness in the matter of food-sharing. Anecdotes of isolated "noble" or altruistic actions evidently do not help in any great measure.

PARENT-YOUNG RELATIONS

Maternal care of the young is so essential for species survival that it is naturally manifested far down in the mammalian orders and even in other classes of vertebrates. The data at our command do not permit us to conclude that maternal care becomes more extensive and skillful as one ascends the ranks of the primates, except in so far as the great apes have longer periods of infancy and dependence and thus prolong parent-child relationship. One may guess that chimpanzee mothers, at any rate, do a good deal more for their children than gibbon or monkey mothers, but it would be unsafe to go much farther. One of the complicating factors which ought to prevent facile generalization, even on this point, is that such apes as the chimpanzee certainly show a great deal of individual variation in the matters of maternal solicitude and the efficacy of the mother's care of her offspring.

The primate father apparently has little to do with his children beyond the occasional help or protection which he may extend to any infant or juvenile of the group which may be in difficulty or danger. Savage males may indeed be an active menace to infants closely associated with their mothers, when the male makes a sexual attack upon the oestrous female. Zuckerman records instances in which baboon males have killed infants under such circumstances, whether their own or not. Some interest in the newly born infant and some solicitude for its welfare have indeed been noted in gibbons, orang-utans, and chimpanzees, but ordinarily it has been the practice in zoological gardens to separate the male from the pregnant female or to remove the father after the birth, so that opportunities for observation of the father-child relation have been limited. On the whole, it seems probable that males regard their young with indifference. It is possible that this stricture does not hold in the case of apes, but it is probably valid for monkeys.

GROUP CO-ORDINATION

Group leadership is not the prerogative of any one male or of the male sex in general among the New World monkeys which have been studied by Carpenter, nor in the monogamous gibbon families. Lack of such fixed leadership is due to absence of dominance, but it does not imply that group control and co-ordination are missing. On the contrary, leadership is assumed by different individuals from time to time, and systems of signaling by cries or gestures are well developed. Among the baboons and macaques dominance is highly important, and in a family group the dominant male always is the leader and controls the group movements. In spite of all the folklore about baboon sentinels and social organization, it seems doubtful that there is any fixed individual leadership in troops composed of a number of family or clan groups. Among the great anthropoid apes, which apparently go about for the most part in families, either monogamous or polygamous, the male apparently leads and directs, but data on this subject are extraordinarily meager.

TERRITORIALITY

Territoriality, or the residence of a primate group within well-defined territorial limits, has been established for howler monkeys, red spider monkeys, various baboons, gibbons, and, in all probability, orang-utans. The list is restricted by the number of field studies made. It is quite possible that nearly all primate genera share this habit of remaining within a certain area which they regard as their own and from which they attempt to expel trespassers, especially those belonging to their own species. If, as is stated, different species of lemurs in Madagascar are separated by fairly easily traversable natural boundaries, such as narrow rivers, it would appear that this primate tendency to maintain territoriality must be closely bound up with the differentiation of races and varieties, and even of species, by selection and inbreeding. Further, it would seem necessary to postulate some such innate or acquired habit of relative immobility within a narrow environmental range to account for the early differentiation of the very distinct physical varieties or races of man.

Thus it would appear that the feeling of ownership of real estate or of a certain habitat area is a very ancient primate inheritance. Under these circumstances it is little wonder that most of the wars of mankind have been over landed possessions and that increased facilities for migration and communication have brought more trouble to man than any other cultural acquisition. The nature of man changes very little. Throughout the ages human groups have desired to defend their territorial integrity if they live in a favorable environment and to migrate and invade better lands if they happen to reside in poor places. However, global wars are impossible until problems of transportation are solved. The migrations of arboreal primates are limited by discontinuities of the forest zone as well as by other geographical barriers. Ground-dwelling primates ought to have a wider range, whether they are quadrupedal or bipedal. It is rather strange that terrestrial monkeys, such as baboons, mandrills, and "Barbary apes," have not a wider distribution. In some way or other, their spread has probably been restricted by competition with other mammals of a more predatory character, possibly carnivores; certainly the human carnivore. The human primate could not have become migratory to the extent which he must have been, even in early prehistoric times, if he had not developed a carnivorous propensity. In short, it seems to me that the term, "territoriality," indicates a finding in regard to infrahuman groups of our order that is possibly the most significant discovery of students of primate sociology.

PERSONALITY, INDIVIDUALITY

The classification of personality traits in man has reached only a very crude and tentative status, in spite of the fact that this subject may be the most important aspect of psychology, in so far as society is concerned. It seems to this mere biological anthropologist that the simplification of problems of individuality which is essential for the beginner in analysis and classification may well be sought among the lower primates—at the lemur and the monkey levels. It is obvious that civilized man presents a complexity of personality that has hitherto baffled the scientific student. Clearly, at the great-ape level personality traits are already so widely diversified and so intricately interwoven that the problem of analysis and classification is not much easier than in the case of man himself.

The somewhat amorphous discipline which goes under the name of "sociology" could profit enormously from the development of a considerable body of psychologically and biologically trained field observers who would undertake to extend the work so magnificently begun by Carpenter and one or two other men upon the infrahuman primates. One really cannot begin the study of mathematics with calculus, and that is what sociologists have attempted to do. The social anthropologist has at least got back to algebra in beginning with savages, but the arithmetic is to be learned most securely in the infrahuman primates. The addition, multiplication, subtraction, and division start with the lemurs and the monkeys.

CHAPTER XIII

Blood and Relationship

BLOOD SYMBOLIZES LIFE and relationship in most human groups, from the sophisticates of civilization to the crude savages. This is one of the most nearly accurate assumptions which man has made about the significance of structure and function within the animal organism or between different organisms. The idea that the heart is the seat of the emotions is a bad guess, but the scientific investigations relative to the morphology of blood cells, the crystallography of the hemoglobins, the reaction of the blood to various sera, the different types or groups of blood, and the specificity of the red cells all confirm the supposition that degrees of relationship between various classes of animals are measurably shown by similarities and differences in the composition and physiology of their respective bloods.

SEROLOGY

Dr. S. Zuckerman has summarized the data derived from research upon the blood of the primates up to 1933, and the present writer, whose ignorance in this field is even more profound than in most of the other subjects discussed in this book, can venture nothing more than a simplified interpretation of Zuckerman's excellent résumé, together with some additions from more recent writings of serologists who are believed to be reliable authorities.[1] Everyone knows that the blood is composed of a colorless fluid called plasma, together with the red corpuscles and the white corpuscles. We also know that the blood circulates in the arteries and veins and that the solid tissues take from it their food and oxygen and discharge into it their waste products.

The blood cells of the primates have been extensively studied by

[1]Zuckerman 1933, Chap. V, pp. 48–61.

Ponder, Yeager, and Charipper and the results are summarized in a table of measurements and counts from which I propose to abstract whatever seems intelligible and interesting to a mere anthropologist. If we start at the bottom of the primate order with ordinary lemurs (one a brown lemur and the other ring-tailed) we find that both of these animals in comparison with man have more than twice as many white cells per cubic millimeter and from roughly 1½ to nearly 2 times as many red cells. The red blood corpuscles in man have an averaged diameter of 7.9 microns, and those of the brown and ring-tailed lemur are 6.7 and 6.8 microns respectively. If we then scan the rest of the list of the primates whose blood has been studied we find these lemurs are "tops" in regard to numbers of red and white cells per cubic millimeter, and, most notably so, in the number of white cells. The mean diameter of their red corpuscles is also smaller than that of any of the other primates except the American squirrel monkey, which incidentally pushes the lemurs most closely in number of red cells, but is nosed out for third place in number of white cells by a green cercopitheque monkey.

Several New World and Old World monkeys appear to have substantially the same number of red cells and white cells as man possesses. The closest fit to man is the "Moor·Macaque," which has a few more white cells and a few less red cells per cubic millimeter and a slightly higher mean diameter of red corpuscles. The hemoglobin percentage for man is given by Ponder as 105, which is 10 per cent above any other primate in the list. Closest to man are the brown capuchin and the common macaque. The only other count in which man stands out is that of large mononuclear leucocytes, which in our species reaches 5 per cent, but is closely approached by the gorilla (4 per cent). A careful inspection of this table leaves one with the impression that the great gap in hematological characters lies between the lemurs and the Anthropoidea, including man. Also one suspects that these counts and measurements may be quite variable and that the samples for infrahuman primates may be based upon so few cases as to be unreliable. Zuckerman says that, with the exception of the green monkey, the marmoset, the capuchin, and the ring-tailed lemur, the red blood corpuscles of all species investigated are more resistant to hypotonic saline than are human red blood corpuscles.

Reichert and Brown have carried out some investigations upon the form of the crystals of the hemoglobins in primates, but these were limited to the ordinary ring-tailed lemurs, three species of baboons, the drill, and the mandrill. Apparently, the globin or proteid fraction of the hemoglobin is the same in all animals, but the hematin part differs. The baboons and mandrills seem to have three types of crystals which belong in the same crystallographic system (isomorphous) as do the blood crystals of man. Two of the human types studied were orthorhombic and strikingly similar to those of the baboons. However, the crystals of the lemurs also belong to the same series.

One of the most familiar methods of testing blood relationship is by means of serum precipitin reactions. Rabbits are immunized against ape, human, and monkey sera. Then the anti-human, anti-ape, and anti-monkey sera obtained from the immunized rabbits are tested with the sera of various primates and the amount of precipitate thrown down is observed or measured. It should be noted that when bloods mingle harmoniously there is no precipitin reaction, but when the sera of markedly different properties are injected into the blood stream or mixed with the blood of any species there results this reaction which produces a more or less dense precipitate. This indicates a marked physiological and biochemical difference. Nuttal and other investigators began this type of work early in the present century. The results are in general as follows: anti-human sera give virtually as marked precipitates when mixed with chimpanzee and orang blood as they do when mixed with human blood. Taking the human reaction to anti-human sera as 100, the precipitate in volume produced by mixing anti-human sera with chimpanzee blood is 130 (but the precipitate is less compact). In the case of the gorilla it drops to 64, in the orang and the mandrill to 42, in the guinea baboon and the spider monkey to 20. In general, the bloods of Old World monkeys show slighter precipitin reactions to anti-human sera than do those of the great apes; the bloods of New World monkeys produce scarcely any reactions at all, and the bloods of true lemurs and the tarsier fail to produce any reaction whatsoever to anti-human sera.

In more recent studies of serum precipitin reactions Von Krogh has been able to show not only the comparative nearness of relationship between various primates, but the probable extent also to which the blood of each has differentiated from the common primate prototype.[2] The latter conclusions are based upon the differentials of the cross-reactions in various pairs of primates. Thus it is found invariably that when anti-human serum is used for testing purposes the chimpanzee throws down a precipitate which is quantitatively nearer to that of man (100 per cent) than the amount of precipitate man produces in his blood when tested with anti-chimpanzee serum. A brief tabulation of the data will make this point clear; *human anti-*

[2]Krogh 1937, pp. 240–47.

serum: chimpanzee 84.5 per cent, orang 70.6 per cent, baboon 64.8 per cent, macaque 63.5 per cent; *chimpanzee anti-serum:* orang 84.9 per cent, macaque 74 per cent, baboon 72.4 per cent, man 62.9 per cent; *orang anti-serum:* baboon 47.5 per cent, chimpanzee 44.3 per cent, macaque 42.2 per cent, man 38.8 per cent; *macaque anti-serum:* baboon 83.3 per cent, chimpanzee 46.4 per cent, man 45.3 per cent, orang 33.7 per cent; *baboon anti-serum:* macaque 60.8 per cent, chimpanzee 42.1 per cent, man 39.8 per cent, orang 33.9 per cent.

The fact that the chimpanzee gives 84.5 per cent of optimum reaction with anti-human serum, whereas man gives only 62.9 per cent reaction with anti-chimpanzee serum, indicates that the chimpanzee has a higher proportion of the substances which are common to the blood of it and of man than man has of these substances. It is further deduced from this and from other serological evidence that the species furthest differentiated from the common stock retains the smallest proportions of ancestral blood substances. Each animal when tested with homologous anti-serum (that of its own species) gives a maximum precipitate. Closer relationships are indicated in the list of precipitate amounts thrown down when an animal is tested with its own anti-serum and other animals are measured by that scale than when the animal is in the secondary position of being tested with some heterologous serum (that of the species to which it does not belong).

These serological studies suggest that man is furthest differentiated from the primate serological ancestral type; that the chimpanzee is further differentiated than orang, macaque, or baboon, and the macaque than the baboon. Again, man has most proteals (antigens) in common with the chimpanzee, notably less with the macaque, and still less with the baboon and the orang. The chimpanzee has the closest blood resemblance to man, much less to the macaque, orang-utan, and baboon. The orang-utan is closest to the chimpanzee, somewhat farther from man, and much farther from the baboon and the macaque. The baboon and the macaque are very close to each other, and not far from chimpanzee and man (the macaque nearer), but both have less in common serologically with the orang-utan.

The weak similarity of the orang-utan to all other species indicates a lengthy process of separate development for this animal and also a somewhat protracted period of separation from the stock of the chimpanzee and of man. The macaque seems to have branched off the ancestral stock later than the baboon, but to have paralleled in serological differentiation, in greater degree, man and the chimpanzee.

BLOOD GROUPS

Experiments with blood transfusions, notably among the wounded of the first World War, showed that it was not possible indiscriminately to transfuse the blood of one human being into another without setting up serious reactions in the form of agglutination or clotting. It developed that in many instances the blood serum contains substances known as iso-agglutinins which cause the red blood corpuscles of alien character to clot. Similarly, the red blood corpuscles contain iso-agglutinogens or receptors which cause them to clot under the stimulus of alien sera. There are four human blood groups: in O the agglutinogens in the red cells are lacking, as are also the agglutinins in the serum. The second group has an agglutinogen known as A, the third B, and the fourth both A and B. In clinical transfusions the blood of the donor is first typed by testing with known sera. The recipient receives transfusions of his own type of blood and no other. Otherwise clotting would result from the transfusion. Theoretically, type O blood could be transfused into the blood stream of any other type since its red cells, having no agglutinogens, would not be clotted by the serum of the recipient. Practically, it is inexpedient to "monkey" with such mixtures of types in transfusions. Furthermore, there are two other iso-agglutinogens, M and N, which exist in human blood quite independently of the A, B pair. To climax it all there are several subvarieties of A. Human blood also contains in its serum some substances which clot the corpuscles of apes, called hetero-agglutinins. In order to compare human blood with ape blood methods of absorbing these hetero-agglutinins must first be employed.

The early investigations of the blood groups among the infra-human primates apparently showed that they were present in all the anthropoid apes, absent in the Old World monkeys, and represented by some sort of B factor in New World monkeys. Very recently Dr. P. B. Candela began to enlarge the series of apes tested by using a technique to obtain the agglutinogen reaction from urine and feces.[3] Although these excretions are weak in agglutinogen content they give positive results in the blood tests.

The available data on the chimpanzee, including 12 specimens grouped by Candela from the urine, now total 108 animals. Of these, 96 are A and 12 are O. Thus the chimpanzee is completely lacking in B and consequently in AB.

Of 24 orangs, 9 are A, 10 are B, and 5 AB. The 11 gibbons tested

[3] Candela 1940a, pp. 209–21.

include 2 A, 7 B, and 2 AB. When Candela first tested 7 gorillas by the urine method he found 2 A, 3 B, and, apparently, 2 AB. An error of interpretation of the blood groups of the 2 gorillas thought to be AB led to such important advances in the serology of the infrahuman primates that it is worth while to recount here the course of Candela's experiments.

Candela, after publishing the results of such tests of 11 apes, including the 7 gorillas, was subsequently able to obtain samples of the blood of the mountain gorilla, Janet Penserosa, which had been purchased from the New York Zoological Society by Yale University for the purposes of study upon cerebral localization.[4] Janet's urine had been tested by Dr. Candela, who found it to be AB. When samples of her blood were tested, the erythrocytes gave a weak B reaction both upon direct agglutination and in the adsorption tests, while the plasma contained a definite a agglutinin. This result was also checked by Dr. Wiener. Extracts of the parotid and submaxillary salivary glands of this gorilla were also obtained. That from the parotid gland resulted in a negative reaction, as in man, while that of the submaxillary gland gave a strong B reaction. Thus it was found that Janet did not belong to AB, but to B, and that the B factor in her blood was not identical with human B, but much weaker, resembling somewhat the weak A_2 factor present in some human beings belonging to A.

Since no such subgroup of B has ever been reported in man, or heretofore in apes, some doubt was cast upon the previous assumptions that factors of the blood groups are in all cases identical in man and anthropoid apes. Therefore Candela set to work again with the urines of Janet and Susie, another gorilla whose urine had given an AB reaction, and retested them over a much wider range of dilutions. He then discovered that these 2 urines, tested in dilutions much too weak to give any reactions in other ape and human urines, yielded B reactions. The "AB" reactions attained at normal dilution levels were "due to a very high degree of non-specific adsorptive or inhibitory power not previously known to exist in urine." Thus of the 7 gorillas tested by the urine method only the 2 in the San Diego Zoo really possess the A factor. Of the remaining 5, 3 gave urine reactions indistinguishable from those obtained from human B urines, "implying, perhaps, that the blood factor may also be comparable." The remaining 2 urines when tested in proper dilutions gave weak B reactions. In one of these from which the blood was also available, a weak B was found in the blood, although a strong B reaction re-

[4] Candela 1940b, pp. 479–80.

sulted from extract of the salivary gland. Thus Candela suspects that gorillas may have 2 kinds of B, one possibly identical with human B, as the chimpanzee's A is identical with human A, while the other has a B factor which might be called B_2, comparable to the subgroup A_2 in men. These new findings do not invalidate the results obtained from grouping by means of the urines of the other apes studied by Candela. They only change the grouping of the 2 gorillas, Susie and Janet, thought to be AB, because of the insufficient application of the adsorption method to their urines in testing.

At present reliable tests of 15 unrelated gorillas are available, after the groupings of 4 gorillas previously reported in the literature have been discarded as unacceptable. Of these 15 gorillas the only 2 mountain gorillas are A, and the 13 lowland or coastal gorillas are all B. A specimen of preserved muscle of a third mountain gorilla, tested by Candela, failed to give a definite reaction. More of the mountain-gorilla material is urgently needed.

As the matter now stands the chimpanzee is the only ape which lacks B, and consequently AB, and has O. The other 3 apes have A and B but no O.

Dr. Candela has also cleared up the confusion which has existed in regard to blood groups among the monkeys.[5] In lower primates the specific group factors are present in the body tissues and secretions, as in man and the anthropoid apes, and these factors are accompanied by the appropriate agglutins in the blood serum. However, the blood-group factors of New World monkeys are seldom identifiable in the red-blood cells and those of Old World monkeys are never so identified. Thus in previous studies of the rhesus monkey inexplicable results were obtained because the sera of all were found to contain anti-A agglutin, whereas the B factor, which consequently ought to be found in the cells, was not demonstrable. Testing the tissues, organs, saliva, or urine of this monkey shows that it actually belongs to group B, but differs in the unavailability of the group-specific factor in the red-blood cells. Candela's grouping of Old World monkeys by new methods which take into consideration the difficulties just mentioned show that the rhesus macaque is all B, but the Java macaque appears to have all 4 blood groups (*M. irus:* 2 O, 9 A, 1 B, 2 AB). However, there is the possibility that the Java macaques tested by Candela have a rhesus strain in them, so that B is not fully established in this species. In the *Cercopithecus* monkeys tested Candela found no B and no anti-A agglutinin. According to literature all members of the *Cercopithecus* genus have anti-B in the blood serum and thus

[5]Candela 1942.

should be A. In 2 of 9 animals Candela found reactions indicating group O. In 7 mangabey monkeys (*Cerocebus*) Candela found 1 O, 4 A, 2 B, and in 2 baboons (*P. papio*), 1 O and 1 B.

In 21 American monkeys tested by Dr. Candela an O reaction was found but once. It seems to be fully established, however, that this O is comparable to the human O. In New World monkeys Landsteiner, Levine, and Candela have been able to agglutinate the actual blood cells and to identify therein the B factor. Among the unrelated spider monkeys tested by Candela all of 6 black spider monkeys belonged in A, and of 5 gray spider monkeys 4 are B and the other is definitely O.

In a personal communication Dr. Candela emphasizes the fact that the A and B factors in many of the infrahuman primates do not react exactly like the corresponding human blood-group factors. He considers that these variations either may be due to a real biochemical difference or may be "merely functions of their association with different proteid and lipid substances which modify the behavior of blood group substances with respect to the testing fluids." In view of the apparently closer serological relationships of the factors in some of the American monkeys with human factors, he is inclined to favor the latter hypothesis.

Candela has also made progress in tracing the distribution and patterning of the blood groups in man and has succeeded where others have failed in showing that there are specific patterns, sometimes for major physical divisions, and at other times for subdivisions or varieties. However, apart from the very high frequency of group O in Negroids, none of the branches of mankind is characterized by a single blood group. The most interesting suggestion made by this serologist has to do with the co-ordination of the infrahuman and human blood-group data. Since group O is the rarest by far in apes and monkeys and the commonest in all branches of mankind, it is hardly likely that A and B can be recent mutations in man, occurring against a background of "primitive" group O. On the contrary, these facts suggest that O is phylogenetically the most recent and may be closely associated with the attainment of the humanoid status. Further, since in all apes and monkeys certain blood-group patterns are specific for species or subspecies, the demonstration of similarly definite group patterns for different varieties of man, correlated with racial differences, raises the possibility that the modern races of man have arisen from incomplete fusion of several different species or subspecies.

CHAPTER XIV

Brains and Behavior

EVOLUTION OF THE BRAIN IN PRIMATES

THE LATE Frederic Tilney, Professor of Neurology in Columbia University, published in 1928 a vast and formidable monograph on the evolution of the primate brain.[1] Much of the material in this work is so technical that it is comprehensible only to a neurologist, yet it is so important that a brief and simple summary of it must be attempted here.

The cerebral hemispheres constitute the forebrain or neopallium, the cortex, or covering, of which is the seat of consciousness, of the control of reflex actions, of the adaptation and readjustment of motor acts, of the senses. Most of the evolutionary and physiological studies of the brain have naturally been concentrated upon the cerebrum or forebrain. The cerebellum, or hind brain, consists of 2 lateral lobes and a median lobe. It lies below the hinder part of the cerebral hemispheres. Much less is known of the physiology of the cerebellum, which seems to be the seat of co-ordination of voluntary movements. The third major part of the brain is the medulla oblongata, which is the transitional part between the spinal cord, the forebrain, and the hind brain. Still less is known of this part of the central nervous system.

Tilney's work, although not neglecting the forebrain, concentrated upon the brain stem, which includes the medulla oblongata, the cerebellum, the pons Varolii, the midbrain, and the interbrain. In addition to gross morphological observations and microscopic studies, Tilney made measurements upon cross sections of brain stems whereby the areas of various structures were estimated in relation to total cross section by means of a planimeter. This method yielded an excellent metrical basis for the comparison of corresponding areas in different groups of primates. The resulting coefficients afford some idea of the range of variation in the more plastic elements of recent

[1] Tilney 1928.

acquisition in the brain stem (and presumably particularly susceptible to adaptive influences), as well as the archaic components which are fundamentally very stable.

The encephalic indices express the relationship of the forebrain by volume and by weight to the total brain. These indices set the primates off by themselves, since they are all above 80 per cent. Animals whose pectoral limbs are specialized as wings, fins, or paddles do

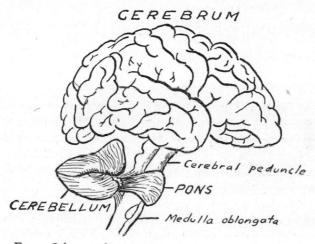

CEREBRUM

Cerebral peduncle

PONS

CEREBELLUM

Medulla oblongata

FIG. 1. Scheme of parts of the brain (*After Schwalbe*).

not exceed 60 per cent in forebrain index. Usually they are much lower than this. Animals which have developed claws, hoofs, and paws may have a forebrain index which rises to 80 per cent, as in the case of the camel, the horse, and the dog, but most of this class fall below such a maximum. In the primates the volumetric indices range as follows: lemur 81, marmoset 80.5, howling monkey 81.6, baboon 83, macaque 84, gibbon 81, orang-utan 83, chimpanzee 83, gorilla 84, man 86–89. *Tarsius*, for which Tilney gives no exact volumetric index of the forebrain, is also only slightly above 80.[2]

In fissural pattern the brain of the lemur is not entirely harmonious with that of other primates, but is, in a degree, reminiscent of a carnivore type of brain in that there is a tendency for the fissures to arrange themselves in circum-Sylvian arches. However, in its temporal lobe it manifests a distinct advance over any subprimate type, and the fissure of Sylvius begins to assume the more oblique relations notable in the primates. What the lemur brain lacks is any extensive occipital specialization.

[2]Tilney 1928, II, 941–42, 950.

The fissural pattern of *Tarsius* is extremely simple, presenting a single indentation, the fissure of Sylvius. It is in this sense the most generalized of all primate brains, but it is more pithecoid than that of the lemur in the development of the visual cortex and in the appearance of a posterior cornu in the lateral ventricle. The brain of *Tarsius,* with its combination of generalized and pithecoid characters, serves well as a transition upward toward a simian type from some preprimate, insectivore-like type of brain. The brain of the marmoset is also very simple and generalized. It is smooth, except in the presence of a well-defined fissure of Sylvius and the faint beginning of a superior temporal sulcus. Tilney regards the simplicity of the marmoset brain as retrogressive. In the other New World monkeys the fissural pattern is more complex. The Sylvian fissure takes a more oblique course upward and backward, separating the parietal from the temporal lobe. The temporal and parietal lobes show considerable fissural specialization, but the frontal and occipital regions still show only slight indentations.

In the Old World monkeys the simian characters of the brain come into full development. There is now a fissure of Sylvius, a fissure of Rolando, which forms the boundary between the frontal and parietal lobes, and a simian fissure which separates the parietal from the occipital lobe. In the baboon, the macaque, and the gibbon the fissural relations are essentially similar. In all three the most prominent and deepest fissuring is found in the parieto-temporal area; in the frontal area only the beginning of the superior frontal fissure is apparent. In the great apes the fissural pattern has increased considerably in complexity, although the fissure of Sylvius, the fissure of Rolando, and the simian fissure still constitute the main landmarks. Notable expansions occur in the frontal and occipital lobes, with the greatest complexity apparent in the arrangement of the fissures. The central sulcus of Rolando tends to take on the major genuflections characteristic of the human brain in a series beginning with orang and passing through chimpanzee to gorilla, where they stand out most prominently. The parieto-temporal region shows the greatest fissural intricacy, as in all other primate brains, but it is not in such striking contrast with the frontal area where the superior, middle, and inferior frontal fissures are well marked. The occipital lobe is also more richly fissured. The lateral occipital fissure becomes more pronounced, passing from orang to gorilla. The fissure of Sylvius becomes more horizontal and the fissure of Rolando diverges from the superior longitudinal fissure at an angle of less than 75°.

LEMUR
Actual length, 75 mm.

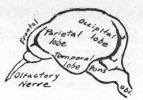

TARSIUS
Actual length, 21 mm.

MARMOSET
Actual length, 31 mm.

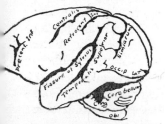

HOWLING MONKEY
Actual length, 52 mm.

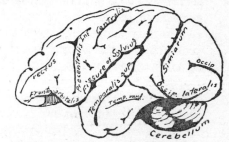

BABOON
Actual length, 89 mm.

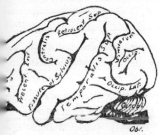

GIBBON
Actual length, 73 mm.

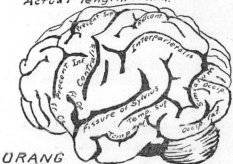

URANG
Actual length, 96 mm.

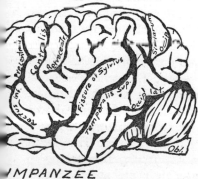

IMPANZEE
ual length 100 mm.

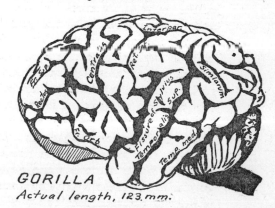

GORILLA
Actual length, 123 mm.

FIG. 2. Fissural patterns of primates (*After Tilney*).

In man the fissural pattern attains its greatest complexity, so that it becomes difficult to identify the characteristic sulci which stand out so prominently in the simpler brains of lower primates. The fissure of Rolando now has an angle of inclination with the superior longitudinal fissure of about 71°; the fissure of Sylvius is nearer the horizontal than in any other species; the simian sulcus of the lower forms has disappeared, although a homologue of it may occasionally appear in the sulcus lunatus described by Elliot Smith.

In the lemur the identification of the four lobes of the brain characteristic of primates is difficult because of the incipient state of the sulcus of Rolando. The occipital lobe is laterally almost entirely wanting. Similar difficulties are encountered in distinguishing the various lobes of the smooth-brained *Tarsius* and marmoset, although their occipital lobes are better developed and overhang the cerebellum. In the howler monkey and succeeding monkey forms the lobation is better defined and an incipient simian sulcus divides the parietal lobe from the occipital. In the Old World monkeys the fissuration is still more marked, but the development of frontal and occipital lobes lags behind the temporal and parietal areas. The great anthropoids present a more advanced condition, but in man the full physiological significance of cerebral evolution becomes apparent in the advance made in the frontal and occipital areas. This advance especially affects the prefrontal region wherein supposedly are synthesized the neural impulses which are the basis of human experience and personality. The planimetric estimates of separate areas and indices derived therefrom are most instructive. They are as follows for the index of the frontal lobe: anteater 9 per cent, horse 13 per cent, sea lion 16 per cent, leopard 20 per cent, brown bear 21 per cent, dog 29 per cent, lemur 23 per cent, spider monkey 31 per cent, baboon 31 per cent, chimpanzee 33 per cent, gorilla 32 per cent, man 47 per cent.[3]

Some of the basal structures of the brain show a corresponding evolutionary sequence. On the base of the cerebrum the roof of the orbit in lower primates produces a deep concavity, which decreases as the frontal area of the hemisphere enlarges. This orbital concavity on the base of the cerebrum is most pronounced in the lower primates, is prominent in the intermediate forms, conspicuous still in the brains of the orang and the chimpanzee, and shows its first marked decrease in the gorilla. In the human species it is hardly discernible. Associated with the two orbital concavities is an interorbital keel which diminishes similarly.

The olfactory bulb and tract in *Tarsius* are much larger than in

[3] Tilney 1928, II, 968.

other primates and recall the development in carnivores and un-
gulates. These features progressively diminish as one passes upward
in the primate order. This decrease is concomitant with lessened
acuity of the sense of smell.

In the lower primates the cerebellum deeply indents the basal surface of the occipital lobes. This concavity is less marked in the lemur
than in higher species, because the lemuroid occipital lobes scarcely
overhang the cerebellum. In the intermediate primates the lateral ex-
tensions of this cerebellar concavity, and especially the postsplenial
fossa, are less prominent; least so in the gorilla. In man there is
merely a vestige of the postsplenial fossa left to accommodate the
vermis of the cerebellum. More simply, the undersurface of the occipital lobe evolves from concavity to something approaching convexity. Also in the cerebellum there is an expansion of the lateral
lobes which represent co-ordinative control of the upper and lower
extremities. The central lobe or vermis does not increase proportionately. In the lower and intermediate primates the vermis is still
the most conspicuous feature of cerebellar organization, and it is not
until the great anthropoids are reached that the real changes become
apparent.

The differentiation of features upon the ventral surface of the brain
stem is connected with the new system in mammals of motor
control by the neopallium. Three prominent structures advance:
the pyramid, the pons, and the cerebral peduncle. The pyramid
is a tract on the ventral surface of the medulla oblongata which lies
between the central fissure and the antero-lateral fissure. The pons
Varolii is a structure on the forepart of the hind brain in front of
the cerebellum consisting externally of transverse fibers arched like a
bridge across the middle line and gathered on either side into compact masses. From the superior surface of the pons arise the cerebral
peduncles, one on each side. These three elements of the brain stem
in the lemur show slight advance over the condition found in still
lower mammals. The marmoset adds little in development, but a
definite advance is notable in all the Cebidae, and still more in the
Old World monkeys and the gibbon. There is a decisive change,
however, in the large apes. The pyramid is more prominent, the pons
Varolii more protuberant, the cerebral peduncles larger and more
clearly defined. All these developments culminate in man, indicating,
according to Tilney, the ultimate development of motor capabilities
made possible by manual specialization.

In the internal structure of the brain stem the evolutionary advance
from the lowest primates to man has to do largely with increasing

definition of nuclei which give rise to the various nerves. Thus the hypoglossal nuclear aggregation, which innervates the muscles of the tongue, shows increasing individuality, as does also the facial nucleus, which innervates those muscles which have to do with facial expression, as well as with the older functions of mastication and deglutition. Similar increase in definition may be traced in other

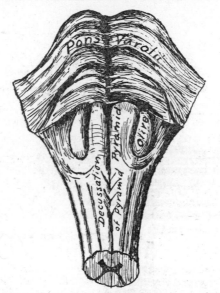

FIG. 3. Ventral surface of the human brain stem (*After Gray*).

nuclear masses as one goes from the lowest to the highest primates. The vestibular nuclei are developed in accordance with the equilibratory or balancing needs of the particular species, although, in the main, the receiving stations for this function maintain a minimal standard. *Tarsius* and the howling monkey have the highest coefficients in the vestibular complex. Tilney attributes the development of the vestibular complex in the latter to the use of the prehensile tail, but passes over the former. In other species, according to this author, the archaic structures representing the balancing mechanism are relatively constant.

In the dorsal part of the medulla are sensory nuclei which indicate variations in the differentiation of the extremities. Thus the clava (the column and nucleus of Goll) represents the lower extremity, foot, and tail, while the cuneus (column and nucleus of Burdach) represents the upper extremity and the hand. The course of primate evolution is from a status in which the clava is distinctly larger than the cuneus to one in which the latter, representing the hand and arm, is at least twice the size of the former. In the macaque and the gorilla the two sensory elements are about equal, but in the gibbon, orang, and chimpanzee, the cuneus begins to get the upper hand. This course of evolution seems to be conditioned upon the loss of function of the tail, but, more especially, upon the increasingly skilled use of the hands.

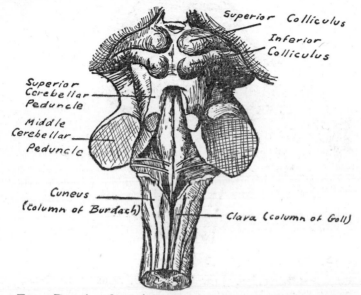

FIG. 4. Dorsal surface of the human brain stem (*After Toldt*).

A third element in the dorsal sensory field is the nucleus of Rolando, which has diminished in all primate types in comparison with lower mammals. This diminution, somewhat more marked in the higher primates, is stated by Tilney to be connected, in all probability, with decreased importance of the head and face as specialized areas for guiding the course of locomotion. These elements of the brain—the cranial nuclei, reticular formation, and nuclei of the dorsal sensory field—are archaic and control such primordial characters as respiration, cardiac activity and digestion, mastication and deglutition, balancing, ocular movements, etc. There are, however, brain elements which are much more responsive to adaptive influences and in general more plastic. These elements are concerned with a new mammalian sphere of action which Tilney calls "neokinesis" (the word means exactly that—new activity). Actually, these elements have to do with the differentiation of cortical areas for voluntary control over muscular movements. They add the quality of judgment for manual guidance and the factors of creative imagination. The brain-stem structures thus functioning are the pontile nuclei, the pyramid, the peduncle, and the olive. As stated above, the pyramid is an antero-medial.tract in the upper part of the ventral side of the medulla. The olive is a swelling shaped like that fruit and about 1.25 cm. long (in man), just lateral to the pyramid.

The planimetric coefficients of the pyramid range as follows: *Tarsius* .032, lemur .110, marmoset .064, howler .137, macaque .147,

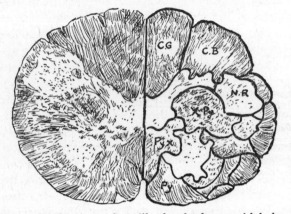

C.G. Column of Goll
C.B. Column of Burdach
N.R. Nucleus of Rolando
XPy Crossed pyramidal tract
Pyx Pyramidal decussation
Py Pyramid
(*After Tilney*).

Fig. 5. Brain stem of gorilla, level of pyramidal decussation. Diagram to illustrate Tilney's method of obtaining planimetric coefficients of the brain stem.

baboon .143, gibbon .138, orang .160, chimpanzee .172, gorilla .161, man .183.[4] The difference between man and the lowest forms represents a remarkable increment in the volume of the human pyramid when it is considered that the pyramidal tract has to accommodate itself to a portion of the neuraxis through which many other equally important conduction systems make their way. This pyramidal system represents a conduction pathway from the motor or precentral area of the neopallium. Each specialized area of the motor cortex (leg or arm, for example) contributes axons to the pyramidal tract. The expansion of the precentral cortex in the primates is one of the most noteworthy features of cranial evolution. The motor area is activated by many other regions of the neopallium. It is, in Tilney's expression, "the mouthpiece of the cerebral hemispheres" and sublimates into effective motor patterns all the afferent impulses which enter the brain. These motor patterns, which determine the animal's

[4] Tilney 1928, I, 245; II, 1008.

external behavior, find their ultimate conveyance through the pyramidal tract. But this tract cannot keep pace with the expansion of the neopallium. Otherwise it would become too large for the brain stem and the spinal cord. Therefore, the pyramidal tract increases only fractionally with cortical expansion and reflects the effort toward condensation which is everywhere necessary in the neuraxis.

The pontile nuclei serve to relay fibers from several areas of the neopallium, and the axons arising in them terminate in the lateral lobes of the cerebellum. The lateral lobes of the cerebellum appear to be an acquisition of the central nervous system for the distribution of co-ordinative impulses to the muscles of the extremities. Many of the fibers running to pontile nuclei take origin in the parietal lobe, which has to do with the reception of sensory stimuli and the up-building of discriminative sensibility. Similarly, fibers arising in the temporo-parietal region seem to be connections between the conscious fields of equilibratory sense, of touch and muscle-joint sense, on the one hand, and the cerebellum, on the other. Thus they serve to perfect the co-ordinative control of muscular activity. There is also a contingent of fibers from the occipital lobe which may blend in visual elements in the co-ordinative guidance of movements of the extremities. The frontal lobe also communicates with the lateral lobes of the cerebellum through pontile fibers. The immediately precentral area probably has control over highly skilled motor performances and represents some phase of neokinetic activity in its connection with the cerebellum. On the whole, Tilney has no doubt that the entire pallio—ponto—cerebellar connection is a reliable indicator of neo-kinetic expansion. Thus, he regards as highly significant from an evolutionary point of view the following array of planimetric coefficients of the pontile nuclei: lemur .055, *Tarsius* .057, marmoset .095, howler .103, macaque .150, baboon .164, gibbon .200, orang .300, chimpanzee .400, gorilla .480, man .550.[5] The cerebral peduncle comprises all the fibers arising from the motor area and including the pyramidal system, as well as all those constituting the pallio-pontile system. Hence it synthesizes in its size the expansion of the cerebral hemisphere. The planimetric coefficients tell practically the same story as in the case of the pontile nuclei and the pyramid.

Tilney tentatively ascribes to the inferior olivary nucleus an activity related to the simultaneous co-ordination of hand, head, and eye. Its coefficients range from .038 in the marmoset to .226 in man.[6]

The superior and inferior colliculi are pairs of rounded eminences

[5] Tilney 1928, I, 273; II, 720, 1008.
[6] Tilney 1928, II, 1037.

forming the dorsal part of the midbrain. They are important in relation to the senses of sight and hearing. These "little hills" (colliculi) are remnants of prominent features in lower vertebrates, such as birds, reptiles, amphibians, and fish. With the appearance of mammals the full force of development is now concentrated upon the neopallium, and each of the special senses, except that of smell, gains representation in the cerebral cortex which affords them more room for functional expansion. Thus in the higher mammals auditory and visual functions tend to be delegated from the midbrain to the cerebral cortex. In this way the capacities for expression of these senses are multiplied, as for example in articulate speech for the auditory sense; reading, writing, and skilled manual movements for the visual sense. Consequently, the colliculi of the midbrain decrease in their planimetric coefficients—in the case of the inferior colliculus from .337 in *Tarsius* to .070 in man.[7] Corresponding with this evidence of cortical transfer of the auditory and visual sense, the oculomotor nuclei increase in the number of their fibers connecting one with the other (decussations). This internuclear connection is essential to the co-operation of movements of the eyeballs required for holding the visual axes parallel in stereoscopic vision. In the lemur, which has no stereoscopic vision, the oculomotor decussation occupies only 16 per cent of the entire nucleus; in the marmoset, whose eyes look forward and are not widely separated, binocular vision is presumably present and the longitudinal coefficient of oculomotor decussation rises to .380, in the howling monkey to .690, orang .710, chimpanzee .860, gorilla .880, and man .90.[8]

The same motive runs through all the measurable areas of the brain stem which are modified by neokinesis, the new motor specialization introduced by mammals. This new element of motor organization substitutes the deliberately considered act for direct reflex reaction, and for limited reflex action a more complexly organized motor design.

CEREBRAL FUNCTION

Considerable knowledge of the function of various parts of the cerebral hemispheres has been acquired by training primates in the solution of experimental problems, extirpating certain parts of their brains, and then trying them upon the same problems and observing the effect of the operations.

[7] Tilney 1928, II, 1032.
[8] Tilney 1928, I, 283; II, 724, 926.

Jacobsen, Wolfe, and Jackson trained two chimpanzees in an elaborate series of problems involving the utilization of sticks.[9] The simplest of these merely required the animals to use a stick of suitable length to obtain a piece of food out of reach. Further complications were introduced by arranging a number of sticks—from 2 to 5—on a platform in such a fashion that the nearest stick could be used to draw in a slightly longer stick, which could then be used to secure a third stick, and so on until the last stick, which was long enough to reach the food. In another test the food was placed on one platform and the stick on another. In a third, sticks of varying lengths were placed on two platforms, so that the animal had to shuttle back and forth between the platforms, using one stick to get another, until it finally secured the stick which could reach the food. The uninjured animals easily achieved the solution of these problems. When one side of the frontal area of the brain was cut away, the animals, after recovery, did these tests as well as before. However, when the frontal areas were removed on each side, their performances definitely deteriorated. The animal with the more serious lesion took several minutes to get food with a stick, when she had previously accomplished the task in a few seconds. If the stick was kept on one platform and the food was on the other, the chimp showed increasing facility in carrying the stick from one platform to another, but, if the relation of stick and food was reversed, so that the chimpanzee found the stick on the platform on which she had been accustomed to work for food, she promptly picked up the stick and went to work on the empty platform. Both animals did this and neither could manage the test with multiple sticks on two platforms.

Another experiment with a problem box required the chimpanzees to push three pegs in succession from left to right and then pull out the fourth on the right in order to unlock the food box and get the reward. In this test the animal could fail through errors in sequence or in direction. The animals originally mastered this problem completely. Cutting away the frontal area on one side did not affect their performances. However, the extirpation of the frontal areas on both sides seriously disturbed their performances and brought out again errors of direction and sequence.

A familiar type of delayed-response experiment gave the chimp an opportunity to watch an experimenter conceal a piece of food under one of two cups, and then after the lowering of an opaque screen and a delay of varying lengths, to select the cup under which the food had been placed. One of these chimpanzees scored a high percentage of

[9]Jacobsen, Wolfe, and Jackson 1935, pp. 1–14.

correct' responses after delays up to one minute. Extirpation of one frontal lobe did not affect the performance, but when both were cut away, the animal was no longer able to respond to delays even of 2 seconds. The other chimp failed the test both before and after the operation. She was eager to work, but highly emotional, and went into temper tantrums, rolled on the floor, urinated, and defecated when the opaque screen was lowered. She finally quit trying. After a while she had to be dragged into the experimental cage. She had developed what the physiologists call an "experimental neurosis."

After bilateral temporal extirpation this animal was profoundly changed. In the experimental situation she showed no excitement at all, but chose between the cups with eagerness and alacrity. If she made a mistake (which she usually did), she remained calm and merely played about or plucked her hair. There was no suggestion of a neurosis. The authors remark that it seemed as if the animal "had joined the 'happiness cult of Elder Micheaux' and had placed its burdens on the Lord." Of course, she failed the test even more completely than before, but far less miserably. In order to pick the right cup, even after the smallest delays, these chimps, after their operations, had to point themselves toward the loaded cup and retain that bodily orientation during the whole period of the delay. They had lost their memories. This effect was specifically due to frontal injury and not to generalized injury of the brain cortex, for extirpations of parietal, temporal, and other brain areas did not have the effect of impairing memory.

Jacobsen performed similar tests of the effect of unilateral and bilateral removal of the frontal lobes in macaques, mangabeys, and baboons.[10] The tests included opening various problem boxes—rope pull, crank, hook and handle, etc., all very tricky—delayed-response tests in selecting the right cup after intervals of varying length when the cups were out of sight; visual discrimination between a white and a black card 8 cm. square. It may be remarked that the pre-operational performances of these animals were admirable. After the operation the immature female macaque showed heightened motor activity and constant restlessness. She did most of the box-opening problems as quickly and as easily as before. However, she failed in the delayed-response tests, although previously she had been successful up to delays of 30 seconds. The white-crowned mangabey monkey was even better than the macaque in the pre-operational tests. In delayed responses he was successful for 60 seconds and possibly longer. Injury of the frontal lobes on one side did not disturb the

[10]Jacobsen with co-operation of Elder and Haslerud 1936, pp. 1–68.

performance. When both frontal lobes were removed, the mangabey failed on the delayed-response tests. Yet the animal performed the problem-box tasks and the visual-discrimination tests as well as ever. Results in the case of the baboon were substantially similar.

Klüver and Bucy, as well as other experimenters, have analyzed the functions of the temporal lobes in monkeys by like methods of training the animals in various problems, extirpating one or both temporal lobes, and observing the effect upon subsequent test performances.[11] Cebus monkeys may lose the ability to utilize objects as tools for obtaining food when the temporal lobes have been excised. The one cebus which had undergone this operation could no longer obtain food by using a stick lying near it. His response consisted only of making an examination of the stick by mouth and reaching for the food again and again with his hand. Instead of using the stick, a sack, a wire, or a leather belt to pull in the food, as he had done in preoperative tests, this monkey merely reached for the food and walked around for half an hour or longer, examining the various objects.

Klüver and Bucy worked with a considerable number of rhesus monkeys in the study of temporal-lobe function. In the first place, loss of the temporal lobes afflicts these monkeys with "psychic blindness." The animal approaches without hesitation all sorts of animate and inanimate objects which previously called forth avoidance reactions, extreme excitement, and other forms of emotional response. The monkey attempts to contact every object in sight by mouth rather than by hand. It will pick up and place in its mouth nails, glass, a live mouse, feces, sealing wax, and anything else. If the object is edible it is eaten, otherwise discarded. The animal goes on examining one object after another, even if they are perfectly familiar objects. It may, if free in a large room, examine 100 objects in 30 minutes, passing by food which lies on the floor. It never carries the objects around, but merely picks them up, examines them, and drops them again. A normal monkey will not bother with such objects as nails, unless it wants to do something with them. In pulling-in tests the strings are pulled indiscriminately by the mutilated animals. The senseless oral examination is accompanied by repeated smelling of the objects. The "bilateral temporal" monkey never tears, breaks, or destroys objects in the way a normal macaque always does. In this temporally injured animal there is no diminution of visual grasp or of concentration. The point is that every visual presentation evokes an immediate motor response, which is to contact the thing as soon as possible. These monkeys seem to suffer no auditory disturbance, but

[11]Klüver and Bucy 1939b, pp. 979–1000; 1939a, pp. 170–75.

for several weeks or months they do not vocalize. Such a monkey remains perfectly quiet at feeding time when the rest of the colony is yelling, or even when it is attacked. When it does make sounds, they are different from ordinary vocalizations, and seemingly the animal does not recognize the meaning of familiar sounds.

Motor reactions involved in grasping, picking up, holding, and pulling in objects were not affected by bitemporal injury, but some abnormalities of gait were observed. All monkeys tend to perform antics, but these animals executed ridiculous movements, such as putting both feet behind the neck at once, jumping around the floor holding one foot with one hand, "skinning the cat," hanging from the feet and swinging with peculiar twists of the body.

Typically, a normal "wild macaque," when turned loose in a room, tries to get away from the human observer. But the bitemporal monkey loses all such reactions of fear and avoidance. It is as eager to contact the experimenter as any other object and will follow him around to play with him. Some of the monkeys after a few months regain their ability to express emotions facially or otherwise, but they never get angry and bite; they only examine and lick.

In some of the male macaques a few weeks after the operation sexual activity became excessive in comparison with that of the other animals. Many normal monkeys have disgusting sexual habits, but erection, manipulation of the genitals, and rhythmic pelvic movements with presentations are greatly increased in frequency. A bitemporal monkey may copulate with a female almost continuously for as long as a half-hour. Two males caged together are likely to indulge in such violent homosexual activities that they have to be separated lest they injure each other.

One most interesting fact is that two of these bitemporal monkeys after their operations ate animal food, such as bacon, liver sausage, boiled ham, boiled tongue, smoked whitefish, ground beef, and broiled lamb chops. Klüver has never known normal rhesus monkeys to accept such food.

Differential responses, such as reacting positively to a circle instead of a square, were easily established with these rhesus monkeys before operation. An attempt to teach such responses to one animal after bitemporal excision was successful only after hundreds of trials, but the monkey finally did achieve an errorless performance. The monkeys which had been trained in these responses before the operation showed a marked disturbance of their responses after removal of the temporal lobes, but ultimately the responses were re-established. In one animal a response to the lighter of two weights (1050 and 350

grams pair) was unaffected by the operation. These bitemporal monkeys did not lose their ability to respond to visual stimuli, and their
responses were maintained through all the variations in color brightness and form in the tests which required them to react positively to
the circle as against other shapes.

Klüver and Bucy doubt that a monkey turned loose in the wild
would be seriously hampered by the loss of its prefrontal region, its
parietal lobes, or its occipital lobes, as long as small portions of the
striate cortex remained intact. But the ablation of the temporal lobes
seems radically to affect the relation of the animal to its environment.
A monkey which approaches every animal to examine it by mouth
would probably not survive for many hours if turned loose in a region
with a plentiful supply of enemies.

CHAPTER XV

Bones and Body Build

IN ONE OF HIS definitive monographs Professor Adolph H. Schultz has discussed in detail the skeleton of the trunk and limbs of the primates,[1] and we can do no better for the elementary student of primates than to summarize the metric data of this work, adding some functional comments and interpretations.

VERTEBRAL COLUMN

The number of rib-bearing (thoracic) vertebrae in the lemurs varies from 12 to 17, with the lorises generally running highest (14–16 thoracic vertebrae). Several genera of lemurs, however, have but 12 thoracic vertebrae, as in man and the orang-utan. A few of the New World monkeys may have only 12 thoracic vertebrae, but most of the family of Cebidae have 14. Macaques usually have 12 thoracic vertebrae, but most other Old World monkeys have 13. All the anthropoids except the orang have generally 13 rib-bearing vertebrae, but the orang and man have only 12. The most stable primates in numbers of rib-bearing vertebrae are man, the macaque, and the spider monkey.

Some of the lemurs have 6 to 9 lumbar vertebrae, and the majority of cebus monkeys have 6, but in the howlers the number has decreased to an average of a little more than 5 and in *Ateles* to 4. The gibbon, the siamang, and man usually have 5 lumbar vertebrae, but the great apes tend to have only 4 and often, in the case of gorilla and chimpanzee, only 3. Here again man is by far the most stable primate.

Figures on number of sacral vertebrae in lemurs are incomplete, but they vary from 2 to 6, although the higher numbers are probably rare.

[1]Schultz 1930, pp. 303–438.

New World monkeys and Old World monkeys usually have 3 sacral vertebrae; the gibbon family averages 4.4, the orang-utan 5.1, man 5.2, chimpanzee 5.4, and gorilla 5.5. The figures to the right of the decimal point indicate high percentages of the genera which possess a total number of sacral vertebrae equaling the integer above that of the statistical average. The lower primates are far more stable in number of sacral vertebrae than are the higher apes and man.

The number of tail or coccygeal vertebrae naturally depends upon length of tail, which is extremely variable. The maximum in primates is 34 (in a specimen of spider monkey), and the minimum one, found repeatedly in gibbons, siamangs, and orangs. Man has oftenest 4 tail vertebrae and an average of 4.2. Three is the modal number among the great apes, and the averages vary from 3.3 in chimpanzee to 2.8 in orang-utan. The gibbons and siamangs average slightly lower than the great apes. In the gibbon 2 caudal vertebrae are slightly more frequent than one.

The number of cervical or neck vertebrae is 7 throughout the primates. It is evident that in primate evolution the lumbar column has tended to be shortened and that this process has gone farthest in the great apes. More vertebrae have tended to become fused in the sacrum, and again this evolutionary trend has been most pronounced in two of the anthropoids—the chimpanzee and the gorilla. In the reduction of tail vertebrae the gibbon has gone farthest, and man is less advanced than any of the apes, supposedly because his coccyx has been curved around underneath to help close the floor of his overly capacious pelvic cavity. In general, man has a larger number of vertebrae in the spine than any of the anthropoid apes. The orang has fewest. The shortening of the lumbar region is undoubtedly connected with brachiating and the erect or vertical position of the trunk, whether suspended from boughs or in the upright posture on the ground. The long, rodlike lumbar column of the lower primates is adapted for quadrupedal progression and jumping from the hind limbs. It is desirable in the case of upright primates to have the pelvic girdle and limbs knitted more closely to the spine; hence a shorter lumbar column with more segments incorporated in the sacrum.

STERNUM

In the lemurs and monkeys the sternum or breastbone is relatively long and narrow; in the apes and man shorter and broader. The chimpanzee is least advanced in this respect. In the lower primates the segments in the body of the sternum tend to remain separate at maturity and this is true of the gorilla and the orang, but in the chimpanzee, man, and the gibbon there is usually fusion of all or some of the segments. The primitive condition of 5 or 6 segments of the body, not including the xiphoid process, is retained throughout life in lemurs and monkeys, but reduction occurs during growth in the higher primates. Man in adult life has only 2 sternal sections, the manubrium and the body. The gibbon has relatively the shortest sternum of all primates. The apes and man have manubria which are relatively broad and long with reference to the sternal body, as compared with lower primates. Man and the chimpanzee are least divergent from lower primates in these proportions. The spider monkey is an exception in the lower forms, in having a relatively very broad manubrium. It seems probable that the breadth of the manubrium in the anthropoids (and in the spider monkey) is connected with their arm-swinging or brachiating habits. In the gibbon the joint in the sternum is often found at the level of the third costal cartilage, so that the manubrium is united with the first segment of the corpus. Keith regards this condition as a specialization connected with brachiation.

CLAVICLE

The clavicle varies irregularly in its length (relative and absolute) among the primates. The curvature shows marked differences in higher forms. Clavicles of gibbons and siamangs appear to be bow-shaped, those of man and the chimpanzee usually S-shaped, that of the adult orang nearly straight, and in the gorilla straight with a bend at the acromial end. Individual variations are numerous. In the great apes the clavicles are directed more posteriorly and less laterally than in man. In the anthropoids the shoulders are higher. This condition is most marked in the orang-utan.

SCAPULA

The scapula is a very difficult bone to describe by the use of measurements and indices. In man the vertical axis of the glenoid fossa is almost parallel to the vertebral border. The scapular spine is almost at a right angle with the vertebral border and the supraspinous fossa is much smaller than the infraspinous fossa. This shape seems to be connected with the fact that the glenoid fossa looks outward, the arm hangs down, and the general position of the entire arm joint is more lateral and less anterior. In the anthropoid apes the glenoid fossa looks upward and forward, to some extent; therefore the axes of the glenoid and the vertebral border of the scapula converge superiorly. The spine is more diagonal with reference to the vertebral border and the supraspinous fossa is relatively larger as compared with the infraspinous fossa. This anthropoid conformation of the scapula is most marked in the gibbon. If you hold your arms upward and a little forward as if you were hanging from them, you will observe how the entire shoulder joint is pulled upward and forward. This seems to be the anthropoid brachiating and suspensory position, and the shape of the scapula and its position on the back and side of the rib cage are apparently conditioned by this function. If you let your arms hang and square your shoulders, you have the human position and the adaptations of the shoulder blade consequent thereupon. The acromial process is short in monkeys, somewhat longer in the gibbons, longer still in orangs and chimpanzees, and longest in the gorilla and in man. Breadth of the acromion also increases in the higher forms. The vertebral border of the scapula has been demonstrated by Graves to be straight, concave, or convex in human types as a matter of heredity. These variations also are found in the great apes. Schultz has noted that the mountain gorilla's scapula differs from that of the lowland gorilla in that the vertebral border at the root of the scapular spine bulges out. Data on scapular variations in monkeys and lemurs are scanty and existing measurements and indices seem to throw very little light upon the nature and significance of variations.

PELVIS AND SACRUM

In general, the pelves of the lemurs and monkeys, like those of other mammalian quadrupeds, have long, narrow iliac blades, slung parallel to the spine and in almost direct axial continuation with the ischium or haunch bone. The meager articulation of the sacrum with the pelvis is high up on the ilia, far above the level of the true pelvic cavity, the ventral border of which is formed by the pubic bones, the sides by the union of the pubis, ischium, and ilium at the acetabular point. No lateral expansion of the iliac blades is notable in the monkeys, with the exception of the brachiating spider monkey. The lateral flare and expansion of the blade of the ilium, making an anterior concavity, is notable in an incipient stage in the large siamang and the chimpanzee, and more markedly in the orang-utan and the gorilla. The iliac fossa or concavity attains its greatest development in man. Man also has by far the shortest primate ilium, and the posterior part of this bone, including the sacro-iliac articulation, has been bent down so that the sacrum forms the back wall of the pelvic cavity. This bending down of the hinder part of the ilium, forming the sacro-sciatic notch and lowering the level of the sacro-iliac articulation so that the coccyx contributes to the pelvic floor, is unique among the primates. The sacrum in man has also expanded laterally and is much more concave anteriorly than in the apes.

In general, it may be said that the human pelvis shows such a radical transformation from the primitive primate form as to be nearly the most distinctively human part of the skeleton. Even the great apes show only feeble foreshadowing of the human modifications and in their general pelvic form resemble the monkeys and lower primates far more closely than they resemble man. Most of the human pelvic adaptations are obviously connected with the transmission of the total weight through the pelvis to the lower limbs in the erect posture, the balancing requirements of the erect posture (involving shifting of muscular attachments and change of leverage), and, finally, to the large-brained offspring which must pass through the pelvic cavity, necessitating such an expansion of both inlet and outlet as to require radical transformation of the entire structure. The human pelvis has also been bent downward and its inlet turned forward by the flexure of the spinal region just above the sacrum in the lumbar curve. This tilting of the pelvis, absent in the primates, actually places the pelvis in such a relation to the long axis of the trunk that the sacrum tends to be the roof of the pelvic cavity and the pubic symphysis the floor, the inlet being directed forward and a little upward, the outlet backward and slightly downward.

HUMERUS AND RADIUS

In the lemurs and the Old World monkeys the radius is, in general, longer than the humerus, but in the New World monkeys it is slightly shorter. In the gibbons and siamangs the radius greatly exceeds the humerus in length. In the orang the bones are of about the same length, and in the chimpanzee the radius is somewhat shorter than the humerus. The gorilla and man are the only primates which have relatively very short radii, and this condition is more accentuated in man, although individual human specimens can easily fall within the gorilloid range. Similarly, the range of variation of every primate genus overlaps those of its neighbors. The mountain gorilla has a relatively much longer radius than the lowland gorilla. Schultz states that the length of the radius relative to the humerus increases with age in all primates except the gorilla. The length of the entire arms has been markedly increased not only in typical brachiators, but also in quadrupedal forms such as the baboon in which the arms had to grow to parity with the legs in the interests of ground progression. There are no sex differences in the relation of radius to humerus in the anthropoid apes, but in man the female has a relatively shorter radius.

FEMUR AND TIBIA

In the lower extremity the crural index is the length of the tibia expressed as a percentage of the length of the femur. This corresponds to the brachial or radio-humeral index of the arm. The crural index has higher values—frequently above 100—in the lemurs and the monkeys than in the anthropoid apes and man. By far the lowest femoro-tibial or crural index among the primates is found in the gorilla, with the chimpanzee second, and man and the gibbons and siamangs practically tied for third.

The intermembral index is the sum of the lengths of the humerus and radius expressed as a percentage of the sum of the lengths of the femur and tibia. It is thus arm length relative to leg length. In all the lower primates studied by Schultz, with the exception of some spider monkeys and some howlers, the arm is shorter than the leg. The anthropoid apes without exception have intermembral indices over 100, since their arms are longer than their legs. Man stands apart in having, relative to leg length, the shortest arms among the higher primates. The chimpanzee comes closest to man among the apes, but the gap is considerable. The mountain gorilla has proportionately shorter arms than the lowland gorilla. Gibbons have a much lower intermembral index than siamangs. The average value of the index in gibbons ranges between 124 and 133, but in the larger siamangs it is over 148.

HAND

Relative to trunk height, the length of the hand in all the higher primates is greater than in a typical Old World monkey such as the macaque, but in the adult higher primates there are great differences. Proportionately the shortest hand in the adult higher primates is that of the mountain gorilla; man has the second shortest hand, whereas the orang and the gibbon, extreme brachiators, have relatively long hands. Man and the gorilla also have proportionately broad hands, while the gibbons, siamangs, orang-utans, and chimpanzees have relatively narrower hands than such a typical Old World monkey as the macaque. In all the primates studied by Schultz, with the single exception of the gorilla, the hand becomes relatively more slender during growth. In the growing gorilla the reverse is the case. Hence Schultz concludes that the short, broad hand of the gorilla is a relatively late phylogenetic acquisition.

The thumb of man is relatively longer than that of any other primate, but the apparently very short thumbs of the anthropoid apes are illusory in that the rest of the hand has been secondarily elongated. Thus Schultz found that an adult chimpanzee and an adult man each had a thumb length equal to 24 per cent of trunk height, but the total hand length of the man was 37 per cent of trunk height whereas that of the chimpanzee was 49 per cent.[2] Schultz does not regard the short thumbs of anthropoid apes as atrophied. There is another variable in the amount of the thumb which is "free," beyond its place of branching from the palm. According to Midlo the free length of the thumb in percentage of palm length amounts to 71 in the gibbon family, 56 in man, 44 in chimpanzee, 40 in lowland and 35 in mountain gorilla, 34 in orang-utan. The thumb in the Hylobatidae branches from the palm at a place nearer the wrist than in any other primate. In all primates the length of the thumb relative to that of the hand is longer in fetuses than in adults. Some of the lower primates have thumbs that are reduced to a mere vestige —notably the colobus monkey of Africa and the American spider monkey. In these animals the phalanges have suffered the most reduction and the metacarpal bone is still well developed.

The ability to rotate the thumb, which facilitates opposing it to other digits, is little developed in the monkeys and is not present in any fetal primate. Schultz states that all the adult higher primates have this ability and that it is more advanced in some chimpanzees than in the average man.

In all lemurs and monkeys the second finger (index finger) is shorter than the fourth. This is true also in the orang-utan and in the majority of chimpanzees and gorillas. In exceptional African apes the two fingers in question may be of equal length. In man the second finger is frequently longer than the fourth and this condition is frequent also in the gibbons and siamangs.

The lower primates have an extra free bone in the wrist known as the os centrale. In the higher primates the gibbon, siamang, and orang are usually stated to possess this free bone, whereas in the great African apes and in man this element has fused with the navicular. However, Schultz records cases in which the bone is fused in gibbons, siamangs, and orangs, and other cases in gorillas and chimpan-

[2] Schultz 1936, no. 3, pp. 259–83; no. 4, pp. 425–55.

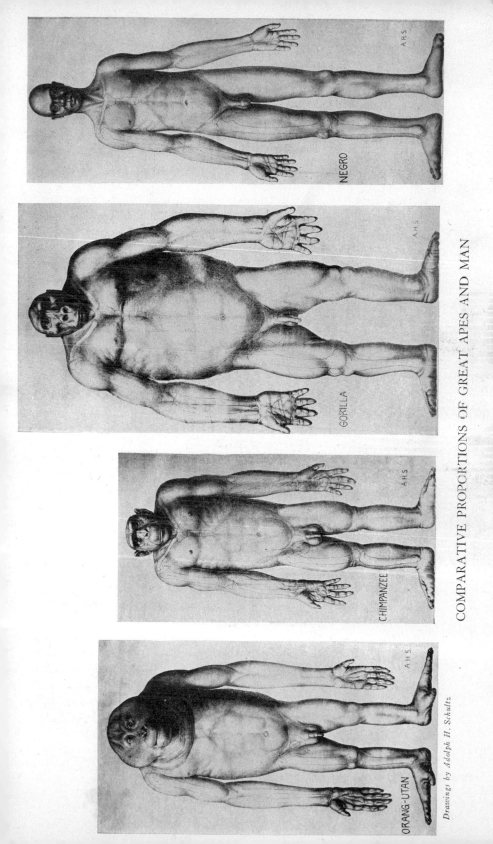

Drawings by Adolph H. Schultz

COMPARATIVE PROPORTIONS OF GREAT APES AND MAN

zees (usually juveniles) in which it is free. In man the os centrale ordinarily fuses with the navicular in the third month of fetal life.

FOOT

Everyone knows that the foot of man has lost most of the prehensile function which it exercises in all other primates and has been modified into an organ of support and locomotion. It is equally common knowledge that in man the heel has been developed backward for support and to afford additional leverage; that the loosely articulated and mobile bones of the generalized primate tarsus have been consolidated into a tightly wedged vault; that the great toe has been brought into line with the long axis of the foot, and that the lateral toes have been shortened. According to Schultz, the tarsus in man is 49.2 per cent of foot length, in the gorilla 40.1 per cent, in the chimpanzee 35.3 per cent, in the orang-utan 26.1 per cent, in the gibbon and siamang 28.2 per cent, and in lower primates 29.2 to 32.3 per cent. Man represents the most specialized condition in tarsal elongation, whereas the gibbons and the orangs have specialized away from the primitive condition in the direction of tarsal shortening. In length of phalanges or toe bones, as represented by the third or middle toe, man shows pronounced shortening in comparison with other primate forms. Length of the phalanges of the third toe relative to foot length range as follows: lower primates 35 to 40, gibbon and siamang 41, orang 43, chimpanzee 36, gorilla 33, man 21. Thus man shows a specialization again divergent from that of the present-day Asiatic apes. Schultz has also shown that the great toe of man has really not elongated to any notable extent. Rather, the lateral toes have been shortened—a process which has resulted in frequent fusion of the phalanges of the "little toe." The orang is the only anthropoid ape which has a degeneratively short great toe. In this animal the terminal phalanx of the great toe, together with the nail, is often missing.

The power of rotating the great toe so that it can be opposed to the other digits depends largely upon the convexity of the joint which carries the great toe and its supporting foot bone, the first metatarsal. The more pulleylike this joint, the farther the great toe can be rotated to oppose the other digits. Similarly, the more oblique the direction of this same endocunieform joint, the farther the great toe can be abducted or swung inward from the long axis of the anteriorly directed foot. Schultz has shown that the gorilla foot is intermediate between those of the other apes and that of man in these characters. Man, in certain races and in individual specimens, still exhibits a considerable obliquity and convexity of this joint, indicating some power of abduction and prehension.

The musculature of the human foot presents surprising resemblance to that of the baboon, and, although the gorilla foot is closest to that of man in this respect also, competent students have concluded that the human foot is more generalized and primitive in its musculature than that of any anthropoid ape. Under these circumstances, the resemblances between the foot of the gorilla and that of man would be due to convergence in evolution.

GENERAL CONCLUSIONS ON SKELETAL AFFINITIES

On the basis of skeletal features of the limbs and trunk, the great apes and man are in a group clearly distinguished from the lower primates, and the gibbons and siamangs are intermediate. However, the great apes stand somewhat apart from man. Schultz says that there is no primate of which it can be stated confidently that its entire skeleton is the most specialized. Man's extreme skeletal specializations, apart from those of the skull, are concentrated in the pelvis, in the proportions of the lower extremity, and in the foot. Most of the conditions found in the spine, sternum, shoulder girdle, and upper extremity are more specialized in one or other of the apes.

Schultz has also made a general appraisal of the affinities of man and the higher primates based upon some 57 characters. These include skeletal features, external proportions of the body, physiological functions (such as duration of pregnancy, duration of postnatal growth, menstrual cycle), morphological features (such as ischial callosities, number of hairs per square centimeter, etc.).[3] According to these findings man resembles the gorilla most closely in 23 characters, the Hylobatidae (gibbons and siamangs) in 15 characters, the chimpanzee in 12 characters, and the orang-utan in 7 characters. The gorilla is closest to the chimpanzee (30 characters), the chimpanzee to the gorilla (28 characters), the orang to the chimpanzee (19 characters), and the Hylobatidae to the orang-utan (23 characters). Of course, these resemblances can hardly be taken as mathematical measures of relationship. It is the opinion of Schultz that the gibbon and siamang family diverged from the common stock of man and the anthropoid apes before the differentiation of any of the giant primates, and with this conclusion most students of primate phylogeny will agree.

Another point of general concordance is the separation of the gorilla

[3] Schultz 1936.

and the chimpanzee from a common African great-ape stock subsequent to the divergence of the orang-utan branch. The most debated question is the time of the human digression from the anthropoid-ape line of progress. The opposite extremes of view are represented by Wood Jones and Weinert. Wood Jones is of the opinion that man represents the development of a progressive "tarsioid" stock which separated from the rest of higher primate stock even before that common stock developed "pithecoid" or monkey tendencies, let alone those of the anthropoids. I am not aware that any other authority on primate development agrees with Professor Wood Jones, who is, nevertheless, one of our most brilliant investigators. At the other end of the range is the German, Hans Weinert, who thinks that man is most closely related to the chimpanzee and, in fact, derives the chimpanzee from the human line of development as late as the end of the Pliocene. This view also is unacceptable to most students. The question then boils down to the divergence of the humanoid line from the common stock before the development of the common *Dryopithecus* family of great apes, or sometime during the flourishing of those giant fossil primates, the surviving descendants of which are represented by the three large anthropoids of today. Schultz is of the opinion that the human line separated from the ape trunk almost as soon as did the branch leading to the gibbons and siamangs. A very similar opinion is held by Sir Arthur Keith, who separates the human from the ape stock in the Oligocene. In contrast, W. K. Gregory and others would derive man from the generalized giant *Dryopithecus* family at about the beginning of the Miocene period. Still another view is that of Broom who, at the moment, thinks that men and the extinct fossil anthropoid apes of South Africa were derived from a *pre-Dryopithecus* ancestor in Miocene times, whereas the gorilla, chimpanzee, and orang branched off somewhat later from the *Dryopithecus* stock.

At present there is insufficient evidence for proving the correctness of any of these phylogenetic theories, but we shall consider the fossil data on which they are based in the next chapter.

CHAPTER XVI

Extinct Ancestors and Collaterals—Mostly Teeth

In TRACING THE DESCENT of modern primates and the relationships of extinct forms we have to depend, for the most part, upon the evidence of teeth, supplemented, sometimes, by that of bones of the skull. When an animal dies, the soft parts of the body decay very rapidly, the bones usually more slowly, and the teeth are generally the most resistant and durable. Thus it is apparent that something is the matter with man in an evolutionary sense when his teeth begin to decay early in the lifetime of the individual. Many animals, at present and in the past, have suffered the fate of being eaten by other animals, but ordinarily their teeth and some of the tougher bony parts are rejected as being both unmasticable and indigestible. Among the notably inedible bones are the lower jaw and some portions of the skull base. Hence the processes of natural decay and the limitations of carnivorous appetites conspire to leave us fossil teeth and some skull bones on which to base our studies of descent. This is a benevolent conspiracy from the point of view of the paleontologist, because teeth and skull bones are perhaps the most instructive parts of the body in regard to the habits, relationships, structure, and adaptations of any animal. Teeth are very informative as to diet, and their details of pattern persistently and conservatively reflect relationship. Since the skull lodges the central nervous system and is the seat of the main sense organs, much can be deduced from it in regard to animal evolution.

EVOLUTION OF PRIMATE DENTITION

The earliest remains of fossil primates are found in the deposits of the beginning of the Tertiary epoch, which may have started some 60 millions of years back. The Secondary epoch was the Age of Reptiles, which witnessed the proliferation and finally the extinction of the dinosaurs. In the latter part of this enormously long period some small and very primitive mammals were in existence, but none of these had reached the primate stage of development. Paleontologists agree that the primates must have developed from ancestors which closely resembled the existing tree shrews (Family Tupaiidae, Order Insectivora). The tree shrews of today are very small, arboreal, insect-eating mammals with five-clawed digits on hands and feet, long pointed snouts, eyes directed laterally, small brains, and many primitive features of the teeth. The earliest fossil primate forms are almost indistinguishable from generalized insectivores.[1]

Fig. 6. Occlusal relations of upper- and lower-cheek teeth in an Eocene Insectivore. Lower teeth in heavy lines (*After Gregory*).

Teeth had already gone through a long and complicated process of evolution before the development of the first mammals. The most primitive teeth are found in early sharks, in which the jaws are cartilaginous rather than bony and the teeth are flattened triangles formed in many successive sets on the skin covering the jaws. In later and progressive forms of fishes the jaws begin to ossify and the teeth are sharply differentiated from scales, those on the margins of the jaws being pointed, with complexly infolded bases. In some of the progressive reptiles the teeth have become small and peglike, and this dental evolution is accompanied by many advances in the structure of the skull which need not concern us here. The mammals developed from mammal-like reptiles in the Triassic, the first period of the Secondary epoch or Age of Reptiles. These advanced, cynodont or dog-toothed reptiles were dwellers on dry land, of predatory food habits. Their teeth had already become differentiated into canines, incisors, premolars, and molars, according to position in the jaws and function. The teeth at the front end of the jaw sweep through a wider arc with more velocity and are necessarily used for biting off food in the case of incisors, and for piercing, holding, and tearing in the case of the canines. The teeth farther back toward the fulcrum of the jaws move

[1]The data of this chapter are derived largely from Gregory 1922.

through a diminished arc and more power can be exerted upon them for crushing and grinding. Their crowns tend to broaden and flatten for these functions. The mammal-like reptiles already had lower jaws in which the several bony elements tended to be reduced, foreshadowing the mammalian condition in which some of the parts of the mandible back of the teeth are transformed into the small bones of the ear. These mammal-like reptiles now had only two sets of teeth—a milk set, followed by a permanent set. These teeth were supported each by a single root. The back teeth or cheek teeth were beginning to take on a triconodont or triangular form. In *Amphitherium,* an insectivorous mammal of the Lower Jurassic, the teeth consist of 4

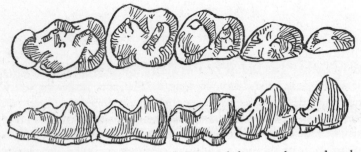

Fig. 7. Primitive Eocene Lemuroid. Lower left premolars and molars of *Pelycodus trigonodus* (*After Matthew and Gregory*). Trigonids of molars higher than talonid. Antero-internal cusps of trigonids retained.

incisors (on each side and in each jaw), one canine, 5 premolars, and 6 molars. The dental formula is written $I\frac{4}{4}$ $C\frac{1}{1}$ $P\frac{5}{5}$ $M\frac{6}{6}$. Probably the upper molars were triangular or 3-cusped, with the apex directed inward. The lower molars were now supported by anterior and posterior roots. The crowns consisted of an anterior cutting triangle with 3 high cusps, the apex outside, and, on the inner side of the crown, a small heel.

In the first insectivorous pre-primates, possibly represented by *Indrodon,* a fossil from the Paleocene (the beginning of the Tertiary in North America), the dental formula has now been reduced to $I\frac{2}{2}$ $C\frac{1}{1}$ $P\frac{4}{4}$ $M\frac{3}{3}$. This *Indrodon* was a small, active, arboreal animal, probably represented in the existing fauna by the tree shrews. The incisors, canines, and first two premolars were simple, with single roots and conical tips. In the last two premolars the internal cingulum, or band surrounding the base of the crown, gives rise to internal spurs, and the posterior part of the cingulum to heels or talonids.

Speaking very generally, it may be stated that in primitive placental mammals the upper molars tend to be triangular, or 3-cusped, with the apex directed inward; the lower molars have an anterior cutting triangle with the apex directed outward and a posterior crushing basin or talonid. The cutting trigonid fits in between the embrasures of the triangular upper molars, which articulate with the posterior crushing basin of the lower molars. But *Indrodon* already shows the tendency of the upper molars to lose their triangularity by the growth of a postero-internal cusp. The upper teeth bite slightly outside of the lowers. Now we have come to the first fossil primates.

FOSSIL LEMURS

In the American deposits the family of Notharctidae can be followed from the base of the Lower Eocene up to the summit of the Middle Eocene. The oldest of this series are very small, with lower molar series only 11–14 mm. in length. The size increases until we reach an animal as big as a howler monkey, with lower molars 20–23 mm. in length. In these Notharctidae the skull and skeleton are very lemuroid. The orbit, as in modern lemurs, has no bony back wall. The formation of the bony auditory swelling or bulla, the canals by which the internal carotid and stapedial arteries enter it, and other anatomical details of the skull are as in modern lemurs, but the brain case is much less expanded and more primitive. The characters of the backbone, pectoral and pelvic girdles, and limbs are also of the lemuroid type. These Notharctidae, confined to the New World, may well have given rise to New World monkeys.

The dental formula of the Notharctidae is $I\frac{2}{2}$ $C\frac{1}{1}$ $P\frac{4}{4}$ $M\frac{3}{3}$. The lower incisors and canines lack all the specializations of modern lemurs, in which the lower incisors are small, compressed teeth which lean forward (procumbent), the lower canines are taken over into the incisor series, and the second lower premolar is modified into an erect pointed tooth like a canine. The premolars of *Notharctus* begin at the front with almost peg-toothed forms and, toward the end of the series, tend to develop broadened crowns which resemble molars. The upper molars have evolved from a trigonal to a quadrangular type, a fourth postero-internal cusp having grown up. In the earliest Notharctidae the lower molars have a high anterior trigonid, with a lower and wider talonid or basin. The anterior trigon forms one V, and 2 cusps and an oblique ridge which have grown up from the talonid form a second, wider V. In later forms of Notharctidae the inner front cusp of the anterior triangle has disappeared or is much reduced; the anterior trigonid is lowered and the level of the talonid or basin with its outgrowing cusps has been raised. All of this has to do with the filling up of the dental interspaces so that the teeth occlude continuously. There is also evidence that transverse widening of the molars is connected with sidewise movements of the lower jaw in chewing a vegetable or mixed diet.

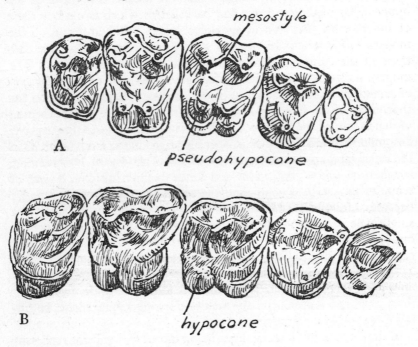

Fig. 8. Upper-cheek teeth of American and European Eocene Lemuroids. A. *Notharctus crassus,* American. B. *Adapis magnus,* European (*After Gregory*).

In Europea related family of Eocene lemuroids called the Adapidae has many characters in common with the American Notharctidae. An important difference lies in the fact that in the American family the new fourth cusp on the upper molars (postero-internal) arises by budding from the antero-internal cusp, whereas in the European series the new fourth cusp arises in the usual mammalian fashion from the postero-internal cingulum (the band around the base of the crown). These differences, according to Gregory, are associated with corresponding differences of the path of the lower jaw in mastication, which is more lateral in the American group and more upright or vertical in the European. Otherwise, the construction of the skull in the European Adapidae represents some advance upon the American family. Probably the modern lemurs developed from the European Adapidae. Some of the modern lemurs have acquired recent, monkey-like modifications of the teeth, but they retain the ancient lemuroid heritage in many less obvious features. An extinct family of Madagascar lemurs, the Archaeolemuridae, tends to present a division of the upper molar teeth into front and back halves which is characteristic of the modern Old World monkeys, but a fossil ancestor of the modern *Indris* lemurs has molars with Vs or crescents that resemble those of the American Notharctidae, but are more specialized. The modern indrisine lemurs (Indrisidae) are an example of the reduction of premolars from 4 to 2 by loss of the anterior 2, dependent upon the shortening of the face and crowding of the teeth due to lengthening of the crowns of the back teeth. That very aberrant form, the aye-aye, has gone very much farther in specialization of the front teeth than the other modern lemurs in whom, as stated above, the lower canine is taken over into the incisor series, the incisors become a sort of scoop or procumbent comb, and the second or third lower premolar becomes caniniform and opposes the upper canine. In the aye-aye a single pair of enormously compressed and enlarged upper incisors opposes a similar pair of enlarged lower teeth which are probably canines, according to Gregory. The other anterior teeth have been lost as far as the last premolar. All the back teeth are degenerate. Presumably, all of this is connected with the rodentlike use of the front teeth in excavating for grubs and the lack of chewing requirements in eating these soft-bodied morsels.

In the opinion of Gregory the existing lorises and galagos represent some of Nature's experiments in evolving large-brained, short-jawed primates from a primitive lemuroid stock. Not much is known of their extinct ancestors. These animals have the lemurine specializations of the front teeth, the primitive projecting rhinarium or snout, and lemuroid hands and feet. Because of their nocturnal habits the orbits have been enlarged and approximated, and the outer rims partly brought forward, but the bony face has not been bent downward beneath the brain case. The cheek teeth (molars) have tended to lose their primitive form and to become rounded and degenerate, especially in the potto. The loris retains more primitive features of dentition. This line of dental evolution is carried still farther in some of the smaller lemurs (mouse lemurs). It contains no promise of human development. As contrasted with the lorises and the pottos, the galagos are more tarsioid, in so far as their hind limbs are specialized for hopping. The skull, as a whole, is longer and narrower, with a more projecting muzzle, and the face even more produced in front of the cranium.

TARSIOIDS

Eocene tarsioids of North America include a number of early specialized side-line developments, with some later but more generalized genera of the Middle Eocene. None of these seems directly ancestral to the existing *Tarsius,* which was probably derived from some Eurasiatic Eocene tarsioid. All the American forms are small and some are minute. In one of them the total length of the three lower molars is only 5 mm. The early tarsioids were nocturnal, with widely expanded brain cases, olfactory parts of the skull reduced, auditory and optical parts enlarged (huge orbits), limbs probably adapted for tree hopping as in the modern tarsier. The jaws were pointed, the lower front teeth variously modified, often with enlarged lower canines or incisors sloped forward, premolar series reduced, upper molars triangular, lowers with small, high trigonids and low, large talonids.

In the European Eocene, tarsioids are represented by seven genera, none of which is common to both hemispheres. The fossil called *Necrolemur* is of a highly modified tarsioid type with excessive enlargement of the auditory bullae and the development of external auditory bony tubes, the interorbital space reduced to a thin septum, and a tendency toward the multiplication of small cusps on the surface of the upper molar crowns. The angle of the mandible is expanded and its posterior border is large and rounded. These specializations take *Necrolemur* far from the primitive tarsioid type. Neither these Eocene relatives nor the contemporary tarsier appear to be in a line directly ancestral to the New World monkeys or to the Old World monkeys and apes. The modern animal has become further specialized in the extreme enlargement of its orbits and the reduction of the lower incisors to one on each side.

Gregory summarizes the evolutionary position of the European fossil tarsioid genera *Necrolemur* and *Microchoerus* as exhibiting certain important advances toward the Old World primates, although none of the latter can be derived from them. Among these advances are the development of quadrate upper molars with subequal anterior and posterior moieties; the development of hypoconulids (fifth postero-median cusps) on the lower molars; the loss of the paraconids (antero-interior cusps) on the lower molars, and the tendency of reduction of the trigonid basin; the tendency of the last two pre-molar teeth to become bicuspid; incipient development of a bony back wall of the orbits; lateral expansion of the base of the brain case; development of a bony tubular external auditory meatus, expansion of the angle of the mandible and enlargement of its posterior border.

FOSSIL NEW WORLD MONKEYS

The only fairly well-preserved specimen of a fossil New World monkey is *Homunculus patagonicus* from the Miocene, represented by the lower jaw and the fore part of the skull. Gregory thinks that this form is closest to some of the smaller Cebidae, especially *Aotus* and *Callithrix* (the douroucouli and teetee monkeys). He considers *Callicebus* (the teetee) to be the most primitive of the existing monkeys of the New World. All these monkeys may have been derived from a tarsioid ancestor or perhaps from the Notharctidae. Several lines of development from the primitive ancestors are recognized: (1) the nocturnal, owl-faced monkeys (*Aotus*) and possibly the marmosets; (2) the large and relatively specialized howlers; (3) the woolly spider monkeys through the true spider monkeys; (4) and (5) the aberrant uakaris and the sakis (both of which have procumbent incisors); (6) and (7) the large-brained cebus monkeys and squirrel monkeys, which are by far the most advanced of the New World group.

There is a controversy as to the position of marmosets. Some anatomists consider them the most primitive of monkeys, particularly because of their claws. Le Gros Clark has proved that the claws of the marmoset are true claws and not degenerated nails. Gregory's view that the marmoset is a degenerate monkey derived from the ancestors of the douroucoulis is questionable. In the marmosets the third molars are suppressed. The upper molars are tritubercular. These molars are almost certainly degenerate.

OLD WORLD MONKEYS

The earliest Old World monkey is *Parapithecus fraasi,* from the Lower Oligocene of Egypt. This small animal is represented by a mandible complete with its teeth. The dental formula is the same as that of the Cercopithecidae, the Simiidae or anthropoid apes, and man. The premolars have been reduced to two. *Parapithecus* is so primitive in its characteristics that it is regarded as standing in, or quite near to, the line of descent which leads to the Old World monkeys, the anthropoids, and man. It is the smallest of the higher primates. The total length of the jaw is 36.5 mm., as against 86 mm. in a modern siamang, which is not a large animal. The two sides of the jaw converge rapidly to a narrow, sharply sloping chin, indicating by the width of the mandibular condyles that the brain had already enlarged transversely. The face must have been shortened, as evidenced by the loss of the first premolars. The canines are not enlarged. The low condyle, sloping ascending ramus, and shallow body suggest that the face was less bent down than in the apes. Gregory says that the small size and lack of modification of the canines, for shearing and tearing, with the blunt, non-sectorial form of premolars and molars, would preclude specialized carnivorous habits, while the gently inclined incisors and low-cusped cheek teeth suggest a mixed diet, possibly of insects, fruit, birds' eggs, and small reptiles. It may be inferred from the bicuspid form of the lower premolars that the uppers were also bicuspid, and from the 5-cusped lower molars that the uppers were quadrate. In these molars the anterior cutting trigonid has been reduced to the level of the talonid; the paraconid (anterior internal cusp of the trigonid) has already been lost, and the primitive V-shaped cusps have become low and conical and have almost lost their crests. The bicuspid premolars contrast strongly with the form of the molars, whereas in primitive mammals there is not such a great difference. Gregory thinks that the skull of *Parapithecus*, if found, would exhibit many tarsioid conditions and others foreshadowing Old World monkey and primitive anthropoid organization. However, the skull has not been found, although the jaw was discovered in 1911. Another Lower Oligocene primate from Egypt is *Apidium*, which in dental characters may represent a stage in which the cercopitheque monkeys were already beginning to separate from the common stock.

The Lower Miocene of Italy, beginning some 19 millions of years ago, has yielded *Oreopithecus,* an early Old World monkey. At this time primitive anthropoids, Old World monkeys, and other mammals had ranged westward over a continuous tract of land, probably from Central Asia. In this form the canines are not yet enlarged; the principal molar cusps are arranged in pairs, but have not yet developed high, transverse ridges joining the opposite cusps. Semnopithecine monkeys, with their specialization for herbivorous diet, are first represented in a Lower Pliocene genus, at which time also fossil representatives of the cercopithecine monkeys (baboons, macaques, etc.) also appear. The principal specialized dental character common to all of the Cercopithecidae, or Old World monkeys, is "bilophodont" molars. This word means that the first and second upper and lower molars are divided into fore-and-aft halves, almost equal, with the paired cusps of each half often united by a high, transverse crest. The fifth cusp on the lower molars is reduced or disappears.

FOSSIL ANTHROPOID APES

From the same Lower Oligocene deposit in Egypt which yielded the primitive monkey or common ancestor of monkeys and anthropoids we have the first small anthropoid ape, *Propliopithecus haeckeli.* The Oligocene period began perhaps 35 millions of years ago. *Propliopithecus* is represented by a lower jaw with all of its teeth but minus the ascending branches or rami, which articulate with the base of the skull. The mandible is somewhat larger than that of *Parapithecus,* whose entire tooth row was only 25 mm. long, as against 30 mm. in this first anthropoid and 51 mm. in the gibbon, the small anthropoid ape of today. The lower canines are not much enlarged; the lower molars have 5 cusps; the lower anterior premolars are not compressed or elongated, but antero posteriorly shortened, somewhat like those of *Parapithecus,* the contemporary primitive monkey. The jaw is shorter and deeper than those of present gibbons and siamangs and the dental arches more convergent in front. Probably the face was less prognathous or projecting. This animal is said to be structurally ancestral to *Pliopithecus,* a fossil of the Upper Miocene and Lower Pliocene of Europe, which in turn leads to the gibbons.

GIANT FOSSIL APES

Beginning with the Lower Miocene, some 19 millions of years ago, there existed in the Old World a family or subfamily of giant anthropoids which originally took its name from *Dryopithecus,* a European genus found in the Upper Miocene and Pliocene. The basic dental characters of this subfamily, called by Gregory and Hellman the Dryopithecinae, are as follows:[2] upper canines tusklike in males, small in females; upper premolars bicuspid, but anterior upper premolar with outside cusp prominent, pointed, and external face sloping upward toward the large canine; both upper premolars with two outside roots; lower anterior premolar compressed with crown set obliquely and the outer anterior surface shearing against the inner posterior surface of the upper canine; upper first and second molars subquadrate with unpaired conical cusps, the fourth cusp (postero-internal) large and the oblique crest retained; the third molar with incipi-

[2]Gregory and Hellman 1939a, pp. 339–73.

ent to better-developed posterior lobe; lower molars with the trigonid fossa reduced to the fovea anterior (front dimple); trigonid cusps reduced nearly to height of talonid cusps, progressive fifth cusp tending to pair with the postero-internal cusp (entoconid); upper dental arch primitively lyriform, becoming variously modified into anteriorly divergent U-form, lower dental arch mostly U-shaped or saddle-shaped; occlusion of molars overlapping-interlocking, jaw movement vertical with considerable side-swing.

The most typical feature of this dentition is what Gregory calls "the fundamental *Dryopithecus* pattern" of the lower molars. If the

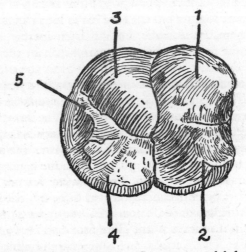

FIG. 9. The Y5 *Dryopithecus* pattern. Lower second left molar of *Dryopithecus frickal* (*After Gregory and Hellman*).

outside cusps are given the odd numbers 1, 3, 5, and the inside 2, 4, the base of cusp 3 (middle outside cusp) is enclosed by two grooves forming a V and the apex of this V meets a transverse groove between 2 and 4, thus forming a Y. The inner apex of cusp 3 protrudes so far to the inside that it separates cusp 1 widely from cusp 4, whereas 2 and 3 are in contact. This is the ancestral cusp pattern from which the lower molar patterns of man and the present apes were derived. It may be called the Y5 pattern. Thus there are 3 cusps on the outside and 2 on the inside, separated by a characteristic pattern of grooves and furrows.

The most primitive of these *Dryopithecus* apes is the form called *Proconsul africanus,* from the Lower Miocene of Africa. The upper canine of *Proconsul* is a nearly straight, vertical, tapering crown grooved in front and with the bladelike, posterior edge co-operating

with the high, pointed outside cusp of the anterior premolar to produce a combination of blade and notch. The upper molars of this
early ape retain some tarsioid features and at the same time show
distinct advance toward the *Dryopithecus* pattern. The *Dryopithecus*
apes were first known from several lower jaws and some teeth from
the Upper Miocene and Pliocene in Europe. Subsequently, a far
richer assortment of forms has been recovered from the Siwalik deposits of the foothills of the Himalayas of northern India. The geological age of these Siwalik anthropoids ranges from the uppermost
Middle Miocene to the Middle Pliocene. A large number of new
forms was added by a Yale expedition to this region in 1935.[3]

All the Miocene anthropoid apes are much larger than *Propliopithecus*. One of them, *Palaeosimia,* known from merely a third upper
molar, is thought to foreshadow the orang-utan in the characters of
the enamel folds and excessive wrinkling. Thus the orang may have
branched off in the Middle Miocene. *Sivapithecus,* another Upper
Miocene form, is regarded by Gregory and Hellman as also progressing somewhat in the orang-utan direction. The lower dental arch,
as reconstructed, can be nearly matched in modern orangs, and specializations of the upper molar cusps and the lower molars are in the
proto-orang pattern. In the forms attributed to the genus *Dryopithecus*
there is a good deal of variation. *Dryopithecus fontani* of Europe is
perhaps the most primitive, according to Gregory, because its lower
molars are relatively narrow, increase in length from the first to the
third, and retain the external cingulum found in *Propliopithecus* and
Pliopithecus. The lower incisors and canines are of moderate size; the
lower molars have the typical *Dryopithecus* pattern, with little or no
wrinkling of enamel and sharply defined cusps; the fifth cusp is more
central and less lateral in position than later forms. *Dryopithecus
chinjiensis* of the Middle Miocene of India shows some gorilloid features of a third lower molar (especially the sixth cusp) and may stand
in or near the gorilla line. *Dryopithecus punjabicus,* another Miocene
Indian species, shows affinities in its teeth both to gorilla and chimpanzee, while *Dryopithecus giganteus* has an enormous lower third
molar which resembles those of chimpanzees except in its more primitive, less-wrinkled character.

Without going into further detail about these Siwalik anthropoids,
mostly represented by a few teeth or isolated teeth with occasional
fragments of the lower jaws, we may repeat the conclusions of
Gregory, Hellman, and Lewis to the effect that they, "taken as a
whole, were on a distinctly infrahuman grade of evolution." Occasion-

[3] Gregory, Hellman and Lewis 1937.

ally, in one or another feature they approach or overlap the human range of variation. Thus the lower second and third molars of *Bramapithecus thorpei* surpass in breadth indices even some human teeth. In general, the minor variations of the *Dryopithecus* patterns of the lower molars, as exhibited in these Siwalik anthropoids, are preserved fully in recent apes and less so in fossil and recent men. These extinct great apes ranged over an enormous area from Spain to India and China, and from Egypt to South Africa, and were extraordinarily variable in jaws and dentition.

South African Man-Apes

Since 1925 our knowledge of fossil anthropoid apes has been greatly enriched by remarkable finds in South Africa. In that year Professor Raymond A. Dart, of Johannesburg, gave the name of *Australopithecus africanus* to a fossilized brain case and incomplete skull of a young ape which had been found in a late Cenozoic limestone fissure deposit at Taungs, near Kimberly in the Transvaal. Professor Dart interpreted the find as belonging to a species of fossil ape distinct from the gorilla and the chimpanzee and in some ways reminiscent of the orang-utan, but more humanoid than any previous find. His report was received with skepticism in many quarters, since it was held that most of the features which he regarded as manlike were infantile. However, subsequent studies proved that Dr. Dart was right. In 1936 and 1937, Dr. Robert Broom, a distinguished South African paleontologist, described the skull and upper teeth of another fossil adult anthropoid ape found in a cave deposit of a limestone quarry at Sterkfontein, about 25 miles northwest of Johannesburg. In 1938 Dr. Broom made available for study to Drs. Gregory and Hellman not only his first find, but also the remains of a third anthropoid ape found in the cave of Kromdraai, presumably in the same general locality. The following account of these South African anthropoids has been summarized largely from the studies made by Gregory and Hellman, supplemented by papers written by Dr. Broom.[4]

The original brain case, face, and lower jaw of the immature anthropoid ape, *Australopithecus,* are probably Early Pleistocene, but may be slightly older. The face and the forehead are nearly complete, but the covering bones of the skull are missing. The greater part of the left side of the skull was filled with limestone which made an exact cast of the external markings of the brain that had filled the cavity. All the milk teeth were present, and, in addition, the first permanent

[4]Gregory and Hellman 1939b, pp. 558–64; 1939a, pp. 339–73; 1940, pp. 211–28. Broom 1941, pp. 314–16.

molars. The cranial capacity of the Taungs skull (*Australopithecus*) is about 500 cc., which is not much more than half of what would be expected in a human child of the same age. However, according to Keith, the gorilla's average cranial capacity at the same stage of development is only 390 cc.[5] The same authority has made a careful study of the brain cast of the Taungs ape and points out that it is laterally more compressed and higher than that of a gorilla. The convolutions of the brain, as far as can be determined from the cast, do not exceed those found in better-developed specimens of gorilla brains.

The face of the Taungs ape is markedly concave, somewhat reminiscent of that of a young orang-utan; the brow ridges are feebly developed, even for so young a specimen. The characters of the nose are retrograde and reminiscent of the condition in the chimpanzee, although the nasal bones are wider than usual for a chimpanzee. The narrow interorbital width in this specimen is also anthropoidal. The premaxillary sutural lines are evident—an ape character. The spheno-parietal articulation in the temporal region is humanoid rather than apelike. The position of the foramen magnum and nuchal muscula ture are such as would indicate ape rather than human affinities. The dentition of *Australopithecus* may be discussed with that of the adult anthropoids discovered by Broom.

The first of these, *Plesianthropus transvaalensis,* was blasted out of a cave deposit in a limestone quarry. The deposit, according to Broom, is Middle Pleistocene. The remains consist of a brain cast, much of the skull base, the supraorbital ridge, portions of the vault bones and the occiput, the right and left maxillae with most of the upper teeth. The third specimen, called by Broom *Paranthropus robustus,* seems not as yet to have been completely described, but evidently includes the zygomatic arches, palate, the right side of the lower jaw, and important teeth.

The brain cast of *Plesianthropus* is estimated by Broom to have a volume of 440 cc., which is not big, even for an ape. The cast is much shorter than the brain cast of a gorilla, but relatively wider, especially in the frontal region. A part of the central area of the brow ridges, together with the nasal bones and nasal aperture, is preserved. The skull top has no bony crest and the temporal crests are not high. The brow ridges form the usual continuous supraorbital torus or bar. The nasal bones are very long, narrow, and markedly concave, the aperture quite narrow. The right maxilla of another specimen of *Plesianthropus* yields additional information concerning this area of

[5]Keith 1932, p. 64.

the face. The alveolar prognathism is pronounced, but less so than in modern apes. In this subnasal region of *Paranthropus* the lower facial plate is peculiarly flattened. In both specimens the configuration of the upper face is entirely apelike, rather more reminiscent of the orang than of the other great apes, with the swelling which marks the root of the zygoma excessively robust, indicating great development of the muscles of mastication necessary for operating the huge lower jaws and massive grinding teeth. The incomplete mandible of *Paranthropus* is enormously thick, but was evidently rather short from front to back.

Probably the most interesting features of these fossil apes of South Africa are the teeth. In both *Australopithecus* and *Plesianthropus* the incisors and canines are much smaller than in existing anthropoid apes. The canines are not tusklike. On the whole, they are more like those of *Sinanthropus,* the fossil man of China, than like those of a chimpanzee. The canine teeth of *Plesianthropus* are directed downward and there must have been an edge-to-edge bite as is normal in ancient forms of man. There are no diastemata, or gaps in the tooth rows, for the interlocking of projecting canines.

The first upper premolar in modern apes has two outer roots and the outer cusp is much higher than the inner. In *Plesianthropus* there is but one outer root and the outer and inner cusps are almost equal in height. Thus the human condition is nearly realized. However, the tooth bears separate outer and inner roots as in apes and not a fused single root as in man. In the fossil great apes the most primitive form of the lower anterior molar occurs in *Proconsul* from East Africa, a Lower Miocene form. It is a pointed tooth with its oblique outer face shearing against the upper canine. In the fossil great apes of India there is a transition to the oval-crowned first premolar found in certain chimpanzees. The first lower premolar in *Plesianthropus* is missing, but in *Paranthropus* it approaches the human bicuspid condition.

The molar teeth of all the South African apes are intermediate in size between those of *Sivapithecus* and the gorilla; they are much larger than those of the chimpanzee, *Sinanthropus,* and modern man. They agree also with *Sivapithecus* and the gorilla in that the third molars are larger than the first. The upper molar buccal cusps of these adult South African anthropoid apes are more obtusely conical than those of the gorilla and the chimpanzee. The crowns wear down into gently rounded surfaces, as in man, and resemble those of orangs, except in the absence of marked wrinklings. In the lower molars the *Dryopithecus* pattern is still discernible, but it is beginning to assume

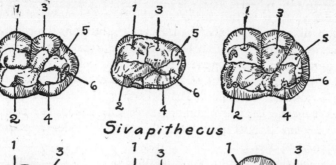

Sivapithecus

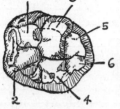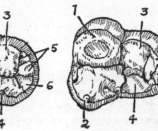

Plesianthropus   Paranthropus   Gigantopithecus

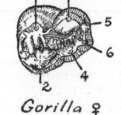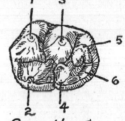

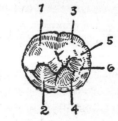

Fossil Orang   Gorilla ♀   Gorilla ♂

Pithecanthropus   Sinanthropus   Heidelberg

FIG. 10. *Dryopithecus* pattern of third right lower molar and some derivatives (*After Gregory and Hellman*).

383

the human plus pattern. There is often a sixth large cusp as in certain men.

Broom has recently pointed out that the milk molars of *Australopithecus* are essentially the same in pattern as those of the baboon and of man, but differ markedly from those of the chimpanzee and the gorilla. These affinities and differences are concentrated in the anterior milk molars. In the gorilla and chimpanzee the upper anterior milk molars have only 2 cusps, whereas in the baboon and in man there are 4 cusps. The lower anterior milk molar in man has 4 cusps and sometimes a fifth and even a sixth posterior cusp. In *Australopithecus* the first lower milk molar is essentially similar. These teeth also have usually a rudimentary anterior cusp in both species. In the gorilla the first lower milk molar is a flattened tooth with a single large median cusp and very small anterior and posterior cusps. It resembles the premolars of a dog. Very similar anterior lower milk molars are found in the chimpanzee and orang. In the baboon and in other Old World monkeys there are 4 subequal cusps with a small anterior cusp and this is evidently the ancestral condition. By this additional evidence of human similarity in the milk molars of *Australopithecus,* Broom fortifies his contention that the living anthropoid apes have descended from a *Dryopithecus* ancestry in Miocene times and that *Australopithecus* probably evolved from a pre-*Dryopithecus* ancestor which survived into Pliocene times. From this subfamily, the Australopithecinae, Broom considers that man evolved in the Upper Pliocene times. Gregory and Hellman have made a careful restoration of the upper dental arch of *Plesianthropus* which shows a posterior divergence of the dental rows and not an anterior divergence as in apes. In the Taungs skull the deciduous upper dental arch is a short, broad U-shape, in contrast to the posteriorly divergent or parabolic form characteristic of man. But this little fossil ape had a broad dental arch instead of the constricted form found in contemporary apes.

There can be no doubt of the close relationship of the three South African fossil apes, although there are some important differences. Very suggestive, in the opinion of Gregory and Hellman, are the resemblances of the Australopithecinae to the orang-utan, over and above their clear human and chimpanzee-gorilla relationships. These resemblances to the orang include facial concavity, molar and premolar patterns, the oranglike appearance of the deciduous cheek teeth of the Taungs specimen, and the resemblance of a lower canine of *Plesianthropus* to that of a fossil orang. These authors suggest that the resemblances between man and the orang may be explained by a

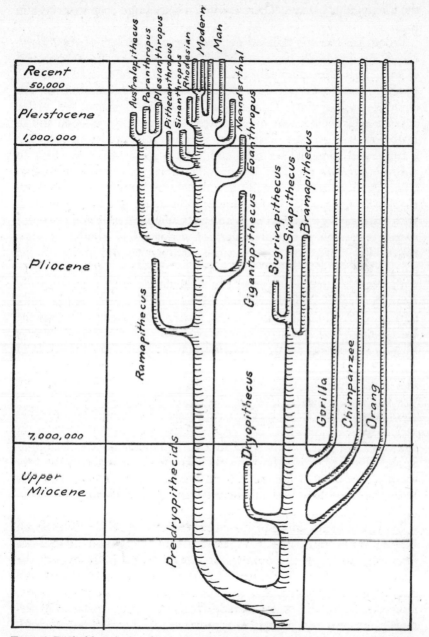

Recent 50,000		
Pleistocene		
1,000,000		
Pliocene		
7,000,000		
Upper Miocene		

FIG. 11. Probable relationships of man and great apes, according to Broom.

rapid and radical divergence of man and the orang from a more chimpanzeelike ancestor, whereas the Australopithecinae exhibit such a mixture of characters because they are late Pleistocene survivors of the common *Dryopithecus* stock and thus truly related to their cousins in the modern chimpanzee-gorilla, orang, and human branches. To the present writer this suggestion does not clarify matters to any appreciable extent.

There can be little doubt that the South African fossil anthropoids represent the persistence or survival into the Pleistocene of a line which in dental characters was much more closely allied to the human stock than any extinct ape forms heretofore discovered. No one supposes that man could be a direct descendant of *Plesianthropus, Paranthropus,* or *Australopithecus,* because it is certain that human forms as well developed as *Pithecanthropus* and *Sinathropus* were contemporary with the African man-apes. The contention of Broom that man evolved in the Upper Pliocene from a more progressive line of the Australopithecinae is at least possible. However, it should be noted that the South African anthropoids, as represented by the adult forms, had brains no larger than those of existing anthropoid apes. It must now be admitted that close resemblances based upon dental characters alone do not imply corresponding similarities of other and more important bodily parts. I myself should expect that the immediate ape precursors of man ought to show at least some tendency toward increase in size of the brain, as compared with the fossil apes in lines leading to contemporary giant primates which have not attained human status. Certainly, we have every reason for supposing that Nature tried a number of experiments in evolving giant primates, not all of which were successful in the sense of surviving up to the present day. That some of these lacked the canine specialization common among present apes and monkeys is not surprising. It does not follow of necessity that these apes with reduced anterior teeth were in other respects more humanoid or more nearly related to man.

CHAPTER XVII

Evolutionary Prospects

Nₒₙₑ OF MAN'S POOR RELATIONS can be said to have a roseate prospect of further and higher evolution. In order to show promise of favorable evolutionary progress an animal group must fulfill certain conditions of present status. In the first place it must show an excess of births over deaths so that it is increasing numerically. Concomitant with such a favorable balance in the ledger of vital statistics must be an opportunity for territorial expansion in order to provide room and adequate subsistence for an increasing population. Probably an animal group which is on an evolutionary upgrade ought to show in its population a frequency of favorable variations in individuals—modifications or mutations which would appear to create new opportunities for utilizing its organic potentialities and for taking advantage of environmental facilities. Structural and physiological specializations which tend to narrow the scope of the animal's activities and to restrict its capability in adapting to new or changing environmental conditions are certainly a bad evolutionary sign. When survival is achieved at the expense of warping the entire organism into some bizarre pattern which will fit only one peculiar set of environmental circumstances, the animal is probably nearing the end of its evolutionary journey, because environment is fickle.

In the light of these requirements we may briefly consider the situation of the suborder Lemuroidea. Most of the genera and species are now confined to a single refuge area, the island of Madagascar. Here they have survived largely because of the absence from that island of predatory carnivores. Further, the island has not been intensively developed by man, so that large areas of primeval forest still exist. There are, of course, in the mainland of Africa the pottos and the bush babies, and in the tropical region of southeastern Asia and Indonesia the single lemuroid family of Lorisidae. Why have the lemuroids been crowded into out-of-the-way corners of the world? In the case of the rodentlike aye-aye it ought to be sufficiently evident that its dietetic specializations and the bodily modifications which are connected with it pin the animal down to a very small range of environment which furnishes for it the one kind of living it can make. The lemurs which have survived outside of the isolated island of Madagascar are all nocturnal animals with eyes specialized for night vision. The galagos, or bush babies, have developed also an extraordinary hopping agility. There are no nocturnal animals among the primates above the lemurs, with the exception of *Tarsius* and *Aotus,* the owl monkey of South America.

In the swamps of Madagascar and in the lake deposits has been found a great variety of remains of extinct lemurs, mostly of late Pleistocene or recent date. Wood Jones considers that the isolation and comparative safety of this island permitted the lemurs to run riot phylogenetically and to follow their various evolutionary trends to extinction. Remains associated with them in the same deposits include crocodiles, lizards, birds, and many mammals. Some of these lemurs are thought to have become extinct as recently as 5 centuries ago. One form, *Palaeopropithecus,* had a skull over 200 mm. in length —roughly as large as a human skull—with an upturned snout and the entire upper surface of the skull flattened. Some authorities have thought that it was an aquatic animal, since its bones have been found in company with those of hippopotami and crocodiles. Several skulls appear to have been bitten or chewed by crocodiles. The largest of all extinct lemurs was *Megaladapis,* which had a skull about 300 mm. long and was about the size of a donkey. There were other lemuroid forms as large as man. It is clear, although little enough is known of these extinct lemuroids, that the process of growing up into gigantic size did not assure survival. Some of the lemuroid skulls in the marsh deposits are much like those of extant Madagascar lemurs, but larger and more robust.

The existing tarsiers, confined to a few islands in the Indo-Malayan Archipelago, are excessively rare, even there. Yet the beginning of the Tertiary witnessed a wide spread of ancestral tarsiers both in North America and in Europe, and, doubtless, in other parts of the Old World. The present tarsier has perhaps survived by dint of extreme specialization, but in a very tenuous manner and in very few out-of-the-way refuge places. More progressive ancestral forms may have developed into higher primates, but there is more than a suggestion that some, at any rate, of these Eocene tarsioids were already specialized in much the same direction as the contemporary animal. In an order which has manifested such an extraordinary evolutionary range as have primates—all the way from lemurs to man—it is obvious that the contemporary survivors from the lower stages represent very conservative ancestral lines. Even if the present-day representatives of these lines have managed to eke out a precarious survival by dint of specialization or by taking refuge in isolated areas, it can hardly be expected that they will manifest in this, the evening of their evolutionary career, any progressive tendencies which will arrest their approaching extinction.

When we reach the intermediate primates, the monkey stage, we find a considerable number of well-adjusted and vigorous types which, although relatively stabilized and perhaps almost "frozen" in their evolutionary status, ought to have a fairly good chance of survival, were it not for that most destructive of primates—man. The high adaptability of some of the monkey strains is manifested in the adoption of a terrestrial habitat by baboons, drills, mandrills, and "Barbary apes." As far as one can learn from the accounts of the distribution of most monkeys in their native haunts, they are in a healthy evolutionary state and might even expand, were it not for man's encroachment upon their areas and his deliberate policy of exterminating them. But, again, the fossil evidence, so far as known, seems to suggest that the period of evolutionary progress in the monkeys is past; that whatever there was of higher possibilities in monkey ancestors was realized in the development of the common anthropoid-human line from the catarrhine ancestors. Both generalized and progressive features seem to occur in fossil monkeys of the earlier geologic strata but, as far back as the Pliocene, ancestors of some of the present types appear to have reached a more or less stable equilibrium in evolution. Further developments from the monkey families seem improbable, unless the alleged giant spider monkey or South African anthropoid is a reality. Even if it is real, it may represent the survival of an unsuccessful experiment rather than an advancing type.

Small anthropoid forms, as far as our present paleontological knowledge takes us, seem to have begun with *Propliopithecus* of the Egyptian Oligocene and to have culminated in the Hylobatidae—the gibbons and the siamangs. Of these two genera the siamang is larger and more advanced toward a giant primate status, but it is more restricted in range than the gibbon, being confined to the island of Sumatra. Further, its generic characteristics which distinguish it from the gibbon—such as the webbing of the digits and the air sac—cannot be regarded as promising features from an evolutionary standpoint. The gibbon, again, would appear to be a fairly well-adapted and stabilized animal, with good prospects for survival if let alone by man. However, its brachiating specializations have crippled its hands as manipulative organs and there seems to be little doubt that the gibbon is, for an ape, a singularly unintelligent animal, representing no advance over the generality of monkeys, and perhaps distinctly inferior to baboons, macaques, and cebus monkeys.

New paleontological finds make it increasingly clear that many diverse types of giant apes existed between the Upper Miocene and the Middle Pleistocene. It is rather discouraging to contemplate the undeniable fact that at least several of these were more like man than the surviving anthropoids and yet, by reason of their humanoid convergence, derived no benefit in the struggle for existence sufficient to keep their lines from dying out. As far as they were concerned, half-a-man seems to have been inferior to an all-out ape. Of the existing great apes the orang-utan is certainly the most specialized and without doubt in a most unfavorable direction. This type of ape is on its degenerate last legs from the point of view of evolution and probably would die out presently, even without the maleficent intervention of man.

The separation of the mountain gorilla from the lowland gorilla implies a restriction of the range of the original generalized gorilla family, together with specializations which are restrictive rather than expansive. It seems to me that the mountain gorilla in particular has embarked upon a quadrupedal career which shows little of evolutionary promise. Again, the gigantism which characterizes the gorillas is probably so excessive as to bode ill for their survival, even if man left them alone.

On the whole, the chimpanzee seems to be the ape endowed with the most physical and mental characteristics which are likely to ensure survival, largely because in many respects it is less specialized than the other two great apes and more adaptable. It has managed a better compromise between arboreal and terrestrial life than either the orang or the gorilla. It has, apparently, far more tool-using capacity and seems to be temperamentally better fitted to withstand environmental changes. It is possible, although not very probable, that, left alone, the chimpanzees might make something of themselves in an evolutionary sense.

Schultz has found out from his anatomical studies of higher primates that, in general, the skeletal features of the great apes tend to be more variable and less stable than those of man. This ought to be an evolutionary factor which would indicate phylogenetic plasticity and some promise of further development. Unfortunately, however, the larger number of ape variations away from the mean or the mode appear to be in the direction of exaggerations of ape features which have already proved disadvantageous in so far as progress in adaptability and intelligence are concerned. Thus, fourth molars, shortening of the lumbar region, and increase of the number of ribs are merely the continuation of presumably orthogenetic trends which lead to no brilliant evolutionary future. One can hardly be optimistic about the prospects of the surviving anthropoid lines.

As for man himself, the way is open, if only he exercises his superior endowment of intelligence to choose to proceed along it. When we contemplate the extent to which the fossil beds are strewn with the *disiecta membra* of unsuccessful, extinct, prehistoric forms of man, some of whom had acquired more than the rudiments of culture, we are forced to conclude that the mere attainment of a human status does not guarantee species survival. When we further recall the recent or imminent disappearance of a considerable number of breeds of modern man, which are culturally, if not morphologically, archaic, it behooves us to look to the evolutionary future of our species.

It is no business of mine to elaborate this subject in the present work, which represents an anthropologist's temporary revulsion from the study of his own kind and his resort to a contemplation of other primates which, if they are monkeys, behave in a manner befitting monkeys, and if they are apes, live up to their apehood. They have probably fulfilled their evolutionary aspirations, if they have any. At least, they make no pretense of being better and more intelligent than they are. If man insists upon aping the apes, he ought, at any rate, to quit posing as an angel. He, of course, has a physical and mental equipment which has permitted him to acquire culture and a dangerous environmental control. If he will utilize his powers judiciously to improve himself, and to select his evolutionary path by a wise control of human genetics, he may well go on to a superprimate status in which, after a couple of hundred thousand years, the superprimate paleontologist may regard our fossilized remains with the same zoological condescension which we feel toward *Pithecanthropus erectus*.

Bibliography

Bibliography

BATES, H. W.
    1863. The Naturalist on the River Amazon, London.

BAUMAN, JOHN E.
    1923. The Strength of the Chimpanzee and Orang, Scien. Mon., vol. XVI, no. 4, April.

    1926. Observations on the Strength of the Chimpanzee and Its Implications, Jr. Mammal., vol. 7, no. 1, February.

BEATTIE, J.
    1927. The Anatomy of the Common Marmoset (Hapale Jacchus Kuhl), Proc. Zool. Soc. London, part 3, September.

BENCHLEY, BELLE J.
    1938. Notes on the Birth and Infancy of a Gibbon, San Diego Zoonooz, vol. X, no. 8, August.

    1940. One Hundred and One Months in the Growth and Development of Mountain Gorillas, San Diego Zoonooz, vol. XII, no. 4, May.

    1942. Mbongo—1926–1942, Parks and Recreation, vol. XXV, no. 9.

BINGHAM, HAROLD C.
    1929a. Chimpanzee Translocation by Means of Boxes, Comp. Psychol. Mono., vol. 5, no. 3, serial no. 25, February.

    1929b. Selective Transportation by Chimpanzees, Comp. Psychol. Mono., vol. 5, no. 4, serial no. 26, May.

    1932. Gorillas in a Native Habitat, Carn. Inst. Wash., pub. no. 426, August.

BONIN, GERHARDT, VON.
    1938. The Cerebral Cortex of the Cebus Monkey, Jr. Comp. Neur., vol. 69, no. 2, October.

BROOM, ROBERT.
    1941. The Milk Molars of Man and the Anthropoids, South African Dent. Jr., vol. XV, no. 11, November.

CANDELA, P. B.
    1940a. New Data on the Serology of the Anthropoid Apes, Am. Jr. Phys. Anth., vol. XXVII, no. 2, September.

CANDELA, P. B.

1940b. Serology of the Anthropoid Apes, Am. Jr. Phys. Anth., vol. XXVII, no. 3, December.

1942. New Data on the Blood Groups of Apes and Monkeys, a paper read before the Am. Assn. Phys. Anth., April 16.

CARPENTER, C. R.

1934. A Field Study of the Behavior and Social Relations of Howling Monkeys (Alouatta Palliata), Comp. Psychol. Mono., vol. 10, no. 2, serial no. 48, May.

1935. Behavior of Red Spider Monkeys in Panama, Jr. Mammal., vol. 16, no. 3, August.

1937. An Observational Study of Two Captive Mountain Gorillas (Gorilla berengei), Human Biol., vol. 9, no. 2, May.

1938. A Survey of Wild Life Conditions in Atjeh, North Sumatra, Neth. Comm. Inter. Nat. Protect., Commun. no. 12, Amsterdam.

1940. A Field Study in Siam of the Behavior and Social Relations of the Gibbon (Hylobates Lar), Comp. Psychol. Mono., vol. 16, no. 5, serial no. 84, December.

1941a. The Menstrual Cycle and Body Temperature in Two Gibbons (Hylobates Lar), Anat. Rec., vol. 79, no. 3, March.

1941b. Societies of Monkeys and Apes, lecture given in a symposium on Levels of Integration in Biological and Social Systems, during a program of the Fiftieth Anniversary at the University of Chicago, September 24.

1942. Sexual Behavior of Free-Ranging Rhesus Monkeys (Macaca Mulatta): I. Specimens, Procedures and Behavioral Characteristics of Estrus; II. Periodicity of Estrus, Homosexual, Autoerotic and Non-Conformist Behavior; Jr. Comp. Psychol., vol. 23, no. 1, February.

CLARK, W. E. LE GROS.

1924. Notes on the Living Tarsier (Tarsius spectrum), Proc. Zool. Soc. London, part I.

CONANT, ROGER.

1941. Meet the Champions, Fauna, vol. 3, no. 2, June.

COOK, NORMAN.

1939. Notes on Captive Tarsius Carbonarius, Jr. Mammal., vol. 20, no. 2, May.

COOLIDGE, HAROLD J., JR.

1929. A Revision of the Genus Gorilla, Mem. Mus. Comp. Zool. Harvard, vol. L, no. 4, August.

1933. Notes on a Family of Breeding Gibbons, Human Biol., vol. V, no. 2, May.

1936. Zoological Results of the George Vanderbilt African Expedition of 1934, part IV, Notes on Four Gorillas from the Sanga River Region, Proc. Acad. Nat. Sci. Phila., vol. LXXXVIII.

COWLES, JOHN T.

1937. Food-Tokens as Incentives for Learning by Chimpanzees, Comp. Psychol. Mono., vol. 14, no. 5, serial no. 71, September.

CRAIG, HUGH.

1897. The Animal Kingdom, vol. I, New York.

CRAWFORD, MEREDITH P.

1937. The Co-operative Solving of Problems by Young Chimpanzees, Comp. Psychol. Mono., vol. 14, no. 2, serial no. 68, June.

1940. The Relation between Social Dominance and the Menstrual Cycle in Female Chimpanzees, Jr. Comp. Psychol., vol. 30, no. 3, December.

1942a. Dominance and the Behavior of Pairs of Female Chimpanzees When They Meet after Varying Intervals of Separation, Jr. Comp. Psychol., vol. 33, no. 2, April.

1942b. Dominance and Social Behavior for Chimpanzees in a Non-competitive Situation, Jr. Comp. Psychol., vol. 33, no. 2, April.

DETWILER, S. A.

1939. Comparative Studies upon the Eyes of Nocturnal Lemuroids, Monkeys, and Man, Anat. Rec., vol. 74, no. 2, June.

DUCKWORTH, W. L. H.

1915. Morphology and Anthropology, Cambridge.

ELDER, JAMES H., and YERKES, ROBERT M.

1936a. Chimpanzee Births in Captivity: A Typical Case History and Report of Sixteen Births, Proc. Royal Soc. London, series B, no. 819, vol. 120, July.

1936b. The Sexual Cycle of the Chimpanzee, Anat. Rec., vol. 67, no. 1, December.

ELLIOT, D. G.

1913. A Review of the Primates, Am. Mus. Nat. Hist., Mono. series, vols. I, II, III, New York.

FINCH, GLEN.

1941a. Chimpanzee Handedness, Science, vol. 94, no. 2431, August.

1941b. The Solution of Patterned String Problems by Chimpanzees, Jr. Comp. Psychol., vol. 32, no. 1, August.

FISH, W. R., YOUNG, W. C., and DORFMAN, R. I.

1941. Excretion of Estrogenic and Androgenic Substances by Female and Male Chimpanzees with Known Mating Behavior Records, Endocrinology, vol. 28, no. 4, April.

FLETCHER, FRANK MILFORD.

1940. Effects of Quantitative Variation of Food-Incentive on the Performance of Physical Work by Chimpanzees, Comp. Psychol. Mono., vol. 16, no. 3, serial no. 82, June.

FLOWER, S. S.

1900. On the Mammalia of Siam and the Malay Peninsula, Proc. Zool. Soc. London.

GALT, W. E.

 1939. The Capacity of the Rhesus and Cebus Monkey and the Gibbon to Acquire Differential Response to Complex Visual Stimuli, Gen. Psychol. Mono., vol. 21, no. 3, August.

GILLMAN, J.

 1939. Some Facts Concerning the Social Life of Chacma Baboons in Captivity, Jr. Mammal., vol. 20, no. 2, May.

GREGORY, W. K.

 1922. The Origin and Evolution of the Human Dentition, Baltimore.

GREGORY, W. K., and HELLMAN, M.

 1939a. The Dentition of the Extinct South African Man-Ape Australopithecus (Plesianthropus) Transvaalensis Broom, A Comparative and Phylogenetic Study, Annals Transvaal Mus., vol. XIX, part 4.

 1939b. The South African Fossil Man-Apes and the Origin of the Human Dentition, Jr. Am. Dent. Assn., vol. 26, April.

 1940. The Upper Dental Arch of Plesianthropus Transvaalensis Broom, and Its Relations to Other Parts of the Skull, Am. Jr. Phys. Anth., vol. 26, March.

GREGORY, W. H., HELLMAN, M., and LEWIS, G. E.

 1937. Fossil Anthropoids of the Yale-Cambridge India Expedition of 1935, Carn. Inst. Wash., pub. no. 495, March.

GRETHER, WALTER F.

 1939. Color Vision and Color Blindness in Monkeys, Comp. Psychol. Mono., vol. 15, no. 4, serial no. 76, June.

 1940a. A Comparison of Human and Chimpanzee Spectral Hue Discrimination Curves, Jr. Exper. Psychol., vol. 26, no. 4, April.

 1940b. Chimpanzee Color Vision: I. Hue Discrimination at Three Spectral Points, II. Color Mixture Proportions, III. Spectral Limits, Jr. Comp. Psychol., vol. 29, no. 2, April.

 1941a. Comparative Visual Acuity Thresholds in Terms of Retinal Image Widths, Jr. Comp. Psychol., vol. 31, no. 1, February.

 1941b. Spectral Saturation Curves for Chimpanzee and Man, Jr. Exper. Psychol., vol. 28, no. 5, May.

 1942. The Magnitude of Simultaneous Color Contrast and Simultaneous Brightness Contrast for Chimpanzee and Man, Jr. Exper. Psychol., vol. 30, no. 1, January.

GRETHER, WALTER F., and YERKES, ROBERT M.

 1940. Weight Norms and Relations for Chimpanzee, Am. Jr. Phys. Anth., vol. XXVII, no. 2, September.

HARLOW, H. F., UEHLING, H., and MASLOW, A. H.

 1932. Comparative Behavior of Primates: I. Delayed Reaction Tests on Primates from the Lemur to the Orang-outan, Jr. Comp. Psychol., vol. 13.

HILL, W. C. OSMAN.
    1939. Observations on a Giant Sumatran Orang, Am. Jr. Phys. Anth.,
        vol. XXIV, no. 3, January–March.
HOOTON, EARNEST A.
    1931. Up from the Ape, New York.
    1937. Apes, Men, and Morons, New York.
HOYT, A. MARIA.
    1941. Toto and I, Philadelphia and New York.
JACOBSEN, CARLYLE F., with co-operation of ELDER, JAMES H., and HAS-
        LERUD, M. G.
    1936. Studies of Cerebral Function in Primates, Comp. Psychol.
        Mono., vol. 13, no. 3, serial no. 63, August.
JACOBSEN, CARLYLE F., and MARION M., and YOSHIOKA, JOSEPH C.
    1932. Development of an Infant Chimpanzee during Her First Year,
        Comp. Psychol. Mono., vol. 9, no. 1, serial no. 41, September.
JACOBSEN, CARLYLE F., WOLFE, J. B., and JACKSON, T. A.
    1935. An Experimental Analysis of the Functions of the Frontal
        Association Areas in Primates, Jr. Nerv. and Ment. Dis., vol.
        82, no. 1, July.
JONES, FREDERIC WOOD.
    1916. Arboreal Man, London.
    1929. Man's Place among the Mammals, New York.
KEITH, SIR ARTHUR.
    1929. The Alleged Discovery of an Anthropoid Ape in South
        America, Man, vol. XXIX, no. 8, August.
    1932. New Discoveries Relating to the Antiquity of Man, New
        York.
KLÜVER, HEINRICH.
    1933. Behavior Mechanisms in Monkeys, Chicago.
    1937. Re-examination of Implement-using Behavior in a Cebus
        Monkey after an Interval of Three Years, Acta Psychol., vol.
        II, no. 3, The Hague.
KLÜVER, HEINRICH, and BUCY, PAUL C.
    1939a. A Preliminary Analysis of the Functions of the Temporal
        Lobes in Monkeys, Trans. Am. Neurol. Ass'n.
    1939b. Preliminary Analysis of Functions of the Temporal Lobes
        in Monkeys, Arch. Neurol. and Psychiat., vol. 42, December.
KÖHLER, WOLFGANG.
    1925. The Mentality of Apes, New York.
KROGH, CHR. VON.
    1937. Serologische Untersuchungen über die stammesgeschichtliche
        Stellung einiger Primaten, Anthrop. Anz., XIII, Stuggart.
LASKER, GABRIEL.
    Primate Diet, manuscript.
LINTZ, GERTRUDE DAVIES.
    1942. Animals Are My Hobby, New York.

LOWTHER, FLORENCE DE L.

    1939. The Feeding and Grooming Habits of the Galago, Zoologica, vol. XXIV, part 4, December.

    1940. A Study of the Activities of a Pair of *Galago senegalensis moholi* in Captivity, Including the Birth and Postnatal Development of Twins, Zoologica, vol. XXV, part 4, December.

LYDEKKER, R.

    1893–94. The Royal Natural History, vol. I, London and New York.

MASLOW, A. H.

    1936. The Role of Dominance in the Social and Sexual Behavior of Infra-Human Primates: IV. The Determination of Hierarchy in Pairs and in a Group, Jr. Gen. Psychol., vol. 49.

    1940. Dominance—Quality and Social Behavior in Infra-Human Primates, Jr. Soc. Psychol., vol. 11.

MASLOW, A. H., and FLANZBAUM, S.

    1936. The Role of Dominance in the Social and Sexual Behavior of Infra-Human Primates: II. An Experimental Determination of the Behavior Syndrome of Dominance, Jr. Gen. Psychol., vol. 48.

MASLOW, A. H., and HARLOW, H. F.

    1932. Comparative Behavior of Primates, II. Delayed Reaction Tests on Primates at Bronx Park Zoo, Jr. Comp. Psychol., vol. XIV.

McCULLOCH, T. L.

    1941. Discrimination of Lifted Weights by Chimpanzees, Jr. Comp. Psychol., vol. 32, no. 3, December.

NISSEN, HENRY W.

    1931. A Field Study of the Chimpanzee, Comp. Psychol. Mono., vol. 8, no. 1, serial no. 36, December.

NISSEN, HENRY W., and CRAWFORD, MEREDITH P.

    1936. A Preliminary Study of Food-sharing Behavior in Young Chimpanzees, Jr. Comp. Psychol., vol. 22, no. 3, December.

NISSEN, HENRY W., RIESEN, A. H., and NOWLIS, VINCENT.

    1938. Delayed Response and Discrimination Learning by Chimpanzees, Jr. Comp. Psychol., vol. 26, no. 2, October.

NOBACK, CHARLES V.

    1930a. Growth of Infant Female Gorilla, Am. Jr. Phys. Anth., vol. XIV, no. 2, April–June.

    1930b. Digital Epiphyses and Carpal Bones in the Growing Infant Female Gorilla with Sitting Height, Weight and Estimated Age, Zoologica, Sc. Cont. New York Zool. Soc., vol. XI, no. 5, December.

    1931. The Zoological Park's Young Female Gorilla, Janet Penserosa, Bull. New York Zool. Soc., vol. XXXIV, no. 3, May–June.

    1936. Abstract no. 12, Am. Jr. Phys. Anth., vol. XXI, suppl. no. 2, Proceed. A. A. P. A.

Nowlis, Vincent.

1941a. Companionship Preference and Dominance in the Social Interaction of Young Chimpanzees, Comp. Psychol. Mono., vol. 17, no. 1, serial no. 85, March.

1941b. The Relation of Degree of Hunger to Competitive Interaction in Chimpanzee, Jr. Comp. Psychol., vol. 32, no. 1, August.

Randall, Francis E.

1942. Osteological Growth and Variation in Gorilla gorilla, Ph.D. Thesis, Harvard University.

Schultz, Adolph H.

1921. The Occurrence of a Sternal Gland in Orang-Utan, Jr. Mammal., vol. 2, no. 4, November.

1926. Studies on the Variability of Platyrrhine Monkeys, Jr. Mammal., vol. 7, no. 4.

1927. Studies on the Growth of Gorilla and of Other Higher Primates with Special Reference to a Fetus of Gorilla, Preserved in the Carnegie Museum, Mem. Carn. Mus., vol. XI, no. 1, November.

1930. The Skeleton of the Trunk and Limbs of Higher Primates, Human Biol., vol. 2, no. 3, September.

1931. The Density of Hair in Primates, Human Biol., vol. 3, no. 3, September.

1933a. Die Körperproportionen der erwachsenen catarrhinen Primaten mit spezieller Berücksichtigung der Menschenaffen, Sond. Anth. Anz., X.

1933b. Notes on the Fetus of an Orang-Utan, with Some Comparative Observations, Lab. Phys. Anth., Johns Hopk. Univ., Rep. Lab. and Mus. Comp. Path., Zool. Sect., Philadelphia.

1933c. Observations on the Growth, Classification and Evolutionary Specialization of Gibbons and Siamangs, Human Biol., vol. 5, no. 2, vol. 5, no. 3, May–September.

1934. Some Distinguishing Characters of the Mountain Gorilla, Jr. Mammal., vol. 15, no. 1, February.

1935. Eruption and Decay of the Permanent Teeth in Primates, Am. Jr. Phys. Anth., vol. 19, no. 4, January–March.

1936. Characters Common to Higher Primates and Characters Specific for Man, Quart. Rev. Biol., vol. II, no. 3, September, no. 4, December.

1937. Fetal Growth and Development of the Rhesus Monkey, Carn. Inst. Wash., pub. no. 479, Cont. to Embry., no. 155, January.

1938. Genital Swelling in the Female Orang-utan, Jr. Mammal., vol. 19, no. 3, August.

1939. Notes on Diseases and Healed Fractures of Wild Apes, Bull. Hist. Med., vol. VII, no. 6, June.

1940a. Growth and Development of the Chimpanzee, Carn. Inst. Wash., pub. no. 518, Cont. to Embry., no. 170, August.

SCHULTZ, ADOLPH H.

1940b. The Place of the Gibbon among the Primates, introduction to C. R. Carpenter's "A Field Study in Siam of the Behavior and Social Relations of the Gibbon (Hylobates Lar)." *See* Carpenter 1940.

1940c. Growth and Development of the Orang-utan, Carn. Inst. Wash., pub. no. 525, Cont. to Embry., no. 182, October.

1942a. Growth and Development of the Proboscis Monkey, Bull. Mus. Comp. Zool., Harvard Univ., vol. LXXXIX, no. 6, March.

1942b. Morphological Observations on a Gorilla and an Orang of Closely Known Age, Am. Jr. Phys. Anth., vol. 29, no. 1, March.

SCHULTZ, ADOLPH H., and SNYDER, F. F.

1935. Observations on Reproduction in the Chimpanzee, Bull. Johns Hopk. Hosp., vol. LVII, no. 4, October.

SCLATER, P. L.

1885. Proc. Zool. Soc. London.

SONNTAG, CHARLES F.

1924. The Morphology and Evolution of the Apes and Man, London.

SPENCE, KENNETH W.

1939. The Solution of Multiple Choice Problems by Chimpanzees, Comp. Psychol. Mono., vol. 15, no. 3, serial no. 75, April.

SPRAGG, S. D. S.

1940. Morphine Addiction in Chimpanzees, Comp. Psychol. Mono., vol. 15, no. 7, serial no. 79, April.

STRAUS, WILLIAM L., JR.

1940. The Posture of the Great Ape Hand in Locomotion and Its Phylogenetic Implications, Am. Jr. Phys. Anth., vol. XXVII, no. 2, September.

TILNEY, F.

1928. The Brain from Ape to Man, New York.

VOLKOV, M.

1900. Le Sommeil hivernal chez les paysans russes, Bull. et Mem. Soc. Anthr. de Paris, 5 me. Serie 1.

YERKES, ROBERT M.

1915. Maternal Instinct in a Monkey, Jr. Anim. Behav., vol. 5, no. 5, September–October.

1916. The Mental Life of Monkeys and Apes: A Study of Ideational Behavior, Behav. Mono., vol. 13, no. 1, serial no. 12.

1927a. The Mind of a Gorilla, Part I, Gen. Psychol. Mono., vol. II, nos. 1 and 2, January–March.

1927b. The Mind of a Gorilla, Part II, Mental Development, Gen. Psychol. Mono., vol. II, no. 6, November.

1928. The Mind of a Gorilla, Part III, Memory, Comp. Psychol. Mono., vol. 5, no. 2, serial no. 24, December.

1934. Modes of Behavioral Adaptation in Chimpanzee to Multiple Choice Problems, Comp. Psychol. Mono., vol. 10, no. 1, serial no. 47, May.

1939. Social Dominance and Sexual Status in the Chimpanzee, Quart. Rev. Biol., vol. 14, no. 2, June.

1940. Social Behavior of Chimpanzees: Dominance between Mates in Relation to Sexual Status, Jr. Comp. Psychol., vol. 30, no. 1, August.

1941. Conjugal Contrasts among Chimpanzees, Jr. Abnorm. and Soc. Psychol., vol. 36, no. 2, April.

YERKES, ROBERT M., and ELDER, JAMES H.

1936. Oestrus, Receptivity, and Mating in Chimpanzee, Comp. Psychol. Mono., vol. 13, no. 5, serial no. 65, October.

YERKES, ROBERT M., and LEARNED, BLANCHE.

1925. Chimpanzee Intelligence and Its Vocal Expressions, Baltimore.

YERKES, ROBERT M., and TOMILIN, MICHAEL I.

1935. Mother-Infant Relations in Chimpanzee, Jr. Comp. Psychol., vol. 20, no. 3, December.

YERKES, ROBERT M., and ADA W.

1929. The Great Apes, New Haven.

1936. Nature and Conditions of Avoidance (Fear) Response in Chimpanzee, Jr. Comp. Psychol., vol. 21, no. 1, February.

YERKES, ROBERT M., and DAVID N.

1928. Concerning Memory in the Chimpanzee, Jr. Comp. Psychol., vol. 8, no. 3, June.

ZUCKERMAN, S.

1932a. The Menstrual Cycle of the Primates, part 6, Further Observations on the Breeding of Primates, with special reference to the Suborders Lemuroidea and Tarsioidea, Proc. Zool. Soc. London.

1932b. The Social Life of Monkeys and Apes, New York.

1933. Functional Affinities of Man, Monkeys, and Apes, New York.

ZUCKERMAN, S., and FISHER, R. B.

1937. Growth of the Brain in the Rhesus Monkey, Proc. Zool. Soc. London, series B, vol. 107, part 4.

INDEX

Index

Absorption, organs of (*see* Digestion)

African pottos, 314–15

Age, chimpanzee, 32–33; gorilla, 65–66; lemur, 293

Air pouches, baboon, 186

Alimentary system, Cebidae, 272–73; Lemuroidea, 320

Alpha, infancy of, 28–32

Altruism, 329–30

Anatomy, Cebidae, 271–74; chimpanzee, 60–62; gibbon, 174–76; gorilla, 109–10; Lemuroidea, 319–20; Old World monkeys, 229–31; orang-utan, 140–41; tarsier, 283–85

Anthropoid apes, fossil, 377–86; South American, 269–71

Arms, *see* Limbs

Aye-Aye, 298–301

Baboon, 179–99; brain, 345–46, 350–51; cerebral function, 354–55; dominance, 325; foot, 366; primate, order of, 1; serology, 337; sexual behavior, 324

Barbary Ape, 220–22; primate, order of, 1

Behavior, howling monkey, 236; macaque, 217–20; spider monkey, 249–50; tarsier, 281–82

Biographies (*see* Alpha *and* Toto)

Birth, gibbon, 161–65

Black Ape of Celebes, 222

Blood, lemur, 293

Blood group, 338–41

Body build, 358–67; baboon, 198–99; colobus monkeys, 224–25; douroucoulis, 264; gibbon, 146–47; guenons, 223; langurs, 225; lemur, 295–96; mangabeys, 223–24; marmoset, 266; orang-utan, 120–22; patas monkeys, 225; proboscis monkey, 226–27; propitheques, 310–11; spider monkey, 247–49; woolly spider monkey, 261

Bones, 358–67

Box-stacking, chimpanzee, 46–48; gorilla, 101; macaque, 216; orang-utan, 134

Brain, Cebidae, 274; cerebral function, 352–57; chimpanzee, 28, 62; evolution of, in primates, 342–52; gibbon, 144; gorilla, 111; marmoset, 266; Old World monkeys, 231; orang-utan, 141; tarsier, 279

Bush Babies, 301–08

Capuchin monkeys (*see* Cebus monkeys)

Cebus monkeys, 256–74; brain, 247; cerebral function, 355; dominance, 214; intelligence, 170; occupation of trees, 156; vision, 215

Cerebral function (*see* Brain)

Chacma, 179–83

Cheek pads, orang-utan, 118

Cheek pouches, baboon, 179; guenons, 223; Old World monkeys, 178

Chimpanzee, 3–62; blood group, 338–39; brain, 345–46, 349–52; cerebral function, 353–54; clavicle, 360; dominance, 327–29; evolutionary prospects, 390; femur and tibia, 363; foot, 365; hand, 363–65; humerus and radius, 362; pelvis and sacrum, 361; primate, order of, 1; scapula, 361; serology, 337; sexual life, 327–29; skeletal affinities, 366–67; sternum, 359–60; vertebral column, 358–59

Clavicle, 360

Climbing, gorilla, 78

407